Τοιοῦτος οὖν μοι ὁ συγγραφεὺς ἔστω, . . .
ξένος ἐν τοῖς βιβλίοις καὶ ἄπολις.
—LUCIAN.

A HISTORY OF

European Scientific Thought
in the
Nineteenth Century

BY
JOHN THEODORE MERZ

in two volumes

VOLUME I

DOVER PUBLICATIONS, INC.
NEW YORK

Published in Canada by General Publishing Company, Ltd., 30 Lesmill Road, Don Mills, Toronto, Ontario.

Published in the United Kingdom by Constable and Company, Ltd., 10 Orange Street, London W.C.2.

Standard Book Number: 486-21349-8
Library of Congress Catalog Card Number 64-18363

Manufactured in the United States of America

Dover Publications, Inc.
180 Varick Street
New York 14, N.Y.

PREFACE.

As the plan of this work is fully given in the Introduction, only a few points, chiefly of a personal character, remain to be touched on here.

The first refers to the motive which led me to a course of studies, extending over more than thirty years, of which this book is the outcome.

The object of the book is philosophical, in the sense now accepted by many and by divergent schools—*i.e.*, it desires to contribute something towards a unification of thought. When in the beginning of my philosophical studies I became convinced that this is the task of philosophy, I felt the necessity of making myself acquainted, at first hand, with the many trains of reasoning by which, in the separate domains of science, of practical and of individual thought, such a unification has been partially and successfully attempted. Such a survey seemed to me indispensable. The possession of a map showing the many lines of thought which our age has cultivated seemed to me the first requisite, the basis from which a more complete

unification would have to start. The following pages
contain the result of this survey. Like every survey, it
can claim to be merely an approximation. It gives outlines
which closer scrutiny will have to correct and fill up.

My original intention was to complete this survey in
three volumes, corresponding to the three divisions of the
subject set out in the Introduction.

Some of my friends, who desired that the publication
of the book should not be unduly delayed, considered that
the Introduction and the earlier chapters of the work would
give something intelligible in themselves, and urged the
advantage of smaller volumes. I therefore decided to complete the first part of the history, which deals with scientific
thought, in two volumes instead of in one.

For the information of my readers, I mention here that
the two last chapters of this volume, which treat of the
astronomical and of the atomic views of Nature, will be
followed in the second volume by similar chapters on
the mechanical, the physical, the biological, the statistical,
and the psychophysical views of Nature, and that it is my
intention to close the first part of my subject by an attempt
to trace concisely the development of mathematical thought
in this century.

My thanks are due to many friends who have supported
me with assistance and encouragement.

I consider myself fortunate in having secured for the
revision of the whole volume the invaluable aid of Mr
Thomas Whittaker, B.A., whose profound erudition, know-

ledge of ancient and modern literature, and great editorial experience, were well known to my late friend Professor Croom Robertson, during his successful editorship of the first series of 'Mind.'

Mr S. Oliver Roberts, M.A., of the Merchant Taylors' School, has kindly read over the fourth, and Professor Phillips Bedson, of the Durham College of Science of this city, the last, chapter of this volume. The Introduction has greatly benefited by a thorough revision by my brother-in-law, Dr Spence Watson, a master of the English language.

I must also thank him and Dr Thomas Hodgkin for having given me what I value as much as assistance — namely, encouragement.

One indeed to whom I am in this respect more indebted, perhaps, than to any one else—whom to have known has meant, for many, a revelation of the power of mind and the reality of spirit—is no more: Ernst Curtius. While I was writing the last pages of this volume, in which he took a warm interest, the tidings arrived that he had passed away. But she who was nearest and dearest to him is still with us—a true priestess of the higher life, who has kept burning in the soul of many a youthful friend the spiritual fire when it was in danger of being quenched by the growing materialism of our age.

J. THEO. MERZ.

THE QUARRIES,
NEWCASTLE-UPON-TYNE, *November* 1896.

CONTENTS OF THE FIRST VOLUME.

INTRODUCTION.

I. Thought, the hidden world, 1; The only moving principle, 2; History of Nature, how to be understood, 2; Not intelligible without intellect, 2; History of savage tribes, what is it? 3; Two ways in which thought enters into history, 4; Definition of thought impossible, 4; Relation of outer and inner worlds undefined, 5; Many meanings of thought, 5; Thought of the present age, 6; Contemporary history, to what extent possible and valuable, 6; Supposed objectivity of historians, 7; Value of contemporary records, 8; Mystery of the life of thought, 8; Latent thought the material for genius, 8; Contemporary record of thought more faithful, 10; Events of the immediate past, 10; Changes of language, 11; Coining of new words, 12; Object of this work, 13; Not a political history, nor a history of science, literature, and art, 13; Influences which have a result on our inner life, 14; Personal knowledge necessary, 14; American influence only touched upon, 14; Only French, German, and English thought treated, 15; Unity of thought, a product of this century, 16; Voltaire, 16; Adam Smith, 16; Coleridge and Wordsworth, 17; Mme. de Staël, 17; Paris the focus of science, 17; Babbage, Herschel, and Peacock, 18; Liebig's laboratory, 18; Comte's philosophy, 18; Constable's influence in France, 19; Science become international, 19; The light which etymology throws on the history of thought, 20; Goethe, 22; Peculiarity of the German language, 22; New thought has found new words, 23; De Bonald and Max Müller, 23; Thought, how expressed in French and German, 24; Philosophy of history, 25; Want of precise terms in German and French, 26; Carlyle, 26.

II. The two factors of intellectual progress, 27 ; Object of the book, 28 ;
Nineteenth century, what it has achieved : (a) Method of knowledge ; (b)
Unity of knowledge, 29 ; Search after truth, 29 ; Method of science, practised by Galileo, &c., defined by Bacon, &c., 30 ; Disintegration of learning, 30 ; Apparent distance between science and poetry, 31 ; Closer connection between science and life, 31 ; What has nineteenth century done
for the ideals ? 32 ; Deeper conception of the unity of human interests,
33 ; Different terms for expressing this unity, 33 ; Definition of thought,
33 ; Age of encyclopædic treatment of learning, 34 ; Unity of knowledge
gradually lost sight of, 35 ; Lectures on " Encyclopädie " in Germany, 37 ;
Encyclopædias did not fulfil their promise, 39 ; French were masters in
science in beginning of the century, 41 ; Reaction in Germany against
metaphysics, 43 ; Reform in school literature, 44 ; Germany has taken
the lead in studying the life of thought, 46 ; Transition from metaphysical to historical method, 47 ; Herbert Spencer, 48 ; Lotze, 48 ;
Herder's ' Ideen,' 50 ; Humboldt's ' Kosmos,' 51 ; Lotze's ' Microcosmus,'
52 ; What the mental life of mankind consists of, 55 ; Methods have
their day and cease to be, 56.

III. Necessity of choosing a road, 57 ; No central event in our age, 58 ; Is
history of thought history of philosophy ? 60 ; Goethe's work involves
the deepest thought of the century, 61 ; Philosophy retrospective, 62 ;
Two questions, 63 ; Speculation, 64 ; Philosophy defined, 65 ; Division
of the book, 65 ; Neither science nor philosophy exhausts "thought," 66 ;
Thought also hidden in literature and art, 66 ; Goethe's and Wordsworth's influence, 67 ; Unmethodical thought, 68 ; Summed up in term
"religious thought," 69 ; Science is exact, 69 ; Subjective interests, 70 ;
Philosophy intermediate between exact science and religion, 71 ; Threefold aspect of thought : scientific, philosophical, individual, 72 ; Difficult
to separate the three aspects, 74 ; French thought centred in science,
75 ; State of philosophy in England, 75 ; Goethe's ' Faust ' representative
of the thought of the century, 76 ; A period of ferment, 76 ; Caused by
the Revolution, 77 ; Thought of century partly radical, partly reactionary,
77 ; Byronic school, 78 ; Revolutionary theories, 79 ; Thought to be considered as a constructive power, 80 ; Darwin, Spencer, and Lotze, 81 ;
Romanticism, 82 ; Scientific thought to be dealt with first, 84 ; Hegel's
doctrine, 85.

EUROPEAN SCIENTIFIC THOUGHT

Three chapters on the growth and the diffusion of the scientific spirit in the first half of the nineteenth century.

CHAPTER I.

THE SCIENTIFIC SPIRIT IN FRANCE.

Our century the scientific century, 89 ; Difference of English and Continental notions of science, 91 ; Relation of science and life, 92 ; Foreseen by Bacon, 93 ; Defect in Bacon's Philosophy, 94 ; Corrected by Newton, 95 ; Bacon's and Newton's ideas taken up by French philosophers : Bacon and Newton compared, 96 ; Laplace's work, 97 ; French Academy of Sciences, 99 ; Continental methods in mathematics, 100 ; Modern analytical methods, 102 ; Older synthetical methods, 103 ; Influence of science on French literature, 104 ; Absence of this influence in England and Germany, 106 ; Schools of science in Paris, 106 ; Promoted by Governments of Revolution, 108 ; Condorcet, 110 ; Lakanal, 111 ; École normale, École polytechnique, 112 ; Monge's 'Descriptive Geometry,' 114 ; Science of Chemistry, 114 ; New mathematical sciences, 116 ; Crystallography, 116 ; Theory of probability, 118 ; Laplace gained his results by disregarding "individuality," 124 ; The centre of interest in the sciences of life, 125 ; Into this centre Cuvier carried exact research, 128 ; Cuvier's training, 133 ; Cuvier the greatest representative of the Academic system, 136 ; Science during the Revolution and First Empire, 138 ; Popularisation of science in France, 142 ; Literary and national popularisation, 142 ; Dangers of the former, 143 ; The Revolution added the practical popularisation, 145 ; Influence of the first Napoleon on science, 149 ; Napoleon favoured the mathematical sciences, 151 ; Discountenanced contemporary philosophy, 152 ; Used statistical methods, 153 ; Prominence given deservedly to French names by Cuvier, 155.

CHAPTER II.

THE SCIENTIFIC SPIRIT IN GERMANY.

Foundation of German universities, 158 ; Development of the universities by the people, 159 ; Geographical distribution of the universities, 162 ; Full development of the German university system, 163 ; Philosophical faculty, 164 ; University of Göttingen, 164 ; Relation of universities and high schools, 166; The university a training-school for research, 167; The ideal of *Wissenschaft*, 168; Developed under the German university system, 170; Reception of exact science in Germany, 174; Science not yet domiciled during the eighteenth century, 178; Scientific periodicals, 180; Gauss's mathematical researches, 181; Scientific spirit enters the universities in second quarter of century, 183; Jacobi's mathematical school, 185; Chemical laboratories established in 1826 through Liebig, 188; Cosmopolitan character of German science, 189; Liebig's organic analysis, 191; Biology a German science, 193; Cellular theory of Schleiden, 194; and Schwann, 195; Ernst Heinrich Weber, 196; and Johannes Müller, 197; Psychophysics, 198; Spirit of exact research and *Wissenschaft*, 202; Encyclopædic view necessary in philosophy and history, 203; Philosophy of Nature, 204; Conflict between the scientific and the philosophical views, 205; A. von Humboldt, 206; Influence of Berzelius on German science, 208; Philosophy of Nature and medical science, 209; Science for its own sake, 211; Bequest of the classical and philosophical school, 211; Completeness and thoroughness of research, 213; Combination of research and teaching, 214; Combination of science and philosophy, 215; Biology grown out of science and philosophy combined, 216; Du Bois-Reymond on Müller, 217; "Vital force" abandoned, 218; Mechanical view in biology, 219; Criticism of principles of mathematics, 221; The exact, the historical, and the critical habits of thought, 222.

CHAPTER III.

THE SCIENTIFIC SPIRIT IN ENGLAND.

Scientific organisation abroad, 226; Similar institutions in Great Britain, 227; English science in the early part of the century, 229; Alleged decline of science in England, 230; Criticisms of Playfair, 231; Babbage's criticisms, 233; Foreign opinions on English science, 235; English replies to Babbage, 238; Foundation of the British Association, 238; Characteristics of higher mental work in England, 239; Academies and universities not always impartial, 240; Fourier, 241; Fresnel, 241; Plücker, 242; Grassmann, 243; Central organisation wanting in England, 243; Thomas Young, 244; Dalton, 245; Faraday, 246; Green, 246; Boole, 247; Babbage, 248; Characteristics of English thought, 249; Absence of schools of scientific thought, 250; Individual character and practical tendency of English science, 251; English peculiarities more pronounced during earlier part of the century, 252; Unique character of English universities, 254; Ideal of "liberal education," 255; Union of education and instruction, 258; Educational organisations in England, 262; The

Royal Institution, 264; Manchester Literary and Philosophical Society, 265; John Dawson of Sedbergh, 267; The Scotch Universities, 267; The Royal Society of Edinburgh, 269; The 'Edinburgh Review,' 270; The Analytical Society of Cambridge, 271; University life in Scotland, 271; The Dublin Mathematical School, 274; Importance of British contributions to science, 276; Diffusion of scientific knowledge on the Continent, 276; Isolation of English men of science, 277; Individualism of the English character, 279; Changes during the last fifty years, 280; British contributions to biology, 282; Jenner, 284; English love of nature, 284; Union of individualism and naturalism in England, 286; White of Selborne, 288; The Geological Society, 290; William Smith, 291; Charles Bell, 292; Historical Geography, 294; Martin William Leake, 296; Work of the three nations compared, 298.

CHAPTER IV.

THE ASTRONOMICAL VIEW OF NATURE.

The scientific spirit in the first and second half of the century, 302; Science become international, 303; Disappearance of national differences, 305; Special scientific ideas, 306; Philosophy of science, 306; Whewell's 'History' and 'Philosophy,' 309; Philosophy and science, 311; Leading scientific ideas mostly very ancient, 312; Mathematical spirit, 314; When first introduced into science, 317; Newton's 'Principia,' 318; The gravitation formula, 319; Lines of thought emanating from it, 321; Element of error, 323; Laplace and Newton, 326; Several interests which promote science, 326; Insufficiency of observation, 328; Practical interest, 328; Focalising effect of mathematical formulæ, 332; Matter and force mathematically defined, 334; Weight and mass, 336; Gravitation not an ultimate property of matter, 338; Attraction and repulsion, 342; Electrical and magnetic action, 344; Law of emanations, 344; Molecular action, 346; The astronomical view: Cosmical, molar, and molecular phenomena, 348; Special interest attached to molar dimensions, 350; Geometrical axioms, 352; Difficulty of measuring gravitation directly, 353; Astronomical view of molecular phenomena, 354; Capillary attraction, 356; Boscovich's extension of the Newtonian formula, 357; Coulomb's measurements, 360; Extended by Gauss and Weber, 360; Davy and Faraday, 363; Ampère and Weber develop the astronomical view, 366; Weber's fundamental measurements, 368; Necessity of developing the infinitesimal methods, 373; Newtonian formula the basis of physical astronomy, 375; The Newtonian formula unique as to universality and accuracy, 377; Is it an ultimate law? 378; Laplace's opinion, 378; Opposition to the astronomical view of nature, 381.

CHAPTER V.

THE ATOMIC VIEW OF NATURE.

Recapitulation, 382; Atomic theory, 385; Lavoisier, 386; Phlogistic theory, 388; Theory of combustion, 389; Rule of fixed proportions, 392; J. Benjamin Richter, 393; Dalton, 394; Berzelius, 396; Atomic theory and gravitation compared, 396; Wollaston's prophecy, 397; Rule of multiple proportions, 398; Equivalents, 399; "Simplex sigillum veri," 401; Prout's hypothesis, 402; Discovery of Isomerism, 405; Organic Chemistry, 407; Liebig's definition of same, 409; Type theory, 411; Uncertainty in chemical theory about middle of century, 413; Two aspects of the atomic theory, 415; A convenient symbolism, 417; Neglect of the study of affinity, 420; Kopp on chemical theory in 1873, 421; The periodic law, 422; Difference between chemical and physical reasoning, 424; The kinetic theory of gases, 425; Avogadro's hypothesis, 427; Neglect of same, 429; Development of the atomic view, 431; Pasteur's discovery of "Chirality," 431; Atom and molecule, 432; Joule's calculations, 434; Clausius's first memoir, 435; Internal energy of molecules, 436; The atomic theory accepted as a physical theory about 1860, 437; Clerk Maxwell: The statistical view of nature, 438; Doctrine of averages, 440; Geometrical arrangement of atoms, 441; Crystallography, 441; Analogy between crystallographic and atomic laws, 444; Isomorphism, 444; Polymorphism, 446; Structural and stereo-chemistry, 447; Valency, 447; Atomic linkage, 449; The carbon tetrahedron, 450; Defects and insufficiency of the atomic view, 451; Theories of chemical affinity, 452; Practical influences, 453; Change in definition of organic chemistry, 454; Criticisms of the atomic view, 455.

A HISTORY OF
EUROPEAN SCIENTIFIC THOUGHT
IN THE NINETEENTH CENTURY

INTRODUCTION.

I.

BEHIND the panorama of external events and changes which history unfolds before our view there lies the hidden world of desires and motives, of passions and energies, which produced or accompanied them; behind the busy scenes of Life lie the inner regions of Thought. Only when facts and events cease to be unconnected, when they appear to us linked together according to some design and purpose, leading us back to some originating cause or forward to some defined end, can we speak of History in the sense which the word has acquired in modern language; and similarly do the hidden motives, desires, and energies which underlie or accompany the external events require to be somehow connected, to present themselves in some order and continuity, before we are able to grasp and record them.

1.
Thought, the hidden world.

That which has made facts and events capable of being chronicled and reviewed, that which underlies and connects them, that which must be reproduced by the historian who unfolds them to us, is the hidden element of Thought. Thought, and thought alone, be it as a principle of action or as the medium of after-contemplation, is capable of arranging and connecting, of combining what is isolated, of moving that which is stagnant, of propelling that which is stationary. Take away thought, and monotony becomes the order.

This assertion may seem bold to many, who would look rather to the grand phenomena of Nature than to the narrow limits of man's activity. A few remarks will, however, suffice to show that my proposition is not opposed to the view which they take. It may be urged that, independent of human life altogether, the earth has a history, the planetary system has a development, and that, according to modern theories, evolution is the principle which governs inanimate as well as animated nature; that rest and sameness are nowhere to be found, everywhere change and unrest. But change and unrest do not necessarily constitute history. Motion and change would be as monotonous as absolute rest, were they merely to repeat themselves endlessly, did the whole movement not produce something more, and were this something more not greater or better than the beginning. But greater and better are terms which imply comparison by a thinking beholder, who attaches to one thing a greater value than to another, judging by certain ideal standards, which are not in the objects or process of nature themselves, but are contained only in his own think-

2.
Thought, the only moving principle.

3.
History of Nature, how to be understood.

4.
Not intelligible without intellect.

ing mind. It may be that a mechanical and mindless series of changes can produce numbers without end, or forms of countless variety: but this process would deserve the name of history only if either the transition from unity to multiplicity, or the production of formal variety, were capable of being understood by a thinking mind,—if the result of the process were a matter of some concern, if an interest were attached to it, if a gain or loss could be recorded. The pendulum which swings backwards and forwards in endless monotony, the planet which moves round the sun in unceasing repetition, the atom of matter which vibrates in the same path, have for us no interest beyond the mathematical formulæ which govern their motions, and which permit us mentally to reproduce, *i.e.*, to think them. A combination of an infinite number of these elementary movements would have as little interest, were it not that out of such a combination there resulted something novel and unforeseen : something that was beautiful to behold or useful to possess, something that was valuable to a thinking mind in a higher or lower meaning of the word.

But if, even in inanimate nature, the processes of change acquire an interest, possess a history, only if referred to a thinking mind which can record, understand, and appreciate them, how much more is this the case when we deal with human affairs, where man is not only the thinking beholder but the principal agent ? Here the historic interest would cease, were the succeeding years and ages to produce no valuable change, were the rule of existence and the order of life to repeat themselves in unceasing monotony. The savage tribes of Africa have a history: but

5.
History of savage tribes, what is it?

this history is all known when the order of the day, the year, at most of a generation, is known. Even the highly complicated but stagnant life of China would have a short historical record—many thousands of years taking up no more space than as many days of modern European history:

"Better fifty years of Europe than a cycle of Cathay."

6.
Two ways
in which
Thought
enters into
History.

Thus it is that Thought becomes in two ways a subject of great interest and importance to the historian. Of every change in nature or human life we can ask: What has been its result in the world of thought? What gain or loss, what progress, has it worked in the minds of men, of us the beholders? Has it increased our knowledge, enriched our stock of ideas, deepened our insight, broadened our views and sympathies—in one word, has it added to our interests? has it made larger and fuller our inner life?

And of every change in human affairs we can ask this further question: What part has thought, the inner life, played in this change? These two questions mark the task of the historian of Thought.

7.
Definition
of Thought
impossible.

I do not think it necessary or practicable at this stage to explain minutely the terms with which we have so far been dealing. Many a one might be tempted to ask for a definition of Thought, or for a preciser statement of the actual relation between Nature, Life, and Thought.[1]

[1] In refusing to define what I mean by Thought, I take up the opposite position to that occupied by Prof. Max Müller in his latest work, 'The Science of Thought,' London, 1887, p. 1, where he says : "I mean by Thought the act of thinking, and by thinking I mean no more than combining. I do not pretend that others have not the right of using Thought in any sense which they prefer, provided only that they will clearly define it." So far as definition is at all a part of the work of the historian, I maintain that it is the result and

Such definitions must be left to the reader himself, if in course of the perusal of these volumes he finds it necessary to form abstract theories on these points. Any definition given now would inevitably involve us in controversies, which would be embarrassing and confusing. I rely upon the general and undefined sense of the word Thought, assuming that every one will connect some intelligible meaning with it, some meaning which will enable him to understand the very general proposition with which we started, the existence of an inner or hidden world behind the world of external events and facts, the continually changing nature of this inner world, and the connection and reaction between the two worlds. Whether in time and in importance the outer or the inner world is the first, whether within the latter equal value attaches to the clearer province of Reason, *i.e.*, defined Thought, to the obscurer regions of Feeling and Imagination, and to the unconscious world of Impulse, these are questions which it is not necessary to answer at present. As it was enough to point to the existence of the two worlds of Life and Thought, so it will be enough to notice that thought does not mean merely defined, clear, methodical thought, but likewise the great region of desire, impulse, feeling, and imagination, all of which play, we must admit, a great part in the inner life of the soul as well as in that of the outer world.

8. Relation of outer and inner world undefined.

9. Many meanings of Thought.

outcome of his narrative, the impression which he leaves on the mind of the reader when he has perused the work. History is not mainly a science which proceeds by analysis; it is the attempt to collect and arrange in a living picture an enormous mass of detail. Too rigid definitions, like lines which are too hard and marked, spoil the total effect.

In this sense of the word we have in the following treatise to deal with the History of Thought: not, however, with the history of thought in general, but with that of a defined period, with that of the present age and the age immediately preceding it,—the age, in fact, to which the writer and his readers belong, of which they have a personal knowledge and recollection more or less wide and intimate. It is the latter circumstance which has made me select this special portion of the history of thought; for it is that portion of which, it seems to me, I and my contemporaries should—if we go about it in the right way—know most. As every person is his own best biographer, so it seems to me every age is, in a certain sense, its own best historian.

10. Thought of the present age.

We know that this has been frequently denied so far as external events (that which many persons call history *par excellence*) are concerned. Contemporary writers do not, it is stated, get beyond mere records of events, records at once one-sided, incomplete, and confusing. It is indeed necessary to have the records in great number and variety: because the true and real record can only be given by him who combines all these many records into one, who avoids the errors arising from special points of view, from narrowness of outlook, from individual ignorance, blindness, or prejudice. Still, in spite of such defects, the contemporary records will always remain the most valuable sources for the future historian who may succeed in sifting their various testimonies, combining and utilising them to produce a fuller and more consistent picture of the bygone age. But while his work may be only temporarily valuable, theirs is

11. Contemporary history, to what extent possible and valuable.

lasting. It is hardly doubtful that, after hundreds or thousands of years have passed, the simple, detailed, and perhaps contradictory, narratives of contemporary witnesses will outlive those more elaborate and artistic efforts of the historian which are so largely inspired and coloured by the convictions of another—*viz.*, his own—age. For as Goethe has remarked: "History must from time to time be rewritten, not because many new facts have been discovered, but because new aspects come into view, because the participant in the progress of an age is led to standpoints from which the past can be regarded and judged in a novel manner."[1]

Most of the great historians whom our age has produced will, centuries hence, probably be more interesting as exhibiting special methods of research, special views on political, social, and literary progress, than as faithful and reliable chroniclers of events; and the objectivity on which some of them pride themselves will be looked upon not as freedom from but as unconsciousness on their part of the preconceived notions which have governed them. But where the facts recorded and the mind which records them both belong to the same age, we have a double testimony regarding that age. The events, and the contemplating mind, supplement each other to form a more complete picture, inasmuch as the matter and the medium through which it is viewed belong to the same time. And so it comes to pass that historians like Thucydides, Tacitus, and Machiavelli are looked upon as

12.
Supposed
Objectivity
of histor-
ians.

---

[1] 'Materialien zur Geschichte der Farbenlehre,' Werke, 2te Abtheilung, Band 3, p. 239. I quote from the new edition, brought out by the German Goethe Society.

perfect models in the art of writing history, and the memoirs of many modern statesmen are more lastingly valuable than the more elaborate and connected narratives of remote and secluded scholars.

13.
Value of contemporary records, both of Facts and Thought.

But if the contemporary record of facts will always have a peculiar value, however incomplete it may be, still more must this be the case with the contemporary record of thought; especially if thought means the whole of the inner life of an age, not merely that portion which in the form of defined thought has been incorporated in the written literature of the age. For a large portion of this hidden life is known only to those who have taken part in it.

14.
Mystery of the Life of Thought.

The vague yearnings of thousands who never succeed either in satisfying or expressing them, the hundreds of failures which never become known, the numberless desires which live only in the hearts of men or are painted only in their living features, the uncounted strivings after solutions of practical problems dictated by ambition or by want, the many hours spent by labourers of science in unsuccessful attempts to solve the riddles of nature,—all these hidden and forgotten efforts form indeed the bulk of a nation's thought, of which only a small fraction comes to the surface, or shows itself in the literature, science, poetry, art, and practical achievements of the age.

15.
Latent Thought the material for genius.

Equally important, though not equally prominent, this large body of forgotten thought has nevertheless been that which made the measure full, which heaped the fuel ready for the match to kindle; it constitutes the great propelling force which, stored up, awaits the time and aid of individual talent or genius to set it free. Philosophers tell us of the wastefulness of organic life, of the thousands of germs which perish, of the huge volume of seed scattered uselessly. A similar fate seems to fall on the larger portion of intellectual and moral effort; but here a deeper conviction tells us that it is not the sacrifice but the co-operation of the many which makes the few succeed, that excellence is the prize of united effort, that many must run so that one may reach a higher goal. What other feeling could console those legions of honest workers who spend their lives in trying to deal with the seemingly unconquerable host of social evils, the apparently growing vice and misery of large towns, who raise a cry for oppressed nationalities, or preach against the curses of war and militarism? Or what higher and unselfish satisfaction could an author derive from spending half a lifetime in producing a work which in the end may fall dead-born from the press, if it were not the conviction that in the cause in which he has failed another after him may succeed, and that his failure may be a portion of the silent and hidden efforts that co-operate towards a useful end?[1] But who in after-ages can write the history of this forgotten and hidden work of a nation? Whose historical sense is delicate enough to feel where the pressure was greatest and the effort longest ere the new life appeared, whose eye penetrating and discerning enough to follow up the dim streaks

---

[1] "Sehen wir nun während unseres Lebensganges dasjenige von anderen gelestet, wozu wir selbst früher einen Beruf fühlten, ihn aber, mit manchem andern, aufgeben mussten, dann tritt das schöne Gefühl ein, dass die Menschheit zusammen erst der wahre Mensch ist, und dass der Einzelne nur froh und glücklich sein kann, wenn er den Muth hat, sich im Ganzen zu fühlen."—Goethe, 'Wahrheit und Dichtung,' 9th Book; Werke, 27, 277.

of twilight, dazzled as he must be by the blaze of the

16.
Contempor-
ary record
of Thought
more faith-
ful.

risen sun ? We who live in the expectation of the light
which is to come, surrounded by the shadows, difficulties,
and obstacles ; we who belong to the army, and are not
leaders, who live in, not after, the fight,—we claim to be
better able to tell the tale of endless hopes and endeavours, of efforts common to many, of the hidden intellectual and moral work of our age.[1]

How far back we who have lived during the second
half of the present century may extend the period of
which we claim to have a personal knowledge, is a point
of further interest. Certain it is that in our parents and
immediate forefathers we have known the representatives
of a generation which witnessed and laboured in the in-

17.
Events of
the imme-
diate past.

terests of the great Anti-Slavery, the Reform, and the Anti-
Corn-Law movements, who experienced the revolutions
worked by the introduction of steam-power and gas, who
took part in the great work of national and popular education abroad and in the reform of school-life in England.
They themselves went through the enthusiasm of the
anti-Napoleonic Revolution in Germany, came under the
influence of Goethe's mature manhood, were fascinated by
the stories from the pen of the Wizard of the North, par-

[1] Compare what A. de Tocqueville
says, ' Œuv. comp.,' vol. viii. p. 170 :
" Nous sommes encore trop près des
évènements pour en connaître les
détails. Cela paraît singulier, mais
est vrai. Les détails ne s'appren-
nent que par les révélations post-
humes, contenues dans les Mémoires, et sont souvent ignorés des
contemporains. Ce qu'ils savent
mieux que la posterité, c'est le
mouvement des esprits, les passions générales du temps, dont ils
sentent encore les derniers frémis-
sements dans leur esprit ou dans
leur cœur ; c'est le rapport vrai des
principaux personnages et des principaux faits entre eux. Voilà ce
que les voisins des temps racontés
aperçoivent mieux que ne fait la
postérité."

took of the spirit of the Romantic School, felt the electrical touch of Lord Byron's verse, listened to the great orators of the third French Revolution, and could tell us of the now forgotten spell which Napoleon I. exercised over millions of reluctant admirers. Most of these fascinations and interests live only in the narratives of contemporaries and surviving witnesses, few of whom have succeeded in perpetuating them with pen or brush, making them intelligible to a future age ; most of them die with the generation itself. Not only have we listened to their words and seen in their features the traces of the anxieties they lived through, in their eyes the reflected enthusiasms and aspirations, in their glances and in the trembling of their voices the last quiverings of bygone passion and joy,—we have received from them a still more eloquent testimonial, a more living inheritance. But this we cannot hand down to our children in the form in which it was given to us : it has not passed through our hands unaltered. This inheritance is the language which our parents have taught us. Unknowingly they have themselves altered the tongue, the words and sentences, which they received, depositing in these altered words and modes of speech the spirit, the ideas, the thought of their lifetime. These words and modes of speech they handed to us in our infancy, as the mould wherein to shape our minds, as the shell wherein to envelop our slowly growing thoughts, as the instrument with which to convey our ideas. In their language, in the phrases and catchwords peculiar to them, we learnt to distinguish what was important and interesting from what was trivial or indifferent, the subjects which

18. Changes which Language undergoes from parent to child, a proof of the changing life of Thought.

should occupy our thoughts, the aims we should follow, the principles and methods which we should make use of. The bulk and substance of this they indeed inherited themselves; but the finer distinctions of their reasoning, the delicate shading of their feelings and aspirations, they added and modified for themselves, modelling for their own special use the pliable and elastic medium of the mother tongue. With this finer moulding we have inherited the spirit of the former generation : predisposing us to certain phases of thought and placing in our path a difficulty in acquiring otherwise than by gradual and almost imperceptible degrees the faculty of assimilating new and unexpected opinions, tastes, and feelings. Many of us adhere to the special character and phase of thought acquired in our youth. Some by learning foreign languages, and living in other countries, gain a facility for understanding quite different phases of thought : very few among us develop so much original thought that they burst the shell of conventional speech, coining new words and expressions for themselves, embodying in them the fleeting ideas of their time, the indefinable spirit of their age. Once expressed, these new terms are rapidly circulated, and if we look back on the period of a generation, we note easily the progress and development of opinion and tastes in the altered terms and style of our language.

19.
Inadequacy
of conventional
speech for
original
thought.
Coining of
new words.

Thus it is that the writer, and those of his readers whose memory carries them back to the middle of the century, and whose schooling and education embodied the ideas of a generation before that time, can claim to have some personal knowledge of the greater portion of the nineteenth century, of the interests which it created and the thoughts which stirred it.[1] It is the object of these volumes to fix, if possible, this possession; to rescue from oblivion that which appears to me to be our secret property; in the last and dying hour of a remarkable age to throw the light upon the fading outlines of its mental life; to try to trace them, and with the aid of all possible information, gained from the written testimonies or the records of others, to work them into a coherent picture, which may give those who follow some idea of the peculiar manner in which our age looked upon the world and life, how it intellectualised and spiritualised them. This attempt is therefore not a history of outward political changes or of industrial achievements: the former will probably be better known to our children than they have been to us; the latter will soon be forgotten as such, or incorporated in the still greater results of the future, for which they will be the preparation. Nor is it a history of Knowledge and Science, of Literature and Art, which I purpose to write; though as these are the outcome of the inner life, and contain it, so to say, in a crystallised form, they will always have to be appealed to for the purpose of verifying the conclusions which we may arrive

20.
Object of this work to retrace the life of Thought through the dying century.

21.
Not a political history, nor a history of Science, Literature, and Art.

___

[1] On the division of History into centuries see what Du Bois-Reymond says ('Reden,' Leipzig, 1886, vol. i. p. 519), and the fuller discussion of the subject by Prof. O. Lorenz, 'Die Geschichts - wissenschaft' (Berlin, 1886, p. 279 *sqq.*) The latter refers to what the first historian says (Herodotus, ii. 142: Καίτοι τριηκόσιαι μὲν ἀνδρῶν γενεαὶ δυνέαται μύρια ἔτεα· γενεαὶ γὰρ τρεῖς ἀνδρῶν ἑκατὸν ἔτεά ἐστι). A person born in 1840 can claim to have a personal knowledge of the last half, and through his parents and teachers a knowledge of the first half, of the century. In this way it may be said that his personal— direct or indirect—knowledge extends over nearly a century. Lorenz says correctly: "Für jeden einzelnen bildet der Vater und der Sohn eine greifbare Kette von Lebensereignissen und Erfahrungen." And that this applies even more to ideas and opinions, to Thought, than to events and facts, is evident.

22.
Where the
interest of
the book
will lie :
in all the
influences
which have
a result on
our inner
life.

at. What will interest us most will be the conscious aims and ends, if such existed, of any political or social movement, and, where they did not exist, at least the results to our inner life which have necessarily followed, the methods by which knowledge was extended or science applied, the principles which underlay literary composition and criticism, and the hidden spiritual treasure which poetry, art, and religious movements aimed at revealing or communicating; in fact the question : What part has the inner world of Thought played in the history of our century,—what development, what progress, what gain has been the result of the external events and changes ?

23.
The personal
knowledge
and experi-
ence neces-
sary for a
true por-
trayal forms
a limitation
of the ex-
tent of
ground to be
traversed.

But if personal knowledge and experience are—as it seems to me—of the greatest importance in an attempt like this; if, without having lived the inner life, a record of it would be either a mere string of names or a criticism of opinions, not a living picture,—so it is also the factor which necessarily limits the extent of the ground which I propose to traverse. Thus I feel obliged in the first place to limit myself to European Thought. Such a limi-tation would hardly have been called for a century ago, because it would have been a matter of course : but the steady growth and peculiar civilisation of a new and vigorous people on the other side of the Atlantic force

24.
American
influence
only
touched
upon.

from me the twofold confession, that there is a large world of growing importance of which I have no personal knowledge, and to estimate which I therefore feel un-qualified and unprepared; and further, that I am equally unable to picture to myself the aspect which the whole of our European culture in its present state may assume to an outside and far-removed observer who is placed in the

New World.   As this New World grows not only in
numbers and national wealth, but also in mental depth,
as it becomes more and more intellectualised and
spiritualised, so it will no doubt experience the desire of
recording its own inner life and culture, emphasising the
peculiarities which distinguish it as a whole from our
civilisation.   But the tendencies of this new culture are
to me vague and enigmatical, and I frankly admit that
I am unable to say anything definite on this subject.   Convinced as I am that in human affairs all outer life is the
vessel which contains an inner substance, the shell which
envelops a growing kernel, I am, nevertheless, unable in
this case to penetrate to either, and must therefore content
myself with taking notice of this vast new element of
nineteenth-century culture only where it comes into
immediate contact with European thought, which has
indeed been powerfully influenced by it.   And of Euro-   25.
pean thought itself I am forced to select likewise only   Only French,
the central portion, the thought embodied in French,   German,
and English
German, and English Literature.   I have to admit that   thought the
subject of
the present
work.
Italian, Scandinavian, and Russian influences are all
around this centre, sometimes penetrating far into it;
but here again languages unknown and interests foreign
to me have made it impossible to identify myself ever so
superficially with the new life that is contained in them.
I must therefore here also confine myself to very imperfect and casual notices, which make no attempt to
do justice to the subject.

The subject before us, then, is European Thought—*i.e.*,
the thought of France, Germany, and England—during the
greater part of the nineteenth century.   Circumscribed as

this subject is by the limits of time and space which I
have mentioned, it is, nevertheless, still vast, intricate, and
bewildering. And yet it is my intention, throughout the
inquiries which I have to institute and in the various outlines and sketches which I have to draw, never to lose
sight of the unity of the whole. This unity, I maintain,
the progress of our age has more and more forced upon
us. It is itself a result of the work of the century. A
hundred years—even fifty years—ago, it would have been
impossible to speak of European Thought in the manner
in which I do now. For the seventeenth and eighteenth
centuries mark the period in which, owing to the use of
the several vernacular languages of Europe in the place
of the mediæval Latin, thought became nationalised, in
which there grew up first the separate literature and then
the separate thought of the different civilised countries of
Western Europe. Thus it was that in the last century,
and at the beginning of this, people could make journeys
of exploration in the region of thought from one country
to another, bringing home with them new and fresh ideas.
Such journeys of discovery, followed by importation of new
ideas, were those of Voltaire[1] to England in 1726, where
he found the philosophy of Newton and Locke, at that
time not known and therefore not popularly appreciated
in France; the journey of Adam Smith in 1765 to France,
where he became acquainted with the economic system of
Quesnay and the opinions of the so-called " physiocrats,"
which formed the starting-point of his own great work,

*26.
Unity of
Thought a
product
of this
century.*

*27.
Voltaire.*

*28.
Adam
Smith.*

---

[1] For a most complete collection
of data referring to this subject
see Du Bois-Reymond's address in
the Berlin Academy, 30th January
1868, reprinted in the collection of
his 'Reden,' Leipzig, 1886, vol. i.

individual thought of each of the three nations has found refuge.[1] Any one who has attempted to translate from one of these languages into another, be it prose or be it lyrical, philosophical, or descriptive poetry, will have experienced the necessity of studying minutely the meaning or hidden thought which a word or a phrase may signify : he will have been led to notice what is common and what is peculiar to different languages,

[1] The only books which treat of words in the sense mentioned above, and which have come under my notice, are Horne Tooke's 'Diversions of Purley' and Archbishop Trench's little volumes on 'The Study of Words' and 'English Past and Present.' So far as the use of merely philosophical terms is concerned, I may refer to R. Eucken, 'Geschichte der philosophischen Terminologie,' Leipzig, 1879. A great deal of material for a research of this kind may be found in the large Dictionaries of Grimm, Littré, and Murray, though I do not feel sure that the great change which has come over language, through the expansion, deepening, and differentiation of ideas and of thought in our age, has been specially taken note of. The plan of Grimm's Dictionary, which aims at embracing the German language in its development during three centuries, beginning with Luther and ending with Goethe (see Wilh. Grimm's 'Kleinere Schriften,' vol. i. p. 508), almost excludes the period which I am reviewing.

It is interesting to remember that Diderot, the first writer who attempted to collect the great body of modern Thought and Learning into an encyclopædic whole, referred to Language very much in the same manner as we do now, a hundred and fifty years later.

See the article "Encyclopédie," where Diderot says that a Dictionary is only an exact collection of titles, to be filled in by the Encyclopædia ; and further on, p. 639 : "Si l'on compte les hommes de génie, et qu'on les répande sur toute la durée des siècles écoulés, il est évident qu'ils seront en petit nombre dans chaque nation et pour chaque siècle, et qu'on n'en trouvera presqu'aucun qui n'ait perfectionné la langue. Les hommes créateurs portent ce caractère particulier. Comme ce n'est pas seulement en feuilletant les productions de leur contemporains qu'ils rencontrent les idées qu'ils ont à employer dans leurs écrits, mais que c'est tantôt en descendant profondément en eux-mêmes, tantôt en s'élançant au dehors, et portant des regards plus attentifs et plus pénétrans sur les natures qu'ils environnent, ils sont obligés, surtout à l'origine des langues, d'inventer des signes pour rendre avec exactitude et avec force ce qu'ils y decouvrent les premiers. C'est la chaleur de l'imagination et la méditation profonde qui enrichissent une langue d'expressions nouvelles : c'est la justesse de l'esprit et la sévérité de la dialectique qui en perfectionnent la syntaxe ; c'est la commodité des organes de la parole qui l'adoucit; c'est la sensibilité de l'oreille qui la rend harmonieuse."

39.
Goethe.

and the thought which they express. Of Goethe it may be said that he created to a large extent the language and style of that which is best in the modern literature of his country. No such supreme influence belonging to a single individual can probably be found in any other German, French, or English writer in our century, for reasons which are obvious : but the great French novelists, the German metaphysicians, and the original poetical minds of modern England have enlarged and enriched the vocabulary of their respective languages, and have added a number of useful and novel modes of expression (*tournures, Wendungen*). Carlyle's influence has been great in introducing novel epithets, borrowed or imported frequently from the German. Matthew Arnold has laboured in a similar direction, his models being, besides Goethe and Heine, mostly French authors, such as Sainte-Beuve and the introspective school. Germany has been less fortunate

40.
Peculiarity
of the
German
Language.

in extending her vernacular vocabulary : the facility which her language possesses of assimilating foreign words and using them almost without any alteration has done much to complicate German style, destroying its simplicity, its graces, the poetical element. It will, however, probably be found that by far the greatest accession to the vocabularies—though not to the finer modelling—of the modern languages has come from the influence of the

41.
Growth in
the mean-
ings of
words.

sciences on general culture and literature. Well-known words, long in use, have at the same time through this influence acquired altered or more specific meanings.

The vaguer word " development " has been supplanted by " evolution." " Differentiation " has a definite philosophic—not only a mathematical—meaning. The word "positive" has, besides the logical signification, acquired at least two meanings which are very specific, and which it did not possess formerly. "Energy" has, besides the general meaning, and the philosophical one which Aristotle assigned to it, acquired a special meaning, having first in England and then abroad taken the place of "force" as a more correct and definable term. In connection with it, "correlation" and "conservation" are terms of very specific value. The word "fittest" and the phrase "struggle for existence" mean something different from what they meant fifty years ago. Then there are the terms "exact" and "science" themselves, which mean something different now from what they meant formerly. And coming out of the more recent doctrines of the limits of human and conscious individual knowledge, there are the words "unconscious," "unknowable," and "agnostic," which indicate whole trains of novel thought. It would indeed be an interesting and useful investigation to follow up to their origin the many new words and phrases, or the altered meanings of well-known and familiar words, in which the three principal European languages abound. It would be a methodical study of the changes which thought has undergone.

42.
New thought has found new words.

Nor need such an undertaking be based upon any particular or one-sided theory as to the connection of Civilisation, Thought, and Language. This century has not been wanting in such, from the extreme theory of De Bonald,[1] who saw in Language an immediate Divine revelation, to the most recent and more scientific view

43.
De Bonald's theory of revealed Language and Max Müller's Science of Language.

[1] De Bonald (1754-1840), 'Législation primitive,' Paris, 1802.

of Max Müller, who would absorb philosophy in the science of Language[1] in the same way as Astronomy has to many become merely " une question d'analyse." In a certain sense we can agree with both of these thinkers. Without discussing the vexed question of the origin of Language and Thought, to us as individuals, born in a civilised and intellectual age, words certainly came earlier than clear and conscious thought. The easy manner also in which, through the use of our parents' tongue, we became introduced into a complex and bewildering labyrinth of highly abstract reasoning is little short of a miraculous revelation. But, as I mentioned above, it is not my intention to study the development of European thought during this century by means of a close analysis of the changes and growth of the three principal languages. Such an enterprise would demand an amount of lexico-graphical knowledge possessed only by the authors of dictionaries like those of Grimm, Littré, and Murray. But though I am not qualified for such a task, there is one special point on which I cannot avoid being drawn into a grammatical discussion. It refers to the word Thought

44. Thought, how expressed in French and German. itself. How is the meaning which I and my readers connect with this word to be expressed in French and German? How are we to translate the word? The subject we deal with does not belong to England alone, but as much to France and to Germany: it must thus have a name in each of their languages. Now I believe that the word *pensée* expresses in French very nearly the same thing which we mean in English by thought. It is some-

[1] See his 'Science of Thought,' London, 1887, especially pp. 292 and 550.

what more difficult to find a corresponding word in German. I have for some time hesitated whether to use the word *Geist* or *Weltanschauung*, two terms frequently used to express the aggregate of the inner life of an age: but have finally resolved to use the word *Denken*, as this word lends itself to the same contrasts of Life and Action (*Leben und Handeln*), denoting the inner world, whereas the opposite of *Geist* is *Stoff* (matter), and *Weltanschauung*, though an expressive and untranslatable word, denotes rather the outcome, the result, of thought than thought itself. Passing from the word to the subject itself, I find that the greater definiteness of the term in the English language is accompanied also by a more abundant literature of the subject. The larger idea of a Philosophy of History is indeed due mainly to Continental thinkers, especially to Herder, Hegel, Comte, and Guizot, and Voltaire's 'Siècle de Louis XIV.' will always be the model of the historical picture of a period. Still it is— in my opinion—mainly the writings of Carlyle, Buckle, Draper, Lecky, Leslie Stephen, and, considering its size, perhaps more than all, Mark Pattison's 'Essay,'[1] which have fixed in our minds the meaning of the word Thought as the most suitable and comprehensive term to denote the whole of the inner or hidden Life and Activity of a period or a nation. I therefore put in a claim to start with the use of the English word, as sufficiently familiar to most of my readers, and request those who may object to the vagueness of the French

45.
Philosophy
of History
due to Continental
thinkers.

---

[1] See 'Essays and Reviews,' 'Tendencies of Religious Thought in England, 1688-1750,' by Mark Pattison; also Leslie Stephen's remarks on it in the Preface to his 'History of English Thought in the Eighteenth Century.'

and German equivalents to look for a definition of my intention in the English word "Thought." I am not aware that French literature possesses any "histoire de la pensée," either of a longer or shorter period; I know of innumerable works in German which cover a similar field, but they have mostly used the word *Weltanschauung*, or expanded the meaning of Thought into the wider sense of a history of Civilisation (*Kulturgeschichte*) or narrowed it to that of Literature, proving—as it seems to me— the real want of a concise term such as the English language now supplies. And yet, I think I am right in saying that the conception of Thought, in the sense in which I am using it, is truly an outcome of interna- tional, not of specifically English progress, and belongs mainly to the period of which I am treating,—a period characterised, as I have already remarked, by the great interchange of ideas, by the breaking down of intellectual barriers, between the principal European nationalities. It was above all in the mind of Thomas Carlyle, who first among Englishmen made a profound study of the intel- lectual agencies which brought about the great change in modern Europe, that the conception formed itself of an intellectual and spiritual organism, underlying and moving external events. He first gave the peculiar sense to the word Thought, in which we here employ it, and made it an object of special study for those who came after him; an object, indeed, definable in various ways and to be con- templated from differing points of view, but yet a some- thing, a power recognised by every one, and for which no better word could be invented. No other language has a word so comprehensive, denoting at once the process and

46.
Want of
precise term
in German
and French.

47.
Conception
of Thought
neverthe-
less not spe-
cifically
English.

48.
Carlyle the
first to give
a special
meaning to
the word
Thought.

the result, the parts and the ideal whole, of what is felt and meant : it commits us to no preconceived theory, can be used equally by thinkers of the most opposite views, and lends itself to any specialisation which may become necessary.

II.

Two processes have helped to determine the intellectual progress of mankind. These two processes have often been apparently opposed to each other in their operations ; but in reality neither of them can proceed very far without calling the other into existence. They are the extension and the condensation of knowledge. Curiosity, the demands of practical life, the experiences of every day, all tend to an enlargement, to an accumulation of knowledge. Such growing knowledge is, however, of little avail if it be not readily grasped : the command of knowledge is as important as its accumulation. The more extensive the country which we wish to explore, the more we look out for elevated and commanding points of view, which permit us at a glance to overlook a wide landscape measuring the distance behind or the prospect before us. But, however enticing, these elevated views are frequently seductive and misleading. They permit us not only to look backward on the land which we have explored, giving us a clearer picture of its many features, of its winding paths, of the position of its separate objects —these elevated views present to us likewise the regions which we have not yet explored, and suggest the attempt to supersede the laborious process of further exploration

1.
The two factors of intellectual progress.

by the more delightful venture of filling up the dim outlines which we see before us, with analogies of past experience or creations of our imagination.   And even if
we do descend into the plains and continue the minuter
and more laborious search, we cannot rid ourselves of certain preconceived but frequently misleading ideas which
the superficial glance has impressed on our minds.

The condensation may become an idealisation of knowledge.   History affords numerous examples of these different stages of progress; centuries of dull accumulation,
of unmethodical and ill-arranged learning, have been followed by short periods of enlightenment, by the triumphant shout of sudden discovery or the confident hope of
invention.   Patient work and real progress have for a long
time been repressed by the allurements of seductive phantoms, which have had to be abandoned after an immense
waste of labour.   New prospects have suddenly opened
the view into vast unexplored regions, heights have been
gained from which the whole of human knowledge appeared for the moment condensed into a single truth or
idealised into a vision, and again these delightful achievements have for a time appeared lost in an all-pervading
discouragement and dismay.

2.
Object of
the book.

Whether our century has been characterised by any
one or by a succession of several of these varying moods,
is a question which I hope to answer in the sequel.   For
the present it is sufficient to note that in both directions—
in that of accumulating and in that of condensing and
idealising knowledge—the efforts of the nineteenth century have been many and conspicuous.   In the former it
is altogether unparalleled, whereas in the latter it has

3.
Nineteenth
century un-
equalled in
accumula-
tion of
knowledge.

probably not equalled the ideal greatness of Greece in the Periclean age, the brilliancy of the Renaissance in Italy, or the great discoveries of the sixteenth and seventeenth centuries in France and England. But what our century has done is this: it has worked out and deposited in special terms of language a clearer view of the correct methods for extending knowledge, and a peculiar conception of its possible unity. At one time—and that not very long ago—the word truth seemed to indicate to the seeker not only the right method and road for attaining knowledge, but also the end, the crown of knowledge. "Truth, and nothing but truth," seems still to the popular mind the right maxim for seeking knowledge—the whole truth stands before it as the unity of all knowledge, were it found. I think it is now sufficiently clear to the scientific inquirer, as well as to the philosopher, that love of truth, while it does indeed denote the moral attitude of the inquiring mind, is insufficient to define either the path or the end of knowledge. "What is truth?" is still the unsolved question. The criteria of truth are still unsettled. It would, indeed, be a sorrowful experience, a calamity of unparalleled magnitude, if ever the moral ideas of truth and faith should disappear out of the soul of either the active worker or the inquiring thinker; but it is with these as with other treasures of our moral nature, such as goodness and holiness, beauty and poetry—our knowledge of them does not begin, nor does it increase, by definition; and though in the unthinking years of our childhood we acquire and appropriate these moral possessions through the words of our mother-tongue, they rarely gain in depth or meaning by logical distinctions which we may learn,

4. Nineteenth century, what it has achieved: a. Method of knowledge; b. unity of knowledge.

5. Search after truth not the end of knowledge, only the attitude of the inquiring mind.

or to which we have to submit, in later life. These do
not touch the essence, though very frequently they may
succeed in destroying the depth, of our convictions.

In the place, then, of the high-sounding but indefinable
search after truth, modern science has put an elaborate
method of inquiry: this method has to be learnt by patient
practice, and not by listening to a description of it. It is
laid down in the works of those modern heroes of science,
from Galileo and Newton onward, who have practised it
successfully, and from whose writings philosophers from
Bacon to Comte and Mill have—not without misunderstanding and error—tried to extract the *rationale*. These
methods will take up a large portion of our attention.
For the moment it is important to note that the result or
aim of scientific inquiry does not dictate the methods,—the
purely scientific inquirer does not know where the path
will lead him: it is sufficient that it be clearly marked.
Modern science defines the method, not the aim, of its
work. It is based upon numbering and calculating—in
short, upon mathematical processes; and the progress of
science depends as much upon introducing mathematical
notions into subjects which are apparently not mathematical, as upon the extension of mathematical methods
and conceptions themselves. The terms "exact" and "positive" are current in the Continental and English languages
to denote these methods and their application. Now to
any one who does not stand in the midst of the scientific
work of the age, it might appear as if by merely following
a defined method which is capable of numerous modifications,—by treading a clear path which in its course leads
us to endless equally defined ramifications,—the scientific

6.
Method of
scientific
inquiry.
Practised
first by
Galileo,
Newton,&c.,
defined by
Bacon,
Comte,
Mill, &c.

7.
Disintegra-
tion of
learning
only ap-
parent.

inquirer is losing daily more and more those elevated views, those points of condensation, those unifying and idealising aspects on which, as it seems to us, the command and grasp of knowledge depends. This is indeed almost inevitable so far as the older ideas are concerned. Unity of knowledge, order and harmony, even completeness and symmetry, truth and beauty, are indeed no longer of direct use as canons for the scientific inquirer, any more than the mysteries once supposed to be inherent in certain numbers. Though we still live under the charm of such entities, however much we may try to get rid of them, it must nevertheless be admitted that the poetical, philosophical, and religious aspects of things seem to recede into an increasing distance from the scientific ; they do not guide scientific search ; it does not receive from them much support. Have both sides been losers by this change ? So far as science is concerned, it can claim to have attained by it not only a greater formal completeness and certainty of progress, but also another very important advantage which was unknown to ancient and mediæval research.

8. Apparent distance between science and poetry.

This advantage consists in the closer connection between science and practical life. The same mathematical spirit which governs scientific methods rules also in trade, commerce, and industry, and is gradually penetrating into the professions, such as medicine, law, and administration. For all these pursuits have either directly to do with numbers, measures, and weights, with distances of space and time, or they have found it necessary to introduce an elaborate system of statistics and averages through which the irregularity and captiousness of subjective and individual influences are practically eliminated. The

9. Closer connection between science and life.

problems of scientific research have thus enormously increased; each advance in science increases our command
of certain measurable phenomena in practical life; each
new development in the latter prepares a new field for
scientific inquiry. The contact between science and life
has become more intimate in the course of our century.
This to a great extent has counterbalanced the tendency
of modern scientific method, which, operating alone, would
have led to endless specialisation; for it is the peculiarity

10.
Solidarity of
all practical
problems.

of all practical problems that they cannot be isolated in
the same way as scientific experiments—that they, in fact,
force upon us the necessity of looking at a large number
of surrounding and extraneous circumstances, at the totality of life and its interests.[1]

If our century can claim to have firmly established
exact or positive methods in science and life, and to have
furthered in this way the interests of both, the question

11.
What has the
nineteenth
century
done for
the ideals
of life?

remains, Has nothing been done to uphold those older,
those time-hallowed ideals of truth, beauty, and wisdom
which to former ages seemed to denote the unifying and
harmonising principles of science and life? What has
become of philosophy, art, and religion, which were once
intrusted with the special care of those ideals, charged
with preventing the falling asunder of the many branches
of knowledge and practice, and expected to save us from
a loss of the belief in the integrity, interdependence, and
co-operation of all human interests?

---

[1] Science deals with things in the
abstract, in their isolation, *in vacuo.*
Practical life deals with the same
things in their position in the real
world, surrounded by other things.
In this distinction lies the value of
Lotze's definition of the reality of
a thing as "a standing in relation,"
viz., to other things, to all things.
See 'Microcosmus,' book ix.

Unless I believed that our age was elaborating a deeper and more significant conception of this unity of all human interests, of the inner mental life of man and mankind, I do not think I should have deemed it worth while to write the following volumes : for it is really their main end and principal object to trace the co-operation of many agencies in the higher work of our century ; the growing conviction that all mental efforts combine together to produce and uphold the ideal possessions of our race ; that it is not in one special direction nor under one specific term that this treasure can be cultivated, but that individuals and peoples in their combined international life exhibit and perpetuate it.

12.
Deeper conception of the unity of human interests.

A number of words have during this century been introduced by various systems of philosophy to denote this unity of the inner life of mankind : Hegel's *Geist*, Comte's Humanity, Lotze's Microcosm, Spencer's Social Organism, all refer to special sides and aspects of the same subject. And it is interesting to note how the great schools of Idealism in Germany, of Positivism in France, of Evolution—physical and mental—in England, and—in spite of their apparently disintegrating tendencies—how the social changes of the Revolution and the specialisations of science have all combined to emphasise this unity of human life and interests. To show this in detail is the object I have in view. So far we have not committed ourselves to any of the many existing theories : the word Thought seems to me to be capable of the widest application, and to denote in the most catholic spirit whatever of truth and value may be contained in the combined aim and endeavour of

13.
Different terms for expressing this unity.

14.
Definition of Thought.

all these modern aspirations. A history of this thought will be a definition of Thought itself.

Much has been done in the course of this century to prepare for an undertaking such as the one before me. It will be well to review shortly this special side of modern literature. We have indeed passed out of what may be

15.
1750 to 1850.
The age of
encyclopæ-
dic treat-
ment of
learning.

called the age of encyclopædic treatment of learning—the hundred years from the middle of the last to the middle of the present century.[1] The plan of such an arrangement of knowledge belongs to an earlier period, the period immediately succeeding the birth of modern science. Lord Bacon was the father of it, but neither he nor the most encyclopædic intellect of modern times, Leibniz, did much to realise the idea, and it was reserved for the genius and the labours of Diderot and d'Alembert [2] in France, in the

---

[1] "Encyclopædia nomen hodie frequentius auditur quam alias."— Gessner in Göttinger Lections-Katalog for 1756.

[2] Diderot's "Prospectus" to the 'Encyclopédie' appeared 1750; the first volume appeared 1751 with the celebrated "Discours préliminaire" of d'Alembert and a reprint of the "Prospectus." The complete title was 'Encyclopédie ou dictionnaire raisonné des sciences, des arts et métiers, mis en ordre et publié par Diderot et d'Alembert.' The principles which guided the editors, and the object of the work, are explained, with repeated references to Lord Bacon, in this introduction, as well as in the article "Encyclopédie," in the fifth volume (1755), which was written by Diderot, and occupied 28 pages. See also Diderot's 'Pensées sur l'interprétation de la Nature,' published anonymously in 1754.

Copious details about the history, the reception, and the influence of the 'Encyclopédie' are to be found in the correspondence and memoirs of Grimm, d'Alembert, and Voltaire, Madame d'Epinay, the Abbé Morellet, and many others. They are combined into a concise narrative, giving all the important facts, in Rosenkranz's 'Leben und Werke Diderots,' 2 vols., Leipzig, 1866, and in John Morley's 'Diderot.'

It is interesting to note how the idea of the unifying and life-giving influence of thought was as familiar to Diderot as it is to us : "Si l'on bannit l'homme ou l'être pensant et contemplateur de dessus la surface de la terre ; ce spectacle pathétique et sublime de la nature n'est plus qu'une scène triste et muette. L'univers se taît ; le silence et la nuit s'en emparent. Tout se change en une vaste solitude, où les phénomènes inobservés se passent d'une manière obscure et sourde. . . .

middle of the eighteenth century, to carry out the plan, foreshadowed in the 'Novum Organum,' of collecting all knowledge, which had been accumulated ever since science had been liberated from the fetters of theology, into one comprehensive whole. It must, however, be admitted that whilst the practical end of these laborious undertakings, the diffusion of knowledge, has certainly been greatly furthered, the original idea, that the sum of human knowledge is an organic whole, has in the execution been by degrees entirely lost sight of. The unity of thought and knowledge was indeed referred to in Diderot's " Prospectus " and d'Alembert's " Discours préliminaire," and in the introduction to Ersch and Gruber's great Encyclopædia,[1] as also in Coleridge's celebrated essay

16.
Unity of knowledge gradually lost sight of in encyclopædic works.

Voilà ce qui nous a déterminé à chercher dans les facultés principales de l'homme la division générale à laquelle nous avons subordonné notre travail."—Article "Encyclopédie,' p. 641.

[1] Ersch und Gruber's 'Allgemeine Encyclopädie der Wissenschaften und Künste,' Leipzig, 1818 to 1875, unfinished, 151 vols. It was founded by Professor Johann Samuel Ersch, librarian at Halle in 1813, assisted by Hufeland, Gruber, Meier, and Brockhaus, and contained contributions by the most learned and eminent Germans of the century. It is interesting to compare the plan and principles which guided the editors, as expounded in the introductions to the first and second volumes, with the corresponding dissertations prefixed to the 'Encyclopédie' in France and the 'Encyclopædia Metropolitana' in England. The unity aimed at by Bacon was either purely formal, securing only uniformity and completeness of treatment, or it was that of prac-

tical usefulness—the philosophy of fruit and progress. The plan adopted by Diderot and d'Alembert could hardly attain anything more than this. Coleridge, nursed in German philosophy, and deeply impressed with the fact that there is a higher view than that of Lord Bacon, and that such is to be found rather in writers like Plato and Shakespeare, uses the word method in a much wider sense. He was deeply affected by the spirit of the idealistic philosophy, which was foreign to Bacon and unduly despised by him.

In the idealistic systems of the Continent, beginning with Kant, the opinion was current that the methods and treatment of science alone were insufficient to close the circle of knowledge. The truly encyclopædic view was only possible in a scientific investigation specially carried on for that purpose, and this was considered to be one of the main objects of philosophy. Thus Kant in many passages of his works, notably vol. ii. pp. 377, 378,

on the science of method prefixed to the 'Encyclopædia
Metropolitana'; but the result has shown, what was not
evident to Lord Bacon, that neither a systematic division
of learning according to some logical principle, nor the historical identity of the beginnings of all branches of knowledge, can in the end preserve the real unity and integrity
of thought. The work of the advancement of learning,
if it be once handed over to different sciences and intrusted to separate labourers, does not proceed in a cycle
which runs back into itself, but rather in the rings of an
ever-increasing spiral, receding more and more from the
common origin. Such is the impression we get if we
contemplate the unfinished[1] rows of Ersch and Gruber's

613; vol. iii. pp. 188, 212; vol. v.
p. 312 (Rosenkranz's edition), especially the two following: "Philosophy is the only science which can
procure for us inner satisfaction,
for she closes the scientific cycle,
and through her only do the sciences receive order and connection."
And: "Mere '$\pi o \lambda v \iota \sigma \tau o \rho \iota a$' is a
cyclopean learning which wants one
eye—the eye of Philosophy—and
a cyclops among mathematicians,
historians, naturalists, philologists,
and linguists, is a scholar who is
great in all these lines, but having
these considers all philosophy as
superfluous." Still, with Kant
Philosophy is not an "instrument
for the extension," but merely a
study of "the limits of knowledge";
she does not "discover truth,"
but only "prevents error." This
modest definition was given up in
the systems of Fichte, Schelling,
and Hegel, who maintained that a
certain kind of—and this the highest
—knowledge could be attained by
starting from one highest principle
deductively: the all-embracing,
encyclopædic character of philoso-

phical, speculative knowledge was
increasingly emphasised, and this
not only in special lectures on the
subject, as in Fichte's lectures on
"The Nature of the Scholar," in
Schelling's on "The Method of
Academic Study," in Hegel's 'Encyclopædia of Philosophy,' but also
in the regeneration and reform of
many older and in the foundation
of new universities and academies
throughout Germany. The great
'Encyclopædia' of Ersch and Gruber
was planned in a similar spirit, as
the reform of university teaching
and of academic learning. This
reform has been of the greatest importance to the German nation and
to the interests of science and
knowledge. The Encyclopædia, on
the other hand, has remained
incomplete, a huge but abortive
attempt to combine not only the
principles of knowledge, but also
the colossal and growing volume of
it, into a systematic whole.

[1] The promoters of it were evidently not sufficiently impressed
with the two very essential conditions which make a work of this

volumes, or if we recognise the fact that the more useful and popular publications of our day have abandoned the philosophical introductions and preliminary discourses [1] by which the earlier works preserved a semblance of unity and method, and are contented to be merely useful dictionaries of reference. The encyclopædic treatment of knowledge, the execution of Lord Bacon's scheme, has shown that the extension and application of learning leads to the disintegration, not to the unification, of knowledge and thought. A conviction of this sort is no doubt the reason why in German universities lectures on "Encyclopädie" have been abandoned.[2] They were very general and popular in the earlier years of the century, when, under the influence of Kant, Fichte, and

17.
Lectures on
"Encyclo-
pädie"
abandoned
in German
universities.

kind useful—*viz.*, that it must be finished, however imperfect it may be, and that it must be completed within a limited time, on account of the revolutions and smaller changes in thought and knowledge. These essential conditions were always before the mind of Diderot. See his article "Encyclopédie," pp. 636-644.

[1] The object of the philosophical introductions has in course of this century been much more completely attained by such works as Mill's 'Logic' and Jevons's 'Principles of Science'; whilst the "preliminary dissertations," such as were contained in the older editions of the 'Encyclopædia Britannica,' have been partially superseded by works like Whewell's 'History' and his 'Philosophy of the Inductive Sciences,' in which the common origin, the genesis, the continuous development and interdependence of the different sciences, are traced. The value in this respect of an undertaking like that of the Royal Ba-

varian Academy ('Geschichte der Wissenschaften in Deutschland,' vol. i., 1864: it has now reached 22 vols., the science of War significantly filling three large volumes, that of Mathematics one small one) is much diminished by the title suggesting that science is a national, not a cosmopolitan or international concern. Fortunately many of the contributors to this important and highly useful publication have not limited their narratives to purely German science, but have largely taken notice of non-German research. Special reports on the state of any science or branch of science in a nation have, of course, quite a different meaning and value.

[2] The term is still in use for courses of lectures giving a general and comprehensive view of special sciences: thus, "Encyclopädie des Rechts, der Medicin, der Philologie, der Philosophie, der Theologie."

Schleiermacher, university teaching and learning entered on a new era, in which the idea prevailed that completeness, universality, and unity of knowledge could be secured by one and the same arrangement of study.[1] It was the age when philosophy for the last time had got a firm hold of all departments of knowledge, and permeated all scientific pursuits;[2] when, favoured by political events,

[1] On this subject the literature connected with the foundation of the University of Berlin in the year 1809 is of special interest. It was essentially the creation of Wilhelm von Humboldt, though prepared by Wolf and Beyme in 1807. See Seeley, 'Life of Stein,' vol. ii. p. 430 *sqq.* ; Haym, 'Leben W. v. Humboldts,' p. 270 *sqq.* The foundation of this university in the year of Prussia's greatest misery, when the first gleams of liberty in the rising of Spain and the success of Aspern had been extinguished by the defeat of Wagram, the voting of £22,500 per annum for the purposes of the new University and the Academy of Science and Arts, when a crushing war-tax hung over the country, when land was depreciated, the necessaries of life at famine prices, the currency of the country at a large discount, when every one, from the king to the lowest subject, was forced into sacrifices and economies of every kind, was an act as heroic as the great deeds on the battle-field, and as far-seeing as the measures of Stein and Scharnhorst. Interesting from our point of view are the ideas of Fichte on university teaching and academic learning, laid down in his 'Deducirter Plan einer zu Berlin zu errichtenden höheren Lehranstalt,' written at the request of the minister Beyme in 1807. In it a great deal is said about encyclopædic treatment. The question of the position

of philosophy in the encyclopædic or academic treatment of knowledge was easily solved in the Kantian school, to which most of the above-mentioned writers belonged. Later on in the school of Schelling it became more difficult. It was frequently discussed by Schelling himself, who was one of those that initiated the new era in the Academy of Munich, which was remodelled in the year 1807. See, *inter alia*, Schelling's essay, "Suggestions concerning the Occupation of the Philologico-Philosophical Class" of the Academy, and especially the following remarkable passage ('Werke,' vol. viii. p. 464): " If, indeed, Philosophy were denied living contact with real things, if she were obliged to soar in transcendent regions without end and measure, and to rise a hungry guest from the well-appointed table of Nature and Art, of History and Life ; then it would be incomprehensible how she could still find so much support as to be received in an academy, and it would be much better if we also followed the path of other nations, who have lately said good-bye to all philosophy, and have thrown themselves, with the most glowing ardour, upon the exploration of Nature and Reality in every direction."

[2] The principal representatives of the encyclopædic teaching at the German universities were Eschenburg, Krug, and Gruber. The latter, in his introduction to the

ideal aims, a generous spirit of self-sacrifice, and a feeling
of one common duty pervaded the German nation, and
foremost in it the teachers and students of the German
universities.[1] This spirit, as it produced co-operation
and unity of action, also favoured unity of thought, and
contributed much to the popularity of several philosophical systems which promised more than they could give.
Encyclopædic surveys were then supposed to be more
than the empty shell, the mere skeleton of learning
which they have since proved to be; they were looked
upon as being able to grasp and convey the living spirit
of knowledge. This phase of thought, which in the
sequel will largely command our attention, has dis-

18.
Encyclo-
pædias did
not fulfil
what they
appeared
to promise.

second volume of Ersch and Gruber's
'Encyclopädie,' gives a definition
and history of encyclopædic study,
which, according to him, was introduced into the modern (German)
universities together with the philosophical faculty. In the beginning
this was subservient to the three
higher faculties (theology, law, and
medicine), but gradually took the
lead. He argues that only since
university studies have become encyclopædic can they be considered
as furthering true humanity. He
refers to the great crisis through
which in the beginning of the century literature, science, and arts
were passing (p. li), and mentions
the conflicting principles in the
treatment of mathematics, physics,
history, philosophy, and philology.
See also the 'Vorbericht,' vol. i.
p. vii.
[1] Among the mass of literature
dealing with this subject, the
'Memoirs of Frederick Perthes,'
by his son (English translation,
vol. i. chap. xi. *sqq.*), and Steffens's
'Autobiography' ('Was ich erlebte,'

Breslau, 1840-44, 10 vols.), give the
most vivid and exhaustive accounts.
Neither Stein, the great statesman,
nor Goethe, the great poet and
thinker of the age, took part in this
alliance of the patriotic and intellectual interests of the German nation.
Stein's attitude to the idealism of
the age is defined by Seeley, 'Life
of Stein' (vol. i. p. 30, "It is desirable to mark that between him
and the literature and philosophy
of his time and country there was
no connection at all"), and is expressed in a remarkable conversation which he had with Steffens,
March 1813, at Breslau (quoted by
Seeley, vol. iii. p. 119 ; Steffens, vol.
vii. p. 120 *sqq.*) Goethe's position is
defined by his reply to the invitation
to contribute to the 'Deutsches
Museum,' a periodical planned by
the bookseller Perthes. It was to
be a scientific alliance of all the intellect of Germany, and was in time
"to be transformed into a political one possessing the strength and
union necessary for vigorous action"
(Perthes' Memoirs, vol. i. p. 167).

appeared; the second half of our century does not expect to find the essence of knowledge condensed in any philosophical formula, any more than it expects to find the real unity and integrity of thought preserved in the fragmentary articles of an alphabetical dictionary. The purpose of the latter is purely practical; it is a popular and handy instrument for the diffusion of knowledge, whilst philosophical divisions are merely formal, and at best are applicable only to a narrow and limited sphere of research.[1]

The age of encyclopædic representation of learning and the short period of philosophical formalism seem both to belong to the past; but the desire of bringing together what is scattered, of focussing knowledge and learning, and of realising the organic continuity and unity of thought and progress, is as great as, perhaps greater than ever. Neither the shapelessness of a huge dictionary nor the barrenness of a concise formula will satisfy the

---

[1] It is interesting to observe the development and spread of encyclopædic learning in the three countries. Encyclopædias in the modern sense have their origin, like so many other modern institutions and ideas, in England. They were there compiled mainly for practical purposes. France took up the scheme in a philosophical spirit, and carried it as far as it is capable of being carried under this aspect. Attempts to improve and amplify the plan proved impracticable; and when subjected to the vast erudition of Germany, it became evident that unity, depth, and breadth of view could not be maintained. In course of this century the country which produced the classical era of encyclopædism has done least for encyclopædic learning. This has now its home in Germany, where encyclopædic labours have been specialised, and where every science is represented by some compilation or annual register aiming at collecting and systematically arranging the scattered contributions of the whole world. But it would be ungrateful not to mention the Royal Society's catalogue of scientific papers, and the services which America has rendered in summarising the literary productions of the English-speaking nations in such works as Poole's 'Index to Periodical Literature.' Without the aid of such laborious compilations the present work could not have been undertaken.

deeper conviction that all mental work is living, individual, and of endless variety. To stimulate individual thought, to bring about life and change, is nowadays felt to be quite as necessary as to insist on method, system, and order. Prompted by this conviction, the last fifty years have done much to facilitate intellectual interchange, and to record the historical development of all branches of science.

This object has been promoted in three different ways. The French, who in the beginning of the period were the masters in science, led the way by founding a series of periodicals devoted to the development of separate sciences. Germany followed, and still later England.[1] A living

19.
French were the masters in science at the beginning of the century.

[1] The oldest scientific periodical is the 'Journal des Savants,' which was started in 1665 in Paris; next to it comes probably Rozier's 'Observations sur la Physique' (1771), continued under the title 'Journal de Physique' (1778, continued with interruptions from 1794 - 95 till 1823). In opposition to this journal, which defended the older phlogistic theories in chemistry, the 'Annales de Chimie' were started in 1789 by Berthollet, Guyton de Morveau, and Fourcroy, as an organ of Lavoisier's ideas. In 1788 the Société Philomatique started its 'Bulletin,' and in 1795 the 'Journal de l'Ecole Polytechnique' started its influential career. No such periodicals existed for special sciences at that time in any other country, if we perhaps except the 'Transactions of the Royal Linnæan Society,' which started in 1791. 'Nicholson's Journal' started in 1797 ; the 'London, Edinburgh, and Dublin Philosophical Magazine and Journal of Sciences' had its origin in Tilloch's 'Philosophical Magazine'; but

the first journal devoted specially to mathematical sciences in England was probably the 'Cambridge Mathematical Journal,' started in 1839. In the meantime the number of scientific journals in France had grown enormously. In Germany we have Crell's 'Chemische Annalen' (1778), Gehlen's 'Allgemeines Journal für Chemie' (1803), Gren's 'Journal der Physik' (1790), Gilbert's 'Annalen der Physik' (1799), Zach's 'Monatliche Correspondenz' (1800), Crelle's 'Journal für die reine und angewandte Mathematik' (1826), and many others, all periodicals of the first importance. The 'Transactions of the Royal Society,' which of course contain many of the valuable scientific contributions of this country, can nevertheless hardly be looked upon as a repository of the work of English mathematicians and physicists of the period in question,—not even as much as the Memoirs of the Paris Academy in France. In Great Britain a new centre of scientific and literary work existed during the latter part of the last century

intercourse between men of science was greatly promoted
by the British Association for the Advancement of Science,
which held its first meeting at York in 1831.   Associa-
tions and meetings of this kind had their origin ten years
earlier in Germany through Oken;[1] but the line in which
Germany has done most is the establishing of and con-
tinuing annual Reports[2] of the progress of the different

in Edinburgh ('Transactions of the
Royal Society of Edinburgh,' started
in 1788), and somewhat later likewise in Dublin ('Transactions of the
Royal Society of Dublin,' started
1799), and Manchester ('Memoirs
of the Manchester Philosophical
Society,' started in 1789). Many
of the first scientific writers of the
age published in these provincial
papers or in separate pamphlets—
the want of a common collecting
centre being very obvious.

[1] Alexander v. Humboldt supported them, and was instrumental
in giving to the Assembly at Berlin
in 1828—which he called "The in-
vasion of philosophers"—a special
importance. It was, as he says,
"a noble manifestation of scientific
union in Germany; it presents the
spectacle of a nation divided in
politics and religion, revealing its
nationality in the realm of intellectual progress."—Bruhns, 'Life of
A. v. Humboldt,' vol. ii. p. 130.
The British Association for the Advancement of Science was (as Prof.
Owen informs us) at the outset
avowedly organised after the Oken-
ian model.—'Encyclopædia Britannica,' art. "Oken."

[2] The first reports aiming at
giving a statement of the position
of Science were those drawn up by
Delambre and Cuvier at the request
of the Emperor Napoleon I., and
presented in the year 1808 under
the title 'Discours sur les Progrès
des Sciences, Lettres, et Arts depuis

1789 jusqu'à ce jour' (1808). They
were imitated on a larger scale by
the Emperor Napoleon III., on the
occasion of the great Paris Exhibi-
tion 1867, and have been continued
under the Republic. Of the report
of 1808 Cuvier says, "Ce tableau
historique nous servira désormais
de point de départ et nos rapports
annuels en seront autant de con-
tinuations." He also adds significantly, "Dans les relations actives
où nous nous trouvons avec la
plupart de ceux qui cultivent les
sciences, il est bien difficile qu'ils se
fassent en Europe quelques découvertes importantes sans que le
bruit en retentisse promptement
dans cette enceinte, et nous excite
à des travaux qui s'y rapportent
plus ou moins directement."

By far the most important work
of reporting and summarising the
results of scientific labour has been
done by Germany. The first publication of this kind, however, originated with Berzelius, who from the
year 1821 reported regularly to the
Academy of Stockholm on the progress of the physical sciences. Of
Berzelius's periodical Kopp says
('Geschichte der Chemie,' vol. i. p.
403), that it "summarises with the
greatest completeness all that had
been done in chemistry since 1820."
This work, which regularly appeared in German translation, was
continued in Liebig's 'Jahresbericht
der Chemie' (1847). In Berlin the
'Physikalische Gesellschaft' has

sciences, in which all scientific researches are—without regard to nationality—reviewed, classified, and arranged in the most complete manner, according to the place which they occupy in the general development. Invaluable service has also been done in England by special Reports or Addresses, prepared by men of the greatest eminence—frequently at the request of the British Association—in which the position of special branches of science is explained, the work of the past summed up, the leading principles clearly brought out, and the unsolved problems placed prominently before the minds of young and aspiring workers.

In Germany during the first half of the century a reaction set in against the metaphysical treatment of scientific subjects, which had been exaggerated in the schools of Schelling and Hegel. Experimental research, following mainly the great French and English models, was next favoured, and through the establishment of laboratories and observatories, through voyages of discovery and the application of science to the industries, an enormous amount of detailed and minute knowledge was accumulated.[1] For a time—even within the limits

20. Reaction in Germany against metaphysical treatment of scientific subjects.

---

continued to issue regularly since 1845 annual Reports under the title 'Fortschritte der Physik.' But it was only in 1868 that a similar annual was started in Berlin having reference to mathematics, under the title 'Fortschritte der Mathematik.' A 'Jahresbericht' on Zoology has appeared ever since 1879, and one on Botany since 1873.

[1] It was the age which compiled the great repositories of chemical knowledge. Such were Gmelin's 'Handbuch der Chemie' (1st ed., 1817. Translated into English by the Cavendish Society, 1848), and the 'Handwörterbuch der reinen und angewandten Chemie' (edited by Liebig jointly with Poggendorf and Wöhler, 1837). The same age also set going and filled the volumes of Liebig's 'Annalen' (started by Hänle in 1823 under the title 'Magazin der Pharmacie,' it finally assumed the title of 'Annalen der Chemie und Pharmacie' under Liebig's editorship), of Poggendorf's 'Annalen der Physik und Chemie' (1824), and the 'Annales de Chimie et de Physique.'

of exact reasoning—attempts to condense and unify knowledge were discredited. The result—especially in Germany—was that in many sciences information became buried in periodicals and in the memoirs of learned societies: text-books were chiefly written by men of secondary importance, translated from the French and English, and frequently on somewhat antiquated lines.[1] The new spirit which began to leaven scientific research in the middle of the century was confined to a few master minds, who—frequently almost unknown—marched in advance of their age. In the course of the last thirty years this has been entirely changed. The means of intercourse and communication, referred to above, make scientific isolation almost impossible; the necessity has been felt of remodelling the whole of the popular school literature on more modern lines: some of the first in-

21.
Reform in
school litera-
ture.

[1] The greater part of the higher German school literature in mathematics and physics was supplied by the French or modelled on French ideas—Legendre and Monge in elementary and descriptive geometry, Lacroix in the higher branches. Francœur's course of mathematics was introduced in England as well as Germany; Poisson, and later Lagrange and Duhamel, became the models in mechanics, Biot and Pouillet in experimental physics, Regnault in chemistry. The only great popular authorities which did not belong to France were Berzelius and Graham in chemistry, and Euler in mathematics. As late as 1860 hardly any text-book existed in Germany on the theoretical and mathematical portions of physics. The second volume of 'Baumgartner' was a miserable compilation. Beer's 'Höhere Optik' was the first important work of this kind. Germany had indeed not been wanting in original research, but the new ideas of Möbius, Steiner, Staudt, Plücker, and Grassmann in geometry found no adherents till, mainly through the translation of Salmon's text-books by Fiedler, a new spirit came over geometrical teaching. In the meantime Lejeune Dirichlet, and Neumann the elder, cultivated in their academical lectures the higher branches of mathematical physics, and educated a whole generation of mathematicians and physicists. Through them the original researches of Gauss and Jacobi became better known, and an independent school of German mathematical thought was established. In England the influence of French science was much more limited, and to the present day Euclid is preferred to Legendre's more elegant methods.

tellects in science have condescended to write text-books of their subjects, by which a great reform has been brought about in the higher scientific literature.[1] At the same time —after fifty years of experimental research and accumulation of material—it has become necessary to review the fundamental principles on which scientific reasoning rests : a more philosophical, not to say metaphysical, spirit is manifesting itself within the limits of science.[2] In the abstract, and especially the mathematical, sciences, real progress depends now mainly upon the discovery of methods of simplification, on conciseness and elegance of treatment, and on the discovery of unifying principles and generalising aspects.[3]

22. Scientific reasoning more philo- sophical.

[1] This remark refers mainly to England and Germany. In France, as a result of giving lectures at the École Polytechnique, the Bureau des Longitudes, the Faculté des Sciences, &c., the great mathematicians and physicists of the century have frequently worked up their researches in connected treatises. For such we are indebted to Lamé, Cauchy, Poncelet, and many others. But the two works which in England and Germany created probably the greatest reform in the teaching of the principles of natural philosophy were Thomson and Tait's 'Natural Philosophy' (first sketch, 1863, 1st ed., 1867) and Kirchhoff's 'Vorlesungen über Mechanik' (Leipzig, 1877).

[2] I refer principally to the various writings of Helmholtz, following those of Riemann, and the many hints thrown out in Gauss's published papers, and in his correspondence with Schumacher. Helmholtz has—of all purely scientific writers —paid most attention to the metaphysical foundations of geometry and dynamics, and has critically examined the earlier theories of Kant, published a century ago. It is interesting in this respect to note what Kant is reported to have said to Stägemann in 1797 : "I have come with my writings a century too soon ; after a hundred years people will begin to understand me rightly, and will then study my books anew and appreciate them." (See 'Tagebücher,' von Varnhagen von Ense, Leipzig, 1861, vol. i. p. 46.)   Next to Helmholtz we are most indebted to Emil du Bois-Reymond and his brother Paul. See Emil's 'Reden' (Leipzig, 1886- 87, 2 vols.), and the posthumous work of his brother : 'Ueber die Grundlagen der Erkenntniss in den exacten Wissenschaften' (Tübingen, 1890).

[3] An authority on this subject says : "Generality of aspects and methods, precision and elegance of exposition, have, since the time of Lagrange, become the common property of those who claim to be scientific mathematicians. This

All these are merely external signs of the new life, indications of progress and change : the inner reason and result, the altered ways of thinking which underlie or are produced by these external changes, will be the object of closer study hereafter ; they constitute the real substance of this work. What I draw attention to here, by way of introduction, are merely fingers on the dial-plate of a complicated clock-work : their motion and position are patent to every one. Later on I shall invite the reader to remove the outer case, and try with me to understand the delicate working parts and the principle of the mechanism, the prime mover and the mode of transmission of motion within. The general curiosity that exists to follow the internal and hidden workings of thought is manifested especially in that country which in modern history has frequently taken the lead in philosophical reasoning. It is manifested by the huge and increasing historical literature of Germany, which is devoted to tracing out the growth and development of modern science and thought. In that country history seems for the moment to have taken the place of metaphysical speculation. A similar transition from the logical to the historical view can be traced in English literature in the last century, the

23.
Germany
has taken
the lead in
studying
the life of
thought.

generality is sometimes exaggerated at the expense of simplicity and usefulness, and then leads to abstruseness and to the enunciation of theorems which have no special application ; precision may degenerate into an affected brevity which renders a dissertation more difficult to read than to write ; elegance of form has in our days almost become the test of the value of a theorem. Yet in spite of all draw- backs these conditions of efficient progress are of the greatest importance, inasmuch as they keep the scientific matter within those limits which are intrinsically necessary if mathematical research is not to lose itself in minutiæ or be drowned in over - abundance." — Hankel, 'Die Entwickelung der Mathematik in den letzten Jahrhunderten' (Tübingen, 1869).

typical representative of that change being David Hume, who, starting with the metaphysical problems involved in Locke's and Berkeley's writings, was from them led on to the study of moral, political, and economic questions, and ended by devoting himself to the study of history.[1] At the end of his career political and historical writings were as frequent in English literature as metaphysical and theological writings had been at the beginning. The causes which have effected the same transition from the metaphysical to the historical mode of treatment in Germany during the present century are similar to those existing in England in the last century; but the whole movement has taken place on a larger scale, penetrates deeper into the mental life and work of the nation, and cannot be so easily studied in the writings of any great representative.

24. Causes of transition from metaphysical to historical method.

Whilst in Germany historical studies are now foremost,

[1] I am quite aware that generalisations of this kind must be made and used with great caution. I therefore refer my readers to Leslie Stephen's 'History of English Thought in the Eighteenth Century,' especially to the Introduction, where the typical position of Hume is fully discussed, and also to the last chapter of the second volume, where he says of Hume (vol. ii. p. 381, 1st ed.) : "Hume was, in one sense, far in advance of his time, and indeed of the average opinion of the present time. But the change may in many respects be described as a revolt from Hume's opinions, much more than a development of them. . . . The history of philosophical and of theological opinion in England is a history of gradual decay down to the revolutionary era." And p. 444 : "The last half of the century was pre-eminently historical. As civilisation progresses, as records are better preserved, and a greater permanence in social organisation makes men more disposed to look beyond their immediate surroundings, a tendency to historical inquiry is naturally awakened. This cause alone, without the more philosophical considerations which might lead a Hume or a Gibbon to turn from abstract investigations to historical inquiries, may account for the growth of antiquarianism in the latter years." But the mere statistics of English literature in the eighteenth century suffice to prove the decline of argumentative and the growth of realistic literature.

and have almost dislodged systematic philosophy, England has for the first time in her history produced a system of philosophy—that of Mr Herbert Spencer; and this with the distinct understanding that the object of philosophy is the unification of knowledge.[1] It is a remarkable fact, which will occupy our close attention hereafter, that the unifying principle in this system is historical,—a process of development now specially known under the term Evolution. This system forms in a certain way a contrast to the last great system in German philosophy, that of Hermann Lotze. Whereas in all systems of evolution the unity of things is historical, and has to be sought in their common origin, Lotze emphasised the truth that unity must be a living presence, a principle which exists in individual things, not merely a link which connects them by proximity in time or space. His object is to answer the question, How can the human mind represent to itself such a living unity, in what ideas

25. Herbert Spencer the first Englishman who has produced a system of philosophy.

26. Definition of Lotze's system.

[1] See G. H. Lewes ('Problems of Life and Mind,' 1st ed., vol. i. p. 84), who says: "The absence of a philosophy in England during the last two hundred years has been a serious defect in her culture. Science she has had, and poetry and literature, rivalling when not surpassing those of other nations. But a philosophy she has not had, in spite of philosophic thinkers of epoch-making power. Hobbes, Locke, Berkeley, Hume, have produced essays, not systems. There has been no noteworthy attempt to give a conception of the world, of man, and of society, wrought out with systematic harmonising of principles. There has not been an effort to systematise the scattered labours of isolated thinkers. Mr Herbert Spencer is now for the first time deliberately making the attempt to found a philosophy." And in his 'History of Philosophy' (3rd ed., vol. ii. p. 653) the same author says: "Mr Spencer alone of British thinkers has organised a system of philosophy." Croom Robertson would take exception to this in favour of Hobbes, "who attempted a task which no other adherent of the 'mechanical philosophy' conceived—nothing less than such a universal construction of human knowledge as would bring Society and Man within the same principles of scientific explanation as were found applicable to the world of Nature" (Ency. Brit., 9th ed., vol. xii. p. 39).

belonging to human thought can this unity be grasped, by what words of human speech can it be expressed?

Both Mr Herbert Spencer's 'System' and Lotze's 'Microcosmus' are written with the object of establishing the unity of thought, of preserving the conviction that things exist and that events happen in some intelligible connection, and especially that the religious and the scientific views of the world and life are reconcilable. But whereas Mr Spencer is content to point to the underlying unity as the Unknowable, and then betakes himself to the study and exposition of the manner in which events follow and things develop, Lotze considers the whole of this part of philosophy as merely an introduction to the solution of the real problem. To him a process of development is merely the outer form in which some real substance presents itself, a mechanical method by which something of higher value is accomplished. He admits the all-pervading rule of such a mechanism, but he urges the necessity of finding the substance itself, and of gaining a view of the end and aim which is to be attained by this array of processes, by this parade of mechanical means, of the interest that attaches to them, and the result which is to be secured.[1] Knowing the mechanism by which a certain object is accomplished, we may be able to calculate phenomena and events, but to understand[2] them requires a

---

[1] The earliest passage in which Lotze gives us a pretty complete idea of his philosophical methods and aims is to be found in his polemical pamphlet against Fichte the younger ('Streitschriften,' Leipzig, 1857, p. 52 *sqq.*) He there also reviews his attitude to the idealistic school of German Philosophy and to Herbart, whose follower he refuses to be called (*ibid.*, p. 5 *sq.*) It is evident that at that time his system was not yet definitely settled in his mind (p. 58).

[2] The difference between calculating and understanding phenomena is probably to be traced to Leibniz. Lotze emphasises this difference.

further knowledge of the worth of the object which is accomplished, of the result which is gained by the calculation. It is one thing to be able to trace the mechanical conditions upon which the accuracy of a clock depends; it is another to mark the hour which the clock strikes, and to note the time which it measures out to us for our work. Curiosity will lead a child to pry into the former; but the latter depends on our appreciation of the objects of life and the seriousness of our duties.

27.
Lotze's relation to Herder's 'Ideen.'

When Lotze undertook to write the ' Microcosmus,' he referred to two great works of a kindred tendency. Both attempted, yet in very different ways, to give a comprehensive view of a large field of scattered phenomena, to take in at a glance the entire scheme of a great world of facts. The earlier of the two belonged to the last century and was concerned with history, with the uniting bond of all human development. For this Herder, in his ' Ideen zur Philosophie der Geschichte der Menschheit,' had, if not invented, yet endowed the term Humanity with a specific pregnancy, meaning by it the unity of all human interests in their social and historical development—an idea which since Leibniz has governed German literature.[1] The other

See, *inter alia*, the closing paragraph of the first volume of the ' System der Philosophie ' (1st ed., Leipzig, 1874). I cannot omit to notice here the extraordinary and misleading misprint in Erdmann's quotation of this passage : see his valuable ' Geschichte der Philosophie' (3rd ed., Berlin, 1878, vol. ii. p. 861), where instead of *berechnen*, to calculate, we read *bezeichnen*, to designate !

[1] The history of this idea has been written by Hettner in the last two volumes of his ' Literaturgeschichte des 18ten Jahrhunderts.' I quote from the 2nd edition, Braunschweig, 1872. Herder had inherited the spirit of Leibniz (see, *inter alia*, the concluding chapter of my essay on Leibniz, in Blackwood's Philosophical Classics, Edinburgh, 1884). Herder fórmed a kind of centre of thought, inasmuch as he gathered up in his own mind and writings the influences of Leibniz, Rousseau, and the English writers of the eighteenth cen-

great work was that of A. v. Humboldt, who in the course
of a long career, peculiarly favoured by opportunities for
studying Nature on an extensive scale, and for appreciating
the detail of modern research, of which he was an illustrious
representative, had never lost sight of the all-pervading
unity.[1] In an elevated style, in which poetry and science

Lotze
lation
A. v.
boldt
'Kos

tury, together with classical influences and new inspirations drawn from the popular song-literature of all nations. Hettner says (see last volume but one, p. 7): "Herder applied Rousseau's gospel of Nature to the demands of poetical sense and creation. Thus he has become essentially the forerunner of the new school of poets : the last fetters of the moralising style by which even Lessing was still hampered fell, and through the scientific study of the beginnings and development of human culture he became the founder of a new science of Language, Religion, and History, in the lines of which we are still advancing." And p. 101 : "Herder does not belong to the classics of the style of Winckelmann, Lessing, Kant, Goethe, and Schiller ; he is everywhere only suggestive, hardly anywhere conclusive and final. For this reason his writings are to some extent antiquated. Nevertheless Herder is one of our most important and influential spiritual heroes. Herder made so deep an impression on his age that the great poetry of Goethe and Schiller, the so-called Romantic School, the philosophies of Schelling and Hegel, cannot be imagined without Herder as the precursor." The fourth volume of Gervinus, 'Geschichte der deutschen Dichtung,' contains likewise a very important chapter on Herder. But the great authority on Herder is R. Haym, 'Herder nach seinem Leben und seinen Werken' (Berlin, 2 vols., 1880 and 1885).

From the unpublished literary notes, correspondences, and diaries of Herder, which Haym inspected, it is evident that the great idea of writing a History of Humanity originated in Herder's mind as far back as the year 1769, on a voyage from Riga to Nantes (on the way to Paris). His diary closes thus : "History of the progress and of the powers of the human mind in the concurrence of whole ages and nations—a spirit, a good demon, has exhorted me to do this. Be that my life's work, History, work !"

The first attempt to carry out his great idea was published by Herder in the year 1774, with the title : 'Auch eine Philosophie der Geschichte zur Bildung des Menschheit.' Herder was then in his thirtieth year. His chief work appeared ten years later (1784), with the title 'Ideen zur Geschichte der Menschheit.' Herder died in 1803. Goethe's 'Faust,' which is an attempt to deal with the highest problems of human interest, the problems of knowledge, evil, sin, and redemption, as they appear in the history of a great individual, not of the race, had its first beginnings about the same time as Herder's 'History of Mankind.' But the work was not finished till a year before Goethe's death in 1831.

[1] Alex. v. Humboldt, 'Kosmos. Entwurf einer physischen Weltbeschreibung,' 1845. Like Herder's great work on the 'History of Humanity' and Goethe's 'Faust,' Humboldt's 'Kosmos' occupied a

are happily blended, he essayed in the evening of life to unroll before the gaze of his readers a picture of the grand features of nature as his mind had viewed them from the elevated regions of scientific study, and his eyes from the heights of Chimborazo.

In the great picture of the world, in the vast changes of the universe, where is man with his life and his interests ?   In the huge Kosmos where is the Microcosmus ?

29.
otze's 'Mi-
rocosmus.'

This question naturally presented itself to the mind of Lotze.   "It is not," he tells us, " the all-embracing ' kosmos' of the universe which we wish to describe again on the model which has been given to our nation.   As the features of that great world-portrait sink deeper into general consciousness, so much more vividly will they lead us back to our own selves, suggesting anew the question, What significance belongs to man and human life with its lasting characteristics and the changing

long period in the life of its author. Goethe's ' Faust ' deals with the individual problem, Herder's 'Ideen' with the problem of the race or mankind, Humboldt's 'Kosmos' with the same problem as referring to the world, the universe.   In the preface Humboldt confesses "that the image of his work had stood before his mind's eye in undefined outlines for nearly half a century" : *cf.* what Goethe says in the dedication to ' Faust ' (written probably after 1797) :—

"Again ye come, ye hovering forms; I find ye
As early to my clouded sight ye shone,"
&c.
                    — Transl. B. Taylor.

The view of the universe which was given in Humboldt's ' Kosmos ' was prepared by his own publication,

' Die Ansichten der Natur' (1808) ; also by Georg Forster (1754-1794), who wrote an account of the second voyage of Captain Cook round the world, whom he accompanied with his father.   "He conceived of nature as a living whole ; his account is almost the first example of the glowing yet faithful description of natural phenomena, which has since made the knowledge of them the common property of the educated world" (R. Garnett in 'Ency. Brit.,' art. "Forster").   Humboldt confesses to have received from him "die lebhafteste Anregung zu weiten Unternehmungen" ('Kosmos,' vol. i. p. 345, also vol. ii. p. 65, and especially vol. ii. p. 72, where incidentally also Darwin's narrative of the "Adventure" and "Beagle" is mentioned).

course of its history in the great totality of nature?"[1]
And in collecting the answers to this question which
suggest themselves both in and outside of the study,
Lotze professes only to renew the enterprise brilliantly
begun by Herder in his 'Ideen zur Geschichte der
Menschheit.' Both Herder's 'Ideen' and Humboldt's
'Kosmos' belong to the age in which philosophy and
poetry largely influenced science and history. Many may
now think it premature or altogether impossible to try
to combine the detailed studies of modern science and
modern history with the comprehensive view demanded
by philosophers and poets, or to grope through the labyrinth of external phenomena and events to their underlying significance and unity. They may, whilst fully
maintaining the existence of an all-pervading power,
nevertheless relegate it with Mr Spencer to the region
of the Unknowable.[2] Without desiring at present to

---

[1] Microcosmus, 1st ed., Leipzig,
1856, Preface. Hermann Lotze was
born in 1817, and died in 1881.
His first philosophical essay of importance was the 'Metaphysik'
(Leipzig, 1841).

[2] Herbert Spencer's Philosophy
of the "Unknowable" is laid down
in his Introduction to 'First Principles.' I believe the first appearance of the first part of this book
was in 1860, and the first collected
publication in the year 1867. In
defining the region of the Knowable an opposite course has been
adopted by Emil du Bois-Reymond,
who in a series of addresses and
articles, now collected in two volumes with the title 'Reden' (Berlin, 1886 and 1887), tried to lead
up to the limits which are fixed
around scientific knowledge. The
purport of his teaching on the

highest "World-problem" is contained in the four words, *ignoramus,
ignorabimus, dubitemus, laboremus.*
The first of these addresses, which
are full of brilliant suggestions and
vivid illustrations, furnishing in the
notes especially an invaluable store
of historical references on the subject of the philosophy of the sciences, was delivered at the forty-
fifth meeting of the German "Naturforscher und Aertze," and published at Leipzig, August 1872, with
the title 'Die Grenzen des Naturerkennens.' It made a great sensation, and was translated into several
languages. It was followed some
years later by an address delivered
in the Berlin Academy, 1880, and
published with the title 'Die sieben
Welträthsel.' If H. Spencer's philosophy is termed the philosophy
of the Unknowable, Du Bois-Rey-

criticise the weighty considerations which have led them to a view so modest and resigned, I propose in the sequel to test within narrower limits, and by what seems to me a novel method, the validity of the conviction that a true understanding of phenomena and events can be attained only by viewing them in their interdependence and collective effect. If anything in the wide expanse of physical and mental life deserves to be considered as one and indivisible, it is surely human thought in its various branches and manifestations. The attempt to trace its origin in the early ages of civilisation, or to foreshadow the end which it is slowly approaching, may indeed be impossible; but of the age to which we belong, and the literature of which we have witnessed the growth, we may claim to possess a deeper knowledge. Astronomers have succeeded in gaining a view of immense and distant orbits by minutely observing and tracing merely an insignificant portion[1] which came within their view. Comparative anatomy teaches how from a few surviving links to construct the whole framework of an organism. I propose to apply a similar method to the small portion

mond's may be termed the philosophy of the Limits of the Knowable. Both views form a contrast to Lotze's philosophy.

[1] The most brilliant example of this is the discovery of the planet Ceres by Piazzi at Palermo in the New Year's night of 1801; the invention of special methods for calculating the orbit of this planet, which had been lost, by Gauss in the course of 1801; and the rediscovery of it by Olbers, aided by Gauss's ephemeris, in the New Year's night of 1802. After the discovery of this first of the small planets, but before it was known in Germany, Hegel published his 'Dissertatio philosophica de orbitis planetarum,' in which he ridiculed the search for new planets, but which Duke Ernest of Gotha sent to the astronomer Zach with the superscription, "Monumentum insaniæ sæculi decimi noni." See R. Wolf, Geschichte der Astronomie, München, 1877, p. 684 sqq.

of mental progress of which I have been able to take personal notice and of which I have felt the immediate personal influence. A tracing as concisely as possible of this comparatively small portion of the course of European thought may be the first approximation to more accurate delineations, which themselves will be the means of gradually gaining a truer idea of the purport and significance that belong to the larger dimensions of the mental life of mankind.

This life does not consist in the accumulated knowledge of our century, not in the results of scientific inquiry deposited in libraries and museums, not in the many schools for learning and study, not in educational and social reforms, least of all in political and economic institutions. These are all external objects, which are capable of being described or photographed like the external objects of nature. The mental life of mankind consists in the inner processes of reflection, by which these external objects have been produced, by which man has been able to add to the physical creation of nature a new creation of his own, by which he has been able to change the face of the earth, and endow the objects of nature with an ideal meaning. To this end he is always inventing and using methods which change, suggesting and applying principles which turn out to be half true or totally fallacious, guessing at results and aims which have to be abandoned, inventing theories which are short-lived—in fact, erecting scaffoldings with the help of which he raises the structures of Society, Art, and Science : these remain as the historical testimonies of his activity ; the scaffoldings are removed as of merely transient and temporary value ; and yet they

30.
What the
mental life
of mankind
consists of.

alone constitute the mental life which interests us. Only
so far as we have taken part in building the scaffolding,
only in so far as we have witnessed the many contrivances
which have been used, only in so far as we have seen the
growth of any structure from small beginnings, from the
first sketch of the architect, can we say that we know
something of the mental life which lies hidden in and
behind those external signs and documents. A closer
study of what we ourselves have witnessed is thus the
only way of attaining some insight into the workings of
the mind—the spiritual life of mankind. We shall pres-
ently find that in science as well as in philosophy every
period starts from certain assumptions and proceeds according to certain methods, that certain habits of thought
become general, and certain views become accepted; but in
the course of one or two generations we find those assumptions questioned, those methods criticised, a new habit of
thought introduced, and those general views which seemed
so natural and convenient giving way to new and altered
ones. The whole fabric of society, the whole structure of
science and knowledge, all the applications of art, have to
be remodelled on new principles, and to meet our changed
demands. Few indeed, very few, of the old creations
remain. One or two so-called laws of science that sur-
vive, a few dozen books that are re-edited, half-a-dozen
works of art and one or two great poems,—this is about
all that our century will at its close have preserved as the
living inheritance of its early years : all the others will be
relegated to the growing bulk of historical records. Possessed of merely monumental interest as documents of a
bygone life, these creations had to be left aside as incap-

31.
**Methods,
the most
approved,
have their
day, and
cease to be.**

32.
**One century
does not
inherit all
of the past;
it discards
much.**

able of marking or guiding any longer our onward career. A few centuries lapse, and posterity will look upon them as we do on the huge monuments of early Eastern civilisation, on the Sphinx in the desert or the Pyramids of Egypt, wondering by what ingenious contrivances they were raised, what amount of human work and suffering they represent, or what idea lived in the minds of those who planned and placed them where they still remain.

III.

It is the privilege of art to represent at a glance the whole of its object, and thus to produce at once a total effect on the mind of the beholder. Closer scrutiny may follow and may show how the various parts support the whole, how the uniting idea is revealed in all the manifold detail of the component elements: still the impression of the whole remains and supplies the key for the comprehension of every part. Literature, science, and history are denied this privilege of presenting their objects in their entirety, and thus giving from the outset a commanding view, a leading and abiding impression of the whole. We have to ask the student to follow us patiently by an isolated path to the summit: many ways lead to it, and we may err in the choice of the right and convenient one. Even if we succeed in reaching the central position, we may have fatigued the reader on the road or produced sensations which prevent the unbiassed contemplation of the whole view when it is presented. With us the whole is only the sum of its many parts, whereas with the artist the parts are merely fractions of a united whole. In

1.
Necessity of choosing a road.

treating of the thought of the century, even within the
narrow limits which have been prescribed, I am met with
similar difficulties. In the large circumference of the
domain of thought I have to choose a starting-point and
to construct a road which may lead to the central position,
hoping there to gain a comprehensive view of the whole.

2.
Some peri-
ods of his-
tory take
their name
from some
great event
or move-
ment.
Some periods of history are characterised by one great
and central movement which absorbs all active forces
and all intellectual and imaginative power, making
them either subservient to one end and purpose, and
helpful in the elaboration of one idea; or else forcing
them into opposition, where they testify equally to the
importance of this central movement. Such periods
were, for instance, the long centuries of Jewish history,
the early age of the Christian Church, the period of the
culmination of Papal power, the Reformation, the French
Revolution. In studying the thought of such ages, we
are not at a loss where to find the leading idea,—we
easily fix the centre of the vortex which draws into its
motion all the existing forces, all genius and all talent.
In an age like that of the Reformation we can speak of
the Politics of the Reformation, the Religion of the Reformation, the Philosophy, Literature, and Art of the Reformation, and we are pretty sure to embrace under these
various heads an account of all the mental progress and
to trace all the thought of that age, be it friendly or anta-

3.
No central
event in our
age.
gonistic. It is evident that no such central event, no such
all-absorbing vortex of motion, exists in the period which
we have lived through. The uniting bond, if it exists, lies
much deeper; the problem we have been engaged in solving, the prize we are fighting for, does not present itself on

the surface; it is not explicitly stated, it must be implied rather than defined. The great object of our life and labour has not been clear to us, as it seemed clear to those who lived during the Reformation or the Revolution, otherwise we should not have philosophies of the Unconscious and of the Unknowable, and the century would not end in asking, Is life worth living?

Then, again, we find in history long periods of quiet development, where men's minds seemingly run very much in the same direction, exhibiting a general tendency of ideas, the spreading of a defined habit of thought and of simple methods, the application of a few principles: such a period was that preceding the French Revolution, the greater part of the eighteenth century. It has therefore been easy to characterise that century: it has been termed the philosophical century, the century of the *Aufklärung*, the century of Voltaire.[1]   No such one

---

[1] The first who reviewed the literature of the eighteenth century from an international point of view was Villemain, who as early as 1820 was engaged in lecturing at the Sorbonne before the *élite* of the rising literary generation of France on the literature of the eighteenth century, taking France as the centre, and showing the influence of foreign literature, especially English, as likewise the reaction of French ideas abroad.   He was too early to recognise the true meaning of the new spirit which had then already gone forth from Germany. In this respect his ' Cours de Littérature française,' published in 1828 and republished in 1864, remains incomplete. Schlosser next attempted to present in his ' Geschichte des achtzehnten Jahrhunderts,' after the manner of Gibbon, a picture of the combined political and literary work of the last century. The first draft of it appeared in 1824, after Schlosser had passed two years in Paris, where no doubt he must have come under the influence of Villemain.   The work itself began to appear in 1826, and was finished in 1848. It is considered to be Schlosser's greatest work, and had a large circulation. The connection of political and literary history was studied by Gervinus, who with Häusser is usually counted as a pupil of Schlosser.   But the great work which Villemain had begun and Schlosser taken up was adequately carried out by Hettner, who in his ' Literaturgeschichte des achtzehnten Jahrhunderts ' conceived the whole intellectual movement of that age as a battle for enlightenment (*Kampf der Aufklärung*). The

term can be applied to our age, no one name can be found which carries with it the recognition of all the many interests which surround us.

4.
Is history of thought history of philosophy?
It has been suggested by some that the history of thought is equivalent to the history of philosophy; that the different philosophical systems and theories exhibit in the abstract the course which ideas have taken in an age.[1] A history of thought in the nineteenth century would thus mean a history of nineteenth century philosophy. There have indeed been plenty of philosophies and systems during our period, but in spite of their great number and variety—ranging from the extreme idealism of Fichte to the equally extreme materialism of Büchner [2]—we feel that they do not cover the whole area of thought. The period in our century which in England was most barren in philosophy, the first forty years, produced an entirely new literature and a novel conception of art, both containing new sources of mental life, though they have hardly yet found expression in any philosophical system. Equally barren in speculation was France during the Restoration; yet there, too, was a

latter part of his work deals with the reaction against *Aufklärung* and "Rationalism" as it began in England, and was represented on the Continent by Rousseau and the earlier ideals of the French Revolution. Through Rousseau and the Revolution the growing influence of the new spirit of English literature was overpowered and lost for the Continent. And, as we have to regret in Villemain his neglect of the new life of Germany, so we have to deplore that Hettner followed the developments of Rationalism and *Aufklärung* only in the form they assumed in Germany, neglecting to notice the contemporary growth of the new life in English Literature and Art, to which, in fact, no German historian has as yet done justice.

[1] See especially Hegel's Lectures on the History of Philosophy in his collected works, vol. xiii. p. 68 *sqq.* (Complete edition, Berlin, 1832.)

[2] The principal publications of this school are Vogt, 'Physiologische Briefe,' 1845-47; Moleschott, 'Der Kreislauf des Lebens,' 1852; Büchner, 'Kraft und Stoff,' 1855.

brilliant era of literature, and the whole of Europe was illuminated by the light of science which emanated from Paris during the first third of this century.   History of philosophy has little to say about Goethe, though his work embodies for us probably the deepest thought of modern times.   Again, the only great and novel system of philosophy which France has produced during this century is that of Comte, but it has had only small influence in its own country; and who would say that it reflects French thought of the period as Voltaire and Montesquieu reflected the thought of the last century ?   Hegel himself, who was intent upon tracing the working of the human mind in the systems of philosophy, declared that philosophy is the latest fruit of civilisation,—that the special idea which governs any period is already dying out when it appears in a system.[1]

5. Goethe's work involves the deepest thought of the century.

[1] The principal passage expounding this idea of Hegel's is to be found in the introduction to the course of lectures which he delivered at Berlin repeatedly during the years 1816 to 1830. See his collected works, vol. xiii. p. 66 : "Philosophy makes its appearance at the time when the mind of a nation has worked itself out of the indifferent dulness of the early life of nature, as well as out of the period of passionate interest ; inasmuch as the direction towards detail has spent itself, the mind transcends its natural form—it passes on from practical morals, from the force of real life to reflection and comprehension. The consequence is, that it attacks this actual form of existence, these morals, this faith, and disturbs them ; and with this comes the period of decay. The further stage is, that thought tries to collect itself. One may say, that where a people has come out of its concrete forms of life, where distinction and separation of classes has set in, where the nation approaches its fall, where a rupture has taken place between the inner desires and the external reality, where the ruling form of religion, &c., &c., does not satisfy, where the mind shows indifference towards its living existence or lingers discontentedly in it, where moral life is in dissolution— then only does one philosophise. The soul takes refuge in the realms of thought, and in opposition to the real world it creates a world of ideas. Philosophy is then the reparation of the mischief which thought has begun. Philosophy begins with the decline of a real world : when she appears with her abstractions, painting grey in grey, then the freshness of youth and life is already gone ; and her reconciliation is not one in reality, but in an ideal world."

This means that philosophy is retrospective: it sums up, it criticises, it does not prefigure the future. The correctness of this proposition may be doubted. We shall have to deal with it in another place. At present it reminds us that thought, in the sense in which we take it, cannot be identified with philosophy, and hence a history of philosophy in the nineteenth century is not identical with a history of its thought. There is indeed a sense in which the word philosophy is sometimes used, when it approaches more nearly to the meaning of the word thought, as we intend to use it. Whewell has in this sense written the philosophy of the inductive sciences, meaning to trace in that work the processes of thought which are consciously or unconsciously employed in scientific research and reasoning, and which lead to progress in science. Something similar might be attempted in regard to art, commerce, politics, government, religion, and literature generally. In every case philosophy would simply mean the peculiar way of thinking and reasoning which is adopted in these various branches of practical or intellectual life. This is, however, not the sense in which the word philosophy is generally used. It generally denotes something more than a statement of method or a *rationale* of ideas and reflections; it denotes a definite theory, an explanation of a larger or smaller circle of phenomena. As such it certainly forms a part of the thought of the century, probably the most interesting and fascinating part; but it is also that which is most liable to change, most subject to discussion; whereas the other more hidden thoughts and reasonings form, as it were, the ground upon which all the intellectual, artistic, and practical achievements of the age rest.

It would thus appear as if an account of the thought of the century might naturally divide itself into two separate investigations. In the first place, we should regard thought merely as a means to an end, as the method adopted to attain a certain purpose, be it practical or theoretical. It would mean the peculiar kind of reasoning which has been employed in the search for knowledge or in its useful application. As all reasoning starts from certain assumptions, called premisses, or principles, or axioms, and progresses from these by certain methods, this portion of our task would divide itself again into a statement of the principles which underlie, and an account of the methods which have guided, theoretical and practical reasoning. But thought does not exist merely for the sake of increasing our knowledge of things and of applying this to practical purposes. Occupied in this way merely, it remains fragmentary, incomplete, and not infrequently it reveals contradictions. Even those who devote themselves purely to detailed research or to practical work are again and again compelled to take a wider and deeper view of things than their special occupation affords. One may find that the methods which he is using daily become useless for certain practical purposes he has in view, and may thus be forced to question the principles which during half his lifetime he has applied with unquestioning faith in their validity and usefulness. Another may have met with such success in the use of a special method of research, that he wishes to apply it to subjects which were previously handled in a different manner, or elevate it to

8.
Inquiry into thought of the century divided into two questions.

the dignity of a general rule of thought. A third may, accidentally, be interested in two or more pursuits which are seemingly unconnected, but which—being brought side by side in his mind—he feels the wish to unite and harmonise. A fourth may, at a certain time of life, grow tired of the drudgery of petty pursuits which never carry him beyond a very limited sphere of interests : he is tempted to look beyond this narrow range, and gain some wider view of other pursuits and interests. Allowing that ignorance or indifference prevents even the majority of those whose powers are not exhausted in the struggle for mere existence from looking much beyond their narrow circle, allowing also that many of us live—like children—in a blessed trust that the great and important interests of mankind are under higher and better guidance than we can understand or control, there still remain a considerable number of persons who are always on the look-out for something higher, wider, and better, who are driven by an undying thirst after real wisdom, or by an

9. Speculation. inherent restlessness of disposition to inquire into the deepest foundations and the ultimate ends of the world and life. Language has coined a word which denotes the whole of these occupations and endeavours, how various so ever they may be, and for whatsoever purpose they may be undertaken. It calls them speculations. The word also indicates the venturesome and risky nature of these undertakings. They have existed in all ages and countries and languages wherever literature has existed, and have been carried on by the powers of reason or imagination, in prose, verse, or symbol, sometimes in defined and clear terms, more often in mystic allegory. Philosophy may be said to have grown out of these vague and scattered beginnings by the attempt to conduct them according to some method, and to unite them into a complete and consistent whole. Philosophy may thus be defined as speculation carried on according to some clear method, and aiming at systematic unity.[1] Both science and philosophy may be called methodical thought, but the word system is applicable only to the higher and more advanced forms of philosophic thought which aim at unity and completeness.

10.
Philosophy
defined.

We have thus arrived at a second division of our subject. In the first we have to consider thought merely as a means to an end; in the second we have to consider it as its own object, as a reflection on itself, carried on with the object of knowing its own origin, its laws, its validity, of testing its powers, and with the end and aim of gaining certainty, completeness, and unity. The whole of this great division of thought I shall comprise under the

11.
Division of
the book.

[1] This view of the nature and object of Philosophy agrees with Lotze's definition (see 'Grundzüge der Logik,' Leipzig, 1883, § 88): "The *common culture of life* and the *separate sciences* contain a number of suppositions the origin of which is obscure to us, because they have been very gradually formed within us through the comparison of many experiences, or because they have first become conscious by means of such experiences, have then received definite names and become habitual without having been subjected by us to any examination as to the reason, the sense, and the extent of their validity. In this way science and life make use of the notions of *cause* and *effect*, of *matter* and *force*, of *means* and *end*, of *freedom* and *necessity*, of *matter* and mind, and they frequently entangle themselves, owing to the above-mentioned defect, in contradictions, inasmuch as they are unable to fix the limits of validity of these to some extent contradictory assumptions.

"Now we may formally define the task of Philosophy as follows: that it is an endeavour to import unity and connectedness into the scattered directions of cultured thought, to follow each of these directions into its assumptions and into its consequences, to combine them all together, to remove their contradictions, and to form out of them a comprehensive view of the world; mainly, however, to subject those ideas which science and life regard as *principles* to a special scrutiny, in order to determine the limits of their validity."

term Philosophy; and as the first part will deal with the scientific, so will the second deal with the philosophical thought of our century.

Science has gradually risen out of the mass of accumulated but inaccurate and disorderly knowledge by the desire of making it accurate, orderly, and useful. Philosophy has similarly emerged from the great world of speculative thought by the desire of carrying it on methodically and for a defined end and purpose. Nevertheless neither the one nor the other, nor both together, really exhaust the whole meaning of the word "Thought"; neither science nor philosophy covers the whole region of thought. Both are comprised under the term methodical thought; but there remains the great body of immethodical, undefined thought. This is buried in general literature, in poetry, fiction, and art; it shows its practical influence in the artistic, moral, and religious life of our age. It is a reflection of the knowledge of science or the light of philosophy, but, like all reflected light, it not only follows, it also precedes the real and full light: it is not only the dusk that comes after, it is also the dawn that comes before the day, it is the twilight of thought. In it lie hidden the germs of future thought, the undeveloped beginnings of art, philosophy, and science yet unknown and undreamt of; it encloses and surrounds the innermost recesses of the mind, where all thought had its origin, and whence it ever and again draws fresh life and inspiration.[1]

12.
Neither science nor philosophy comprises the whole meaning of the word thought.

13.
Thought also hidden in the literature and art of the age.

[1] This is originally a Leibnizian idea. It is laid down in the doctrine of the *petites perceptions*, as given in the introduction to the 'Nouveaux Essais,' and referred to in many passages of Leibniz's various

No account of the thought of our century would be complete or satisfactory which took no notice of this great volume of immethodical and unsystematic thought which lies buried in the general literature and in the art of the age. Both have shown a vitality, originality, and versatility which exceed that of any except the few favoured periods—those of Athens under Pericles, Italy during the Renaissance, and England under Elizabeth. In one of the arts, in music, our age has, according to the opinion of many competent judges, exceeded in originality and certainly in productiveness all former ages. In poetry Goethe and Wordsworth have raised our tastes and demands to a higher level, in fiction France and England have almost created a new branch of literature, whilst the peculiar features of modern English landscape-painting were unknown to previous centuries. All this, though produced under no scientific or philosophical rule

14. Goethe and Wordsworth raised our tastes.

writings. See 'Nouv. Ess.,' Preface, Leibniz, Philosophische Werke, ed. Gerhardt, vol. v. p. 48 :—

"Ces petites perceptions sont donc de plus grande efficace par leur suites qu'on ne pense. Ce sont elles qui forment ce je ne sçay quoy, ces gouts, ces images des qualités des sens, claires dans l'assemblage, mais confuses dans les parties, ces impressions que des corps environnans font sur nous, qui enveloppent l'infini, cette liaison que chaque estre a avec tout le reste de l'univers. On peut même dire qu'en consequence de ces petites perceptions le present est gros de l'avenir et chargé du passé, que tout est conspirant (σύμπνοια πάντα, comme disoit Hippocrate) et que dans la moindre des substances, des yeux aussi perçans que ceux de Dieu pourraient lire toute la suite des choses de l'univers.

"Quæ sint, quæ fuerint, quæ mox futura trahantur. . . . C'est aussi par les perceptions insensibles que s'explique cette admirable harmonie préestablie de l'âme et du corps, et même de toutes les Monades ou substances simples, qui supplée à l'influence insoûtenable des uns sur les autres, et qui au jugement de l'auteur du plus beau des Dictionnaires exalte la grandeur des perfections divines au delà de ce qu'on eu jamais conçu."

The importance of this idea of Leibniz has been dwelt on at length by Kuno Fischer in his 'Geschichte der neueren Philosophie,' where he also traces its influence in the development of philosophy and literature in Germany after Leibniz.

and very frequently outside of any school, points to novel modes of mental conception, to a fund of ideas yet undeveloped or only partially developed into clear thought. The whole of this productiveness indicates a vast amount of mental work which, though not yet absorbed by science or philosophy, belongs nevertheless, according to our original conception, to the world of thought. The meaning of it may be enigmatical, and the clear expression which it will some day produce in philosophical and scientific reasoning may be far distant and unintelligible to us now. Still there it is, this great body of undefined thought, this volume of diffused light, the focus and centre of which is still hidden from us. We feel that in discussing the thought of the century we cannot pass it by or neglect it.

15. Unmethodical thought.

It is difficult to find any one term under which we could comprise this great body of unmethodical, scattered, and fragmentary thought,—any one word, similar to science and philosophy, in which we could sum up and characterise its general meaning and tendency. So far we have only stated what it is not, what to a large extent it perhaps never will be—*viz.*, methodical. And yet we feel that it contains that kind and portion of thought which touches our deepest interests, our most intimate concerns, our noblest aspirations. Science becomes more and more a mere calculation, *une question d'analyse*, an occupation for the laboratory, the workshop, the manufactory, and the market; philosophy savours at its best too much of the school and lecture-room, runs too much into systems and categories, it fatigues us with definitions and abstractions.　But neither calculation and measure-　^{16.} ment, nor definition and abstraction, suffice to exhaust what is to us, in the quiet and serious moments of life, of the deepest concern—*viz.*, our religion.　I use the word here in its original sense, and I propose to sum up in the term religious thought the whole of the thought contained in that large volume of literature which does not submit to scientific and philosophical treatment, but which never-theless forms so important an outcome of the mental life of the century.

16. Summed up in the term reli-gious thought.

There are other words more or less current in modern literature that may serve to throw some light on the distinction that I am here drawing for the purpose of affording a preliminary view of the course to be pur-sued in the following treatise.

Science is said to be exact, positive, and objective, and it is opposed to such other thought as is inexact, vague, and subjective.　Science is said to convey its results or ideas in defined, direct, and general terms, whereas there is a large department of literature and thought which moves in undefined, symbolical, and indirect expressions. Science professes to rest on clear and precise knowledge, and is thus opposed to such other realms of thought as rest on opinion, belief, and faith.　It may be well to note here that these different terms refer either to the method of treatment or to the matter which is under treatment. Science alone professes to have a rigid and undisputed method.　Other branches of thought either borrow their methods from science, or they have fluctuating, not gener-ally recognised methods, or they refuse to submit to method

17. Science is exact, posi-tive, and objective.

altogether. But so far as the matter under treatment is concerned, a clearer division is possible. Science deals with all such things or objects of thought as are common to a great many persons and—under certain circumstances—are accessible to everybody : it thus claims that its observations and reasonings can be checked and submitted to repeated examination and verification ; so that a large portion of them can always be regarded as settled and agreed upon, and can be taken for granted and used as a secure foundation by those persons who are themselves unable or unwilling to go through the process of verification. But

18. Some interests or objects of thought are personal or subjective.

there are a great many things and interests which centre in the individual mind of each person—which are, in fact, personal, individual, or subjective. They are to all of us just as important as the others. They form the real subject-matter of all'that thought which is separated from science, and in its very nature and aspect opposed to it. In this great province of thought one person cannot do the work for many in the same way as is possible in

19. Agreement on these matters impossible.

science. Proof is almost impossible, and agreement refers always only to a certain number of persons. Doctrines or theories in this region of thought cannot be accepted and taken for granted as they are in science, but every person must go over the same ground for himself before he has any right to accept or make use of what is given to him. The real and true character of all this thought is that it is individual and personal, whereas all scientific thought—whatever its origin may be—must be general and impersonal. At the extreme end of thought in one direction are placed the mathematical sciences, at the extreme end in the other lies religion. Disagreement in the former is almost as unknown [1] as agreement in the latter. There we have an almost universal unity of thought; here unity of thought probably never existed; it is unknown. Popularly we can say that at the one extreme lie knowledge and certainty, at the other faith and belief. There is, however, a very large extent of ground between these two extremes. This is covered by all such intermediate thought as rests partly on knowledge, partly on faith, where certainty is largely mingled with belief. This large intermediate region, where changes and fluctuations are frequent and rapid, is the proper home of philosophy, which occupies itself with the grounds of certainty and belief, the origin of knowledge and faith, and the relations in which both stand to each other. Were all our thoughts either purely mathematical — *i.e.*, referring to number, measurement, and calculation, or purely religious—*i.e.*, referring to our individual concerns and personal convictions,—the need of a continued compromise or mediation would be unnecessary, the question as to the grounds of certainty or belief would never arise. But no sooner do we wish either to apply our strict mathematical notions and processes, or to bring our personal convictions into practical use, than the two kinds of thought come into contact, not to say into conflict, and there is need of some theory according to which this contact may be regulated, this conflict settled. And as the occasions for such contact change with the demands of practical life, or

20. Philosophy intermediate between mathematical science and religion.

[1] It may be doubted whether this is quite correct, looking at the controversies which have been connected with many mathematical theories—such as the theory of parallel lines, the meaning of infinitesimals, the correct measure of force. These controversies, however, referred really to applied, not to pure mathematics, and were settled by introducing correcter and more stringent definitions.

the progress of applied science, these theories must themselves change and develop. Now it may be generally stated that it is the task of philosophy to take note of these different ways by which the strict methods of science are applied and made useful, or by which personal and individual convictions are brought to bear upon practical questions which are not only of personal but of general interest and importance. It does not follow that philosophy must necessarily construct a complete system; but it is a natural and frequent occurrence that the occupation with a great number of detached theories or aspects of thought generates the desire to bring them into harmony and to unite them in a connected whole. Thus the enterprise which was originally purely critical and preparatory, and undertaken merely as a means to an end, may lead to the formation of a general and all-embracing view of things —*i.e.*, to a philosophical system.

From whichever side we approach the matter, we are thus always led to a threefold consideration of thought, as scientific, as individual, and as philosophical. An attempt in which any of these three aspects were neglected could have no value in an account of the thought of our age. There have indeed been schools of thought which identified science with philosophy, or which maintained that no independence belonged to religious, personal, or individual thought, inasmuch as this was merely of a derived character. Though such theories may have exerted considerable influence, they have as a whole failed,[1]

21.
Threefold consideration of thought: scientific, philosophical, individual.

---

[1] This can be said of Hegelianism as well as of Comtism. In the former it was a favourite doctrine that philosophy was the higher wisdom compared with religion and art. See Hegel, 'Geschichte der Philosophie' (Werke, vol. xv. p. 684): "The highest aim and interest of philosophy is to reconcile thought, the idea, with reality.

and we find ourselves at the end of a long and critical period unable to say that any one of the three realms of thought has gained an undisputed victory over the others. Science is more than ever that kind of thought which gives knowledge and certainty. Religion is still the generally recognised abode for those convictions which refer to our deepest personal interests. And more than ever do we feel the need of a reconciliation of both in some theory of life which is neither purely scientific nor purely individualistic; and this means that philosophy is as much needed as ever. Our century has witnessed a great development of scientific thought, a great revival in religious interest, religious feeling, and religious activity, and it is probably richer than any preceding age in philosophical theories and systems.

22. Philosophy the mediator between science and religion.

I must repeat here what I said above, that it is a misfortune that in dealing with a complicated subject we are obliged to divide it,—that we are forced to give preference to some one aspect, and to choose a special

Philosophy is the veritable theodicy, compared with art and religion and their sentiments—this reconciliation of the mind, indeed of that mind which has grasped itself in the freedom and wealth of its reality. It is easy otherwise to find satisfaction in subordinate regions of intuition and feeling," &c., &c. Although it is an exaggeration to say that Hegel desired to absorb or evaporate religious belief in philosophical knowledge, as his lengthy explanation (Introduction to the 'History of Philosophy,' Works, vol. xiii. p. 77 *sqq.*) sufficiently proves, there is no doubt that the sentiment expressed in the above passage indicates that philosophy was coming to the rescue of true religious belief, which threatened to be lost in the rationalistic and mystical schools of the day. And this had the further consequence that a scientific occupation with or interest in religious subjects—be it metaphysical or historical—took the place of a purely religious interest, and that many eminent German theologians became either pure metaphysicians or merely critics, the practical side being lost sight of.

It is probably just as incorrect to accuse Comte of an intention to destroy true religion because he preached the well-known doctrine of the three stages of human thought—the theological, the metaphysical, and the scientific or positive.

point from which to set out. In dealing with the thought of our age, I have been obliged to divide what is in reality connected and coherent; and I am further forced, in examining more closely its different aspects, to select one as the most prominent with which to make a beginning. In reality such a preference does not exist in my plan. I recognise all the aspects of thought as equally important, and I feel that I might begin with any one of the three, and that I should in due course be led on to a consideration of the other two. They are in their actual historical appearance in the course of our period so interwoven that they cannot practically be separated. And it is indeed not difficult to assume various positions in contemplating the whole subject from which either one or the other of the three forms of nineteenth-century thought assumes as it were the ascendancy. Thus it would be undeniable that from a German point of view the great movement of ideas centred in the first third of the century in what I have called philosophy. The number of systems which succeeded each other was astonishing, the influence they had on literature, science, and practical life was without precedent, the enthusiasm with which students from all parts gathered in the lecture-rooms of the great metaphysicians was quite extraordinary, and probably equalled only in the schools of Athens in antiquity, or in the lecture-room of Abelard in the middle ages. From this point of view an account of this great movement—how it grew, flourished, and died away—would no doubt afford a suitable introduction to the history of thought in our century. If after this we were to turn to France and try to fix upon the

23.
Difficult to separate the three aspects of thought.

most striking intellectual feature of the century, it would be the equally great and remarkable array of scientific names of the first magnitude. In France during the early part of the century the foundation of nearly all the modern sciences was laid; many of them were brought under the rule of a strict mathematical treatment. It was there that scientific subjects were made so popular, and clothed with a garment of such elegant diction, that they have since that time greatly entered into general consciousness, and have promoted in literature and art an independent school — the naturalistic. Compared with this mathematical and naturalistic spirit, philosophy proper has found but a meagre development and culture in France: the constructive tendency of idealism has found nourishment for the most part only in leanings to the older systems of Descartes, Plato, and Aristotle, or to the foreign ones of Hegel and other German metaphysicians. Compared with Germany in philosophy, and with France in science, England during the early part of the century appears remarkably unproductive. English science and English philosophy had flourished in the seventeenth and eighteenth centuries, and leavened the whole of European thought, but in the beginning of our period we find neither represented by any great schools. The great discoveries in science belonged to individual names, who frequently stood isolated; the organisation and protection which science could boast of in France was then unknown in England; into popular thought it hardly entered as an element at all. Metaphysics had not recovered from the blow which David Hume had struck, and speculation was confined

24.
French thought centred in science during the first part of the century.

25.
State of philosophy in the early part of the nineteenth century in England.

almost entirely to the novel field of social and economic problems. But against this there was a young growth of ideas springing up in the poetic literature of the nation. It is the freshness of individual thought as clothed in the poetic language of Shelley and Wordsworth, maturing and deepening in the works of Tennyson and Browning, which strikes us as the most original phase of English thought in this century, whether we compare it with Continental thought of the same period, or with English thought of the previous age.

26.
Goethe's
'Faust' re-
presenta-
tive of the
thought of
the century.

And lastly, we might be tempted to make the great work of the greatest mind of the early part of our period, Goethe's 'Faust,' the centre and beginning of our survey, singling it out as a comprehensive embodiment, as the classical expression of nineteenth-century doubts and aspirations, leading us—if we try to understand it— now into the bewildering labyrinth of philosophy, now into the cheerful expanse of natural science, and again into the hidden depths of individual life, of religious faith with its mysteries of sin and redemption.

But from whatsoever point we may start on our journey, from whatsoever easily reached eminence we may cast a first eager glance across the wide country which we wish to explore, there is one feature which impresses itself alike upon our minds from the very beginning. It is not

27.
A period
not of re-
pose but of
ferment.

a country of repose and restfulness, of healthy industry and quiet work, of gradual development, of ripening crops, of sowing or ingathering; it does not present the aspect of a happy division of labour, of successful co-operation, of peaceful regulation of employment. It looks more like a land which has lately been disturbed by great elemental forces, heaved up by an earthquake or visited by a destructive storm. We see some persons employed in filling up great breaches and recently made rents, others trying to lay new foundations; others again are fighting for their possession or trying to divide a disputed territory; even the peaceful workers are called out to help in the battle, or disturbed by the complaints of their neighbours, on whose ground they are trespassing unawares, whose foundations they are unconsciously undermining. If we inquire into the cause of this unrest and anxiety, which seems to be a feature common to nearly all the phases of nineteenth-century thought, we must look back to the age which immediately preceded it. It is the storm of the revolution which passed over Europe, and shook to the foundation all political and social institutions, that has likewise affected our ideas and thoughts in every direction. The period we refer to has thus not incorrectly been termed a century of revolution. If in spite of this I decline to consider nineteenth-century thought as essentially revolutionary, it is because the work of destruction belongs in its earlier and more drastic episodes to the preceding age. The beginning of our period witnesses everywhere the desire to reconstruct, either by laying new foundations or by reverting to older forms of thought and life which it tries to support by new arguments or to enliven by a fresh interest and meaning. We may say that the thought of the century in its practical bearings is partly radical, partly reactionary,—meaning by the former all those constructive attempts which try to go to the root of things and to build up on newly prepared ground; by

28.
Cause of it seen in the century of revolution preceding it.

29.
Nineteenth-century thought not revolutionary.

30.
Thought of this century partly radical, partly reactionary.

the latter all those endeavours which, clinging to historical institutions and beliefs, aim at finding the truth and value which are in them, and the peculiar importance which they may have for the present day. The work of destruction is indeed still going on; in the midst of this constructive or reconstructive work we still witness the workings of the revolutionary spirit. The healthy new life which Burns, Wordsworth, and Coleridge infused into English poetry at the beginning of our period was disturbed in its quiet growth by the revolutionary spirit of the Byronic school. The new thought, which grew up in Kant's philosophy and the idealistic school, degenerated in its further development into a shallow materialism and a hopeless scepticism. But none of these destructive influences, however passingly interesting they may have been, seem to have struck out any new line of thought. Whoever wishes to study the arguments by which social order was subverted and cherished beliefs destroyed will find them brilliantly and consistently expounded in the writers of the eighteenth century, from which many nihilists of our age have drawn their inspiration. This is not the task which I have in view. It has been performed in our time by many writers of great eminence. Nor do I intend to describe the courses which governments and politicians have taken in dealing with the legitimate demands of the people, such as a hundred years ago found a memorable expression in the American Declaration of Independence, and an exaggerated one in the cry of the French Revolution. Only to a small extent has the ideal of that great movement, as it lives in the mind of many a democratic leader, been realised in our century. In

31.
The thought of Burns, Wordsworth, and Coleridge disturbed by the Byronic school.

32.
Destructive spirit in writings of eighteenth century.

most European countries the work of national unification
and consolidation, and the struggle for political independence, have retarded internal reforms; nor have theorists
been able to agree in what form of social organisation
liberty and equality could consistently live side by side.
Their teaching must indeed command special attention
as one of the many forms of the philosophic thought of
the age; but a wide gap separates theory from practical
politics, which have been largely occupied with wars and
diplomatic feats, or, when they really dealt with social problems, have had to be content with awkward compromises
between prejudices and institutions of bygone ages on the
one side, and legitimate demands for freedom on the other.

33.
Revolution-
ary theories
not practi-
cal.

Though much practical thought and much labour have
been spent in achieving even these moderate results, I feel
that they really fall outside of my programme. Wherever
either science or philosophy steps out of the quiet regions
of the study, the lecture-room, and the laboratory, or
wherever religious faith leaves the secret recesses of the
believing soul to solve the problems of life or to perform
the work of the day, the line is crossed which I have felt
obliged to draw around the following sketch. Not that I
do not recognise this borderland, where the spirit subdues
matter, where thought becomes useful, where the idea
attains reality, this field of strife and endeavour, of patient
toil and slow victory, as by far the most important subject
of history, and as that in which our age has probably excelled every earlier period. But an account of this side of
nineteenth-century life could ill afford to limit its view to
the three principal countries of the Old World. For where
are discovery and invention at this moment more at home

than in America; where have political theories, the original rights of man, the ideas of liberty, equality, and brotherhood, been more widely put to the test; where have religious beliefs entered into closer contact with the work of the day; or where in our age has the simple rule of early Christianity been more successfully put into practice? An account of the application of thought taken merely from our European experience, where half our endeavour must always be spent in clearing away obstacles, in removing the *débris* of antiquated institutions, in overcoming prejudice, or battling with evils which have grown to uncontrollable magnitude, would give us but a poor notion of the influence of thought over material circumstances, and a very exaggerated one of the inertia of the mechanism of older societies. With the work of the inventor, the practical statesman, or the lawgiver, I have thus nothing to do at present; only in cases where practical problems have immediately reacted upon scientific research, or where social questions have given rise to special theories, shall we be compelled to cast a glance outside of the inner world of thought into which I invite my readers to retire.

34.
This is not a history of invention or of practical politics.

This inner world has, indeed, not been all rest and peace and quiet development. No age has been so rich in rival theories, so subversive of old ideas, so destructive of principles which stood firm for many ages, as ours. It is not my intention to emphasise this critical or radical tendency more than is necessary. True to the original view which I have already expressed, I intend to look upon thought as a constructive, not a destructive agency; on the world of ideas as a positive acquisition, not as a mere counterpart

35.
Thought to be considered in its constructive, not in its destructive attitude.

or shadow of material existence. Though demanding for its growth an outer stimulus, and unable to proceed very far without external correctives, I nevertheless maintain that the human mind in its individual and collective life encloses an independent source of reality which contact with outer things and thought in all its various forms has to reveal, to preserve, and to develop. To what extent this has been done in our century is the question I propose to answer. With this object in view I shall try to gather my observations and my narrative around the prominent and novel constructive ideas which have sprung up in the course of the century, not omitting the great development which the purely formal side of thought, the method of research, has undergone. Such constructive ideas are those of energy, its conservation and dissipation; the doctrine of averages, statistics, and probabilities; Darwin's and Spencer's ideas of evolution in science and philosophy; the doctrines of individualism and personality, and Lotze's peculiar view of the world of "values" or "worths." Around these centres of thought cluster the many critical oppositions, the great controversies of radical or conservative opponents. As regards these, I shall welcome all radicalism which lays bare the roots of our ideas, which delves deep into the ground of our opinions and principles, or which points out new methods by which we may test the correctness and consistency of our axioms. As such I consider the spirit infused by Kant into all modern thought. That other radicalism, which merely roots up, which destroys without building, which fails to find any ground of certainty, simply because human thought and observation may after

36.
Darwin's, Spencer's, and Lotze's constructive ideas.

37.
The right sort of radicalism.

all be a delusion,—this kind of radicalism I shall try to pass over as meaningless. And equally meaningless appear to me those opposite conservative tendencies which merely annul progress, which shut out the daylight, and preach the doctrine of inertia. But this, again, will not prevent me from recognising the real gain and **38. Reactionary movement of Romanticism.** interest which belong to some reactionary movements, such as lay at the bottom of Romanticism, with its love of the past, its artistic idealisation of the childhood of mankind, of aspects of life in their infancy and primitiveness, with its study of mediævalism and its more sober historical tastes. I shall endeavour always to ask what addition to the great stock of human ideas has resulted; what gain we have to register; convinced that everything that lives must grow, increase, and multiply: and what can be more living than Thought?

But although the school of Critical Thought in Kant, and the Romantic school as centred in Walter Scott and the German Romanticists, are in time almost the first intellectual phases of the century, they will not in the beginning command my special attention.[1]

---

[1] In order to give some idea of the complexity of the different currents of thought in the first years of the century, I place here a carefully selected list of dates. They refer to events or publications which mark epochs or important stages in the history of thought. Of specifically *scientific* importance are—

1796. Laplace's 'Exposition du Système du Monde.'
1799. (2 vols.)—1825. Laplace's 'Mécanique céleste.'
1799. Legendre's 'Théorie des Nombres.'
1801. Gauss's 'Disquisitiones Arithmeticæ.'
1801. Piazzi discovers and
1802 Olbers rediscovers the first of the minor planets, "Ceres," being assisted by Gauss's new methods of calculation, which were published *in extenso* in
1809. Gauss's 'Theoria motus corporum cœlestjum.'
1798. Cuvier's 'Tableau élémentaire d'Histoire naturelle.'
1800-5. Cuvier's 'Leçons d'Anatomie comparée.'

Though somewhat later in point of time than they, the school of exact research seems to have become the more generally recognised agent in nineteenth-century progress.

1809. Lamarck's 'Philosophie zoologique.'

1799. Volta constructs his first electric pile, and announces this in 1800 to Sir Joseph Banks.

In chemistry the early years of the century brought many of Gay-Lussac's important Memoirs, in

1801 Humphry Davy publishes the first of his electro-chemical discoveries, and

1802-3 Berzelius publishes his own.

1803. Berthollet's 'Essai de Statique chimique.'

1810. John Dalton's 'New System of Chemical Philosophy.'

1801. Thomas Young announces to the Royal Society his belief in the undulatory theory of light, which during

1802, 3, and 4 he substantiates further in his papers, and fully expounds during

1802 and following years in his lectures to the Royal Institution.

1808. Malus announces his discovery of the polarisation of light through reflection.

1802. Chladni's 'Akustik.'

Count Rumford's papers, which laid the foundation of the mechanical explanation of heat, belong to the end of the last century, and in

1799 H. Davy publishes his equally important 'Essay on Heat, Light, &c.'

1800. Bichat's 'Recherches physiologiques.'

1801. Bichat's 'Anatomie générale.'

1799-1804. Alexander von Humboldt travels in America, and lays by his observations the foundation of the sciences of physical geography and meteorology.

For the history of the *philosophical* movement of thought the years 1793-1806 witnessed in Germany the great development, expansion, and criticism of Kant's ideas in the writings of

1793 Schiller, 'Briefe über ästhetische Erziehung.'

1796. Schiller, 'Über naive und sentimentalische Dichtung.'

1797. Fichte, 'Wissenschaftslehre.'

1797. Schelling, 'Naturphilosophie.'

1803. Schelling, 'Transcendentaler Idealismus.'

1799. Schleiermacher, 'Reden über die Religion.'

1800. Schleiermacher, 'Monologen.'

1799. Herder, 'Metakritik.'

1799. Jacobi, 'Offener Brief an Fichte.'

1806. Hegel, 'Phänomenologie des Geistes.'

In France—

1804. Destutt de Tracy's 'Idéologie' represents the reigning philosophy, and

1803 Maine de Biran's 'Mémoire sur l'Habitude' the beginning of the later reaction against it.

In England—

1792-1827. Dugald Stewart's 'Elements of the Human Mind' and his

To it are due the great changes in every department of
science, of life, and probably also of literature and art,
the great inventions and the great conflicts of our age.
Science has not only very largely influenced our ideas,
it has also by its applications altered the external face
of the world we live in.   It is therefore simply a tribute
to the popular view, and a desire to start from some
striking and generally conceded position, if I select the

**39.
Scientific
progress to
be consid-
ered first.**

scientific movement of ideas as the first with which
I have to deal.   How has it spread in the course of
the century ?   From what beginnings and through what
influences ?   What are its principles and methods ?   How
have they themselves changed and developed ?   What
has it led to ?   These are some of the questions which

1803   ' Life and Writings of Thomas Reid ' represent the predominant
        Scottish philosophy, and
1804   Thomas Brown, ' Inquiry into the Relation of Cause and Effect,'
        the beginnings of the later associationalist school.   At the same
        period Jeremy Bentham's influence, which cannot be reduced to
        special dates, had already acquired European if not world-wide
        importance.   His long life (1748-1832) was contemporary with
        Goethe's (1749-1832), whose ' Faust' was given to the world in
        successive stages between the years 1790 and 1832.
1794. Thomas Paine's ' Age of Reason.'
1798. Malthus's ' Principles of Population.'
Literary criticism started on a new era and extended its influence in
1802   through the ' Edinburgh Review,' and
1808   the ' Quarterly Review ' ; in Germany somewhat earlier in
1794   Schiller's ' Horen.'
1797. Schiller and Goethe's " Xenien " in the ' Musenalmanach.'
1798. Schlegel's ' Athenæum.'
1802. A. W. v. Schlegel's Berlin lectures.
The *Romantic school* of fiction dates in Germany from 1798, when
Frederick Schlegel uses the term for the first time as characteristic of
a new departure in his review of Goethe's ' Wilhelm-Meister ' (' Athenæum,'
vol. i.)   A literary movement with frequently similar aims and characteristics is represented in this country by Walter Scott (" Lay of the Last
Minstrel," 1805), Southey (" Thalaba," 1802), and Coleridge (" Christabel,"
1806), and spreads later into France.   As the great source of the new
and original *poetic* inspiration of nineteenth-century poetry we have the
" Lyrical Ballads," 1798, and besides ' Faust,' the other principal works of
Goethe and Schiller (died 1805).

I shall try to answer as concisely as possible. This selection does not commit me to any theory on the value of the scientific view as compared with other aspects. Such theories will have to be dealt with in a later portion of the work. They have sprung up in the course of the last hundred years, partly as the inevitable outcome of scientific progress itself, partly in the educational world, where a reaction has set in against the undue importance which former generations attached to classical learning and training. I need not at present do more than note these opinions, nor need I define my position with regard to Comte's celebrated positivist theory on the advancing stages of the human intellect. Curiosity and the consensus of popular opinion suffice for the moment to make me take up the scientific side of the thought of the age. As we proceed, other directions and movements will present themselves, and the interdependence of all human interests will reveal and explain what truth attaches to Hegel's celebrated doctrine of the inherent dialectic of ideas, the spontaneous development of thought.

40. Hegel's doctrine of the spontaneous development of thought.

A HISTORY OF
EUROPEAN SCIENTIFIC THOUGHT
IN THE NINETEENTH CENTURY

CHAPTER I.

THE SCIENTIFIC SPIRIT IN FRANCE.

IT will be generally admitted that the scientific spirit is a prominent feature of the thought of our century as compared with other ages. Some may indeed be inclined to look upon science as the main characteristic of this age. The century may thus be called with some propriety the scientific century, as the last was called the philosophical century, or as the sixteenth was termed the century of the Reformation and the fifteenth the century of the Renaissance. It is therefore natural that we should begin our study of the thought of the age with an examination of this side of modern culture.

It is not necessary to *define* what I mean by science.[1]

---

[1] The use of the word science and its adjective scientific has varied considerably in the English language. We must wait for Dr Murray's great work to give us a history of the word. I venture to assert that it acquired its present definite meaning about the time of the formation of the British Association for the Advancement of Science (1831). The two other great organisations which professedly started for the culture of what we now call science — *viz.,* the Royal Society for the Improvement of Natural Knowledge, and the Royal Institution—did not use the word officially in their charter or title, although it is used frequently in the documents and correspondence connected with the foundation of the younger, and occasionally in those referring to the older Society. The Royal So-

Schools and colleges of science, triposes, examinations, and degrees in science, have established a popular meaning which did not exist a hundred years ago, but which is now well understood. For my purpose it is of some interest to note that the meaning of the word in French is somewhat different, and that the word *Wissenschaft*,[1]

ciety, and sometimes the Royal Institution, use the word "philosophy" in formal and official statements of their object. This is in accordance with older English usage. What we now universally call science was not infrequently termed in the seventeenth century natural knowledge, and Bacon himself translates *scientiæ* by "knowledge," by "learning," and sometimes by "sciences." In France, on the other hand, the word "science" seems to have acquired its present meaning as far back as the middle of the seventeenth century. At the time of the foundation of the "Académie des Sciences," in 1666, the word was used almost in the same sense — embracing the same separate departments of knowledge—as the word "science" is now used in this country when we speak of a college of science. In France, so far as I am aware, a cultivator of science has never been called a philosopher. Science and philosophy have there never been synonymous. But science in France has been made to cover a larger field of knowledge by such adjectives as "moral," "social," "political," and has been narrowed by such other adjectives as "exact" and "natural," in the same way as the word philosophy has been more strictly defined in the English language by the adjectives "natural," "experimental," "moral," "mental," &c. At the head of the sciences in France stood "mathematics," at the base of the

new philosophy in England stood "experiment" and "observation."

[1] The word *Wissenschaft* has a much wider meaning than science in the modern sense, and is the literal translation of the Latin *scientia*. It means knowledge in a systematic form and connected by some method. What the French call *science*, the Germans call *exacte Wissenschaft*. This includes mathematics and *Naturwissenschaft*, which covers the ground covered by the word "sciences" in English. The word *Wissenschaft* plays an important part in German culture, as we shall see later on. The modern term "scientist" is about synonymous with the word *Naturforscher* in German. The word *savant* in French has no synonym in English, but is about equivalent to the term *Gelehrter* in German; and this, again, is partially translated by "scholar" in English. I suppose "man of science" and "scholar" together would be about covered by either *savant* or *Gelehrter*. Those who desire to study the older and modern, the English and foreign, uses of the word science and other kindred terms, should read Bacon'-English writings; Weld's 'History of the Royal Society' (1848, vol. i.); Bence Jones's 'The Royal Institution' (1871); Léon Aucoc's 'L'Institut de France' (Paris, 1889); Alfred Maury, 'Les Académies d'autrefois' (vol. i., Paris, 1864); and the correspondence in connection with the foundation of the British Associa-

by which science is translated into German, requires a qualification in order to cover approximately the same ground. These verbal differences point to differences of thought. Only since Continental ideas and influences have gained ground in this country has the word science gradually taken the place of that which used to be termed natural philosophy or simply philosophy. One reason why science forms such a prominent feature in the culture of this age is the fact that only within the last hundred years has scientific research approached the more intricate phenomena and the more hidden forces and conditions which make up and govern our everyday life. The great inventions of the sixteenth, seventeenth, and eighteenth centuries were made without special scientific knowledge, and frequently by persons who possessed skill rather than learning. They greatly influenced science and promoted knowledge, but they were brought about more by accident or by the practical requirements of the age than by the power of an unusual insight acquired by study.[1] But in the course of the last

2.
Difference of
English and
Continental
notions of
science.

---

tion in Dr Whewell's 'Writings and Correspondence' by Todhunter (2 vols., London, 1876). I believe the word philosophy has lost the specific meaning which it acquired in the Baconian school, as much through the influence of French science on the one side as through that of metaphysics on the other. The latter emanated from Scotland, and from Germany through Coleridge. It reinstated the word philosophy in its original sense.

[1] Examples are plentiful. Not to speak of gunpowder and printing, which came earlier, we have later nearly all the great improvements connected with the manufacture of textiles, the fly-shuttle, the self-acting mule, the power-loom, the spinning-roller, invented by men of little or no scientific education. The same is the case with the older metallurgical processes, the refining of copper and the introduction of cast-iron. Watt was one of the first who brought a trained intellect to his mechanical work. The Royal Society was started with the distinct purpose of cultivating such knowledge as has "a tendency to use"; the Royal Institution still more so. It is, however, still doubtful, view-

hundred years the scientific investigation of *chemical* and *electric* phenomena has taught us to disentangle the intricate web of the elementary forces of nature, to lay bare the many interwoven threads, to break up the equilibrium of actual existence, and to bring within our power and under our control forces of undreamed-of magnitude. The great inventions of former ages were made in countries where practical life, industry, and commerce were most advanced; but the great inventions of the last fifty years in chemistry and electricity and the science of heat have been made in the scientific laboratory: the former were stimulated by practical wants; the latter themselves produced new practical requirements, and created new spheres of labour, industry, and commerce. Science and knowledge have in the course of this century overtaken the march of practical life in many directions.[1] A confused

3.
Relation of
science and
practical
life.

ing the history of the learned societies as well as the rare cases in which highest scientific genius is allied with practical skill in the same person, whether the cultivation of research for its own sake should not preferably be kept distinct from its hasty application. This is the view held by many great thinkers abroad. In England the opposite view has frequently impeded the progress of pure science.

[1] A few examples may suffice. The discovery by Oersted and Ampère of Electromagnetism (1819, 1820) led at once to the idea of electrical telegraphy: the first telegraph over considerable distances was constructed by Gauss and Weber (see 'Wilhelm Weber,' Breslau, 1893, p. 26, &c.) The artificial preparation of an organic substance by Wöhler in 1828 led at once to many attempts at preparing expensive organic compounds—

especially medical substances—by chemical synthesis. The occupation with this problem under A. W. Hofmann's instructions led Perkin in 1856 to the discovery of the first anilin colour (Mauvein, see 'Berichte der deutschen chemischen Gesellschaft,' No. 17, p. 3391). Leblanc's discovery how to make carbonate of soda from salt, for which a prize had been offered by the Paris Academy under Napoleon, led to the enormous development of the sulphuric acid industry in England and on the Continent. Liebig foretold in 1840 the recovery of sulphur from the waste of chemical works and the effect on the sulphur mines of Sicily, fifty years before this process was satisfactorily carried out (see Liebig's familiar 'Letters on Chemistry,' 1st ed., 1843, pp. 22, 31, &c.) But the greatest of all industries created in the laboratory was probably that of

picture of this latest stage of culture lived in the prophetic but essentially unscientific mind of Lord Bacon.
But he did not sufficiently allow for the amount of patient
scientific toil that was needed, nor for the time which the
preparation of the instruments of research would require,
nor for the necessity of destroying existing superstition
and accumulated errors. All that has since been done by
Newton and the great Continental mathematicians in the
former, and by Bayle and Voltaire in the latter sense,
Bacon had hoped to achieve at once by the new philosophy of fruit and progress. Such expectations were
inevitably doomed to disappointment, though posterity
has made amends by all but universally referring to him
as the pioneer of modern thought,—as the herald of a
new era of human civilisation.[1]

making artificially the fertilising
compounds required in common
agriculture which followed on the
publication of Liebig's famous work
on 'Chemistry in its applications
to Agriculture and Physiology' in
1840 (see Hofmann's Faraday
Lecture of 1875, 'The Lifework of
Liebig,' p. 15, &c.) Liebig also
discovered and described in 1832
the properties of chloroform and
chloral, fifteen years before Simpson
introduced the first as an anæsthetic
and twenty years before Oscar
Liebreich discovered the physiological action of chloral (ibid., p. 101,
&c.) Sir Lowthian Bell calculated,
many years before the invention
of the so-called basic process of
making steel, the fertilising value
of the phosphorus which was contained in the ironstone of Cleve-
land, and which then made it useless for the manufacture of high-
class iron and steel. The great
revolution in the theory of the

steam-engine embodied in the work
of Macquorn Rankine is to be traced
back to the patient measurements
by Joule of the mechanical equivalent of heat.
[1] A great controversy arose on
this subject through the publication of Liebig's pamphlet in 1862,
entitled, 'Francis Bacon von Veru-
lam und die Methode der Natur-
forschung.' It was directed mostly
against the exaggerated view taken
by Macaulay in his celebrated essay.
The fact is that Bacon, like Voltaire after him, was much more
of an essayist and a man of the
world than a patient labourer in
any special field of research ; he
was more of a philosopher in a
worldly sense (what the Germans
call "ein Weltweiser") than a profound thinker. He misunderstood
many of the great discoveries of his
age, though he prophetically foresaw the great change in the spirit
of inquiry. He did not appreciate

5.
Defect in
Bacon's
philosophy.

Our age has in many ways inherited the spirit of Bacon's philosophy; but it would be a mistake to attribute its great scientific achievements to the exclusive working of this spirit. Bacon was neither a retired and patient nor an accurate thinker—the desire to apply and make his learning useful led him away from the "sapientum templa serena" into the forum of life: in his own experience, as well as in his writings, he anticipated many of the dangers which beset modern culture—the love of premature application, and the haste for practical results and achievements. Science, which in the hands of patient and diligent observers [1] had just been rescued from the sway of empty metaphysical and theological reasoning,

the enormous part which mathematics would play in the development of science. In this respect Descartes was a genius of much greater originality—his actual contributions to scientific progress, as well as those of Pascal, being far beyond those of Bacon; but they both retained the metaphysical habit of thought which has characterised many, if not all, among the greatest mathematicians. In modern culture the popularisation of novel views and ideas has become so important a factor that writers like Bacon and Voltaire, who combine the scientific and literary taste, are of the greatest importance in the diffusion of new ideas, though none of their works need be looked upon as great repositories of research and knowledge. Before Liebig wrote his pamphlet, a very impartial and temperate estimate of Bacon's philosophy and its relations to actual science was published by Robert Leslie Ellis in his introduction to the philosophical works of Lord Bacon (London, 1857). As the literature of the subject is so large, I cannot but recommend this essay as containing one of the best discussions of it.

[1] A very good and concise account of the achievements of these contemporaries and forerunners of Bacon—of Tycho (1546-1601), Kepler (1571-1630), Galileo (1564-1642), Gilbert (1540-1603), Harriot (1560-1621), Napier (1550-1617), Harvey (1578-1656)—is given by John Nichol in the second volume of his 'Francis Bacon, his Life and Philosophy' (Edinb., 1889), pp. 86, 254. In the same volume (p. 193) there is also a useful summary of Bacon's real claims to a place among physicists, of his ignorances (p. 196), and of the reception which his works met with in England and abroad (p. 233 to end). Not quite so readable, but more complete, is the little volume of Hans Heussler, 'F. Bacon und seine geschichtliche Stellung' (Breslau, 1889), with its flood of references—which exhaust the subject. See especially p. 160, &c., on Bacon's anticipations.

was in danger of falling a prey to hasty generalisation for the purpose of practical ends. Practical demands threatened then, as they frequently still do, to stifle or to force into premature growth the patient thought which had just begun to germinate in the new light and freedom of reason. The narrow view had indeed been widened, and the breadth of the land had been surveyed, but there was little inclination to deepen the view, or to do more than search on the surface. The spirit of Bacon's philosophy required a corrective. For a long time to come the hope of practical application had to be postponed; the thinker and student had to retire into solitude, and there to lay the more permanent foundations of the new research. This was done by Newton for all time. His reputation spread more slowly than that of the great High Chancellor; but it rests on a surer foundation, which baffles every attempt to shake it, and will outlast all coming changes of thought.

6. Corrected by Newton.

The beginnings of modern scientific thought are thus to be found in this country. Lord Bacon foretold prophetically the great change which the new philosophy was destined to work. Newton more patiently drew up the first simple rules and gave the first brilliant application. More than the unfinished and wearisome pages of Bacon's 'Novum Organum' does the 'Principia' deserve to be placed on a line with Aristotle and Euclid as a model work of scientific inquiry.

For a real recognition of the greatness of Newton, as well as for a partial realisation of Bacon's plans, we are, however, mainly indebted to the French philosophers of the second half of the eighteenth century. Bacon's plan of promoting

7. Bacon's and Newton's ideas taken up by French philosophers.

knowledge and research by the co-operation of many was more thoroughly realised in the old French Academy than in the Royal Society of London : his desire to unite all knowledge in a collective work underlies the great productions of Bayle, and still more those of the Encyclopædists. The many problems contained in Newton's 'Principia' were first treated singly by Clairault and Maupertuis; a general knowledge of his view of the universe was introduced into popular literature by Voltaire,[1] who made use of it as a powerful weapon wherewith to combat error and superstition, or, as he termed it, " pour écraser l'infâme "; but for a full announcement of its scientific value and its hidden resources we are indebted to Laplace, whose 'Mécanique céleste' was the first comprehensive elaboration of Newton's ideas, and whose 'Système du Monde' became the scientific gospel of a whole generation of Continental thinkers.

8. Bacon and Newton compared.

We may look upon Lord Bacon as one who inspects a large and newly discovered land,[2] laying plans for the

[1] I believe Voltaire was the author of the term *Newtonianisme*. The modesty and truly scientific spirit of Newton would not have allowed him to apply such a term to his work, and it is doubtful whether Voltaire did not extract from Newton's 'Philosophia Naturalis' a general philosophy which was not conceived in his spirit.

[2] Cowley in his Ode to the Royal Society :—

" Bacon at last, a mighty man, arose, . . .
And boldly undertook the injur'd pupil's cause.
. . . led us forth at last,
The barren wilderness he past;
  Did on the very border stand
  Of the blest promis'd land ;
And, from the mountain's top of his exalted wit,
  Saw it himself, and shew'd us it."

On this Mr Ellis remarks (Bacon's Works, vol. i. p. 63) : " Bacon has been likened to the prophet who, from Mount Pisgah, surveyed the Promised Land, but left it for others to take possession of. Of this happy image, perhaps part of the felicity was not perceived by its author. For though Pisgah was a place of large prospect, yet still the Promised Land was a land of definite extent and known boundaries, and, moreover, it was certain that after no long time the chosen people would be in possession of it all. And this agrees with what Bacon promised to himself and to mankind from the instauration of the sciences. . . . In this respect, as in others, the hopes of Francis Bacon

development of its resources and the gathering of its riches. But the wealth lies deep down, and is only indicated by the first labours of the early pioneers. Newton, following these, unites their beginnings into a systematic exploration, and sinks the main shaft which reaches the lode of rich ore. He opens out the wealth of the mine and marks out the work for his followers. But many difficulties had to be overcome, much united effort and a vast organisation of labour were required, in order to develop to the full Newton's scheme, and to raise the great treasure which he had reached. This was not done until the end of the last century, when Laplace collected, arranged, and condensed the work of French and English mathematicians and observers into a picture of the universe. A variety of circumstances had combined to make the French capital the place above all others where the means and materials for the development of the great work could be most easily procured. Let us glance for a moment at the different factors in operation during the eighteenth century which contributed to the great achievement.

9. Laplace's work.

Whilst Newton was labouring privately and almost unassisted [1] at the greatest scientific work produced in

---

were not destined to be fulfilled. It is neither to the technical part of his method, nor to the details of his view of the nature and progress of science, that his great fame is justly owing. His merits are of another kind. They belong to the spirit rather than to the positive precepts of his philosophy."

[1] It has been stated that Newton, not knowing of Norwood's approximately correct determination of the length of a degree in 1635 (published in his 'Seaman's Practice' in 1637), but relying on the old figure of sixty miles for a degree of latitude (confirmed by Ed. Wright, Cambridge, 1610), was led away from the right supposition, which he entertained as far back as 1665, regarding the moon's orbit, and had to wait for Picard's figures (ascertained about 1669, published in France about 1672, and in the

modern times by any single mind,[1] the penetrating and
far-seeing genius of Colbert had already recognised the
important part which science would one day play in
the government of the world, and had secured the ap-
proval of his royal master to the constitution of an Aca-

Philos. Transactions in 1675), by
applying which he determined that
"the moon appeared to be kept in
her orbit purely by the power of
gravity." See Brewster's 'Life of
Newton,' vol. i. p. 290, &c.; Todhunter's 'History of the Theories of
Attraction,' vol. i. p. 38, &c. This
account is, however, now discredited
(see *infra*, chap. iv.) For the part
which Dr Hooke and Halley took in
the discovery of the "reciprocal
duplicate" ratio, see also Brewster,
loc. cit., vol. i. p. 291, &c. During
the writing of the 'Principia' Newton carried on a useful correspondence with Flamsteed, who was then
Astronomer-Royal. How this happy
co-operation ceased ten years later
can be read at length in Brewster
(*loc. cit.*, vol. i. p. 312; vol. ii. p. 164,
&c.) The greatest material assistance which Newton received was
from Halley, who defrayed the expenses of publishing the 'Principia,'
after the Royal Society, to which it
was dedicated, had reversed its resol-
ution to defray them (Brewster, vol.
i. p. 305, &c.) Nevertheless Weld, in
his 'History of the Royal Society,'
says : "Fortunate indeed was it for
science that such a body as the Royal
Society existed, to whom Newton
could make his scientific communications ; otherwise it is very possible
that the 'Principia' would never
have seen the light." Though one
must lament the differences between Flamsteed and Newton, which
prevented the latter from bringing his investigations of the lunar
and planetary theories to a close
(Brewster, vol. i. p. 312), a word of

deep gratitude is due to Flamsteed's
own exertions in the cause of astronomy. After Charles II. had built
the Observatory in order to have
the places of the fixed stars "anew
observed, examined, and corrected
for the use of his seamen" (Flamsteed, History of his own Life), and
after he had appointed Flamsteed
Astronomer-Royal at a salary of
£100 per annum, the Observatory,
"hurriedly established, was left for
a period of nearly fifteen years
without a single instrument being
furnished by the Government"
(Weld, vol. i. p. 255). The instruments were mostly supplied by
Flamsteed himself or lent by others,
and besides, "the king had ordered
that Flamsteed should instruct
monthly two boys from Christ
Church Hospital, which was a great
annoyance to him, and interfered
with his proper avocations" (Baily,
'Account of the Rev. J. Flamsteed').
"Any other man would probably
have succumbed under the amount
of drudgery appertaining to the
office (earning his salary by labour
harder than thrashing), if indeed,
in the absence of encouragement,
he would have continued in it at
all, and particularly when the reward was so insignificant" (Weld,
vol. i. p. 256).
    [1] "And it may be justly said,
that so many and so valuable Philosophical Truths, as are herein discovered and put past dispute, were
never yet owing to the Capacity
and Industry of any one Man"
(Words of Halley, Philos. Transactions, vol. xvi., 1687).

demy, which was based upon the endowment of research, and which prompted the co-operation of its members in organised [1] scientific work. Whilst the Royal Society of London only received a charter, and existed by the entrance payments and contributions of its own members, augmented by private donations, the Paris Academy had, as far back as 1671, received the funds with which to commence its labours in connection with the survey of the kingdom and its extensive dependencies. It was these labours which led to the measurements of the length of the seconds pendulum, and of the variation of gravity in different latitudes; to the explanation of this variation by Huygens; to the controversy regarding the figure of the earth; to the direct measurements of the arcs of the meridian in Peru and Lapland; and, finally, to Clairault's celebrated work on this subject.[2] It was almost exclusively by these observations that the data were found with which to substantiate Newton's mathematical reasonings : in his own country that fruitful co-operation which

10.
French
Academy
of Sciences.

---

[1] "Le roi assurait l'existence des Académiciens par des pensions et mettait libéralement à leur disposition un fonds destiné à pourvoir aux frais de leurs expériences et de leurs instruments" (Maury, 'Les Académies d'autrefois,' vol. i. p. 13). Organisation and co-operation are difficult to obtain in societies founded on private and voluntary contributions. In England they scarcely existed before the foundation of the British Association, with perhaps one illustrious exception pointed out by Struve ('Description de l'Observatoire de Pulkowa,' 4to, Pétersbourg, p. 5): "Il y a, dans l'histoire de l'observatoire de Greenwich, un point très remarquable, savoir que les astronomes ont travaillé sur un même plan, depuis l'origine de l'établissement jusqu'à l'époque actuelle." Organisation and co-operation were the order in the Paris Academy from the beginning. "On y travaillait de concert"; and, "Dès les premiers mois de 1667, Perrault proposa un plan de travail pour la physique, c'est à dire pour l'ensemble de l'histoire naturelle" (Maury, loc. cit., p. 15).

[2] A full account of these is given in Todhunter ('Hist. of Theories of Attraction, &c.,' vol. i.) Clairault's book was published in 1743, and had the title, 'Théorie de la Figure de la Terre, tirée des Principes de l'Hydrostatique, par Clairault.'

can only be secured by an academic organisation and by endowment of research was wanting. No one since the time of Bacon had been more impressed with this necessary condition of modern progress than Newton's great rival, Leibniz,[1] much of whose time was spent in promoting academies all over Europe—in Berlin, St Petersburg, Dresden, and Vienna—and who had himself been early attracted to Paris and London by the scientific fame of their learned societies, though he significantly pointed out the want of activity and efficiency in the early history of the Royal Society.

11.
Continental
methods in
mathe-
matics.

There was, moreover, another and independent line of scientific thought which had centred in France, the development of which came greatly to the aid of the students of Newton's work. This was the purely mathematical elaboration of the various infinitesimal methods of the French and English mathematicians, by which they were all brought together, simplified, and united into a calculus with strict rules, a practical notation, and an easy algorithm. Newton himself had for the purposes of his great work invented a new and powerful

[1] A collection of Leibniz's writings on this subject will be found in the 7th volume of M. Foucher de Careil's edition of Leibniz's Works, Paris, 1875. Of the projects of Leibniz, only the Academy of Berlin came into existence during his lifetime (1700 and 1701); the others were discussed at great length with the Elector of Saxony, with the Emperor, and with Peter the Great. The Academy of St Petersburg was founded in 1724, eight years after the death of Leibniz. The Academy of Vienna did not come into life till 1846, and in the same year that of Saxony was founded, which has its seat at Leipsic. Leibniz had the largest views on academic life and work: they were to embrace the historical and philosophical studies as well as the purely scientific, and were to stand in relation with the higher and lower educational institutions. His ideas are best realised at Berlin. See Jacob Grimm's interesting discourse, entitled 'Ueber Schule Universität Akademie' (Kleine Schriften, vol. i. p. 211, &c.)

instrument, afterwards called "the method of fluxions"; but he had not made it generally known before the invention of Leibniz was published.[1] This, though much later in time, had been perfected and applied by his friends and followers in a most extensive manner, and had, in fact, become the recognised mathematical language of the Continent. No learned body did more than the Paris Academicians to perfect (with purely scientific

[1] Leibniz seems to have been in possession of his method as early as 1675, and communicated it to Collins in 1677. It was, however, not published before 1684 in the 'Acta Eruditorum,' and then probably only on account of some writings of Tschirnhausen trenching on the same subject. Newton seems to have been in possession of his methods as early as 1665, fully ten years before Leibniz made use of his. Immediately after the publication of Leibniz's paper in 1684, the differential calculus was taken up by the Continental mathematicians, especially by James Bernoulli (1654-1705) and John Bernoulli (1667-1748), and the Marquis de l'Hopital, who published the first treatise on the new calculus in 1696. Newton did not publish any account of his method, though he must have used it extensively in arriving at the results contained in the 'Principia.' Different views have been expressed on the reasons which induced Newton to withhold from publication his new methods, and the question to what extent Leibniz owed the first suggestions of his method to Newton remains also undecided. Those who take an interest in the personal question should refer to the original documents, the 'Commercium Epistolicum,' published by the Royal Society in 1715 ; the pamphlet of Gerhardt,

'Die Erfindung der Differentialrechnung' (Halle, 1848). An extreme view, unfavourable to Leibniz's originality, is taken by Sloman, 'Leibnitzens Anspruch auf die Erfindung der Differentialrechnung' (Leipzig, 1857); but it has not been generally adopted by those who have examined into the subject. As to the superiority of the Continental notation for practical purposes, this seems to have been generally admitted at the beginning of this century, when it was introduced into English mathematical works. In the school of W. R. Hamilton of Dublin the notation used by Newton acquired a peculiar importance, and it is still occasionally used in some important works like Tait and Steele's 'Dynamics of a Particle,' and Thomson and Tait's 'Natural Philosophy.' See on this Tait's article on Hamilton in the 'North British Review' (Sept. 1866). The importance of the labours of the Continental school, headed by Leibniz, for the diffusion of the new methods, is well described by Remont de Montmort in a letter to Brook Taylor, dated 18th December 1718, and given in the appendix to Brewster's 'Life of Newton' (vol. ii. p. 511, &c.) Those who take more interest in the fate of ideas and the progress of thought than in personal matters will do well to read this letter.

interest) this new calculus, which in the course of the
eighteenth century had in the hands of Lagrange been
adapted to all the purposes and problems contained or
suggested in Newton's 'Principia.'

12.
Modern
analytical
methods.

This leads me to a third and yet more important element
of scientific thought, which was peculiar to the Continental,
and especially to the French mathematicians, counting
among them Leibniz, who, though a German, was wholly
trained in the French school. This factor is the establishment of pure mathematics on an independent foundation, and the cultivation of research into the abstract
relations of quantity, without reference either to geometrical or mechanical problems and applications. It is
the modern analytical spirit introduced by the great
French algebraists of the seventeenth century, which
looks upon geometry, mechanics, and astronomy merely
as "questions d'analyse," and makes their solutions depend upon the perfecting of an abstract calculus rather
than on the study of these individual problems themselves. Opposed to this spirit of analysis, which in
general seeks the solution of any given question by
looking upon it as a special case of a wider and more
abstract problem, is the method known to the ancients,
which never loses sight of the actual application, be it a
figure in geometry or a special arrangement of physical
forces, and is more interested in the peculiarities of the
individual case than in the abstract formula of which it
may be considered an application. This opposite view
regards the calculus and mathematics in general merely
as an instrument, the value of which lies solely in its
application to real physical problems. It is usually

termed the synthetical method, and has in modern times survived principally in England, where inductive reasoning, based upon observation of detail, has since the age of Lord Bacon been most successfully cultivated.[1]   These different ways of approaching the same subject will frequently engage my attention in the course of this survey : the greatest mathematicians of modern times have recognised the importance of both aspects, and the enormous progress of the science itself has depended, no doubt, on an alternating employment of them.   Leibniz clearly foresaw this when, in his correspondence with Huygens and others, he urged the necessity of not abandoning the purely geometrical view, or entirely sacrificing the older for the modern methods.[2]   There can, however, be no doubt that

13.
Older synthetical method.

---

[1] See on this point the opinion of an authority, Hermann Hankel, in his highly interesting and suggestive lecture, ' Die Entwickelung der Mathematik in den letzten Jahrhunderten' (Tübingen, 1869, republished by P. du Bois-Reymond, 1884).   Speaking of the age of Leibniz he says : "Though on the Continent mathematicians were not so conservative as in England, where a purely geometrical exposition was considered to be the only one worthy of mathematics, yet the whole spirit of that age was directed to the solution of problems in geometrical clothing, and the result of the calculus had mostly to be retranslated into geometrical forms.   It is the inestimable merit of the great mathematician of Basel, Leonhard Euler, to have freed the analytical calculus from all geometrical fetters, and thus to have established analysis as an independent science.   Analysis places at its entrance the conception of a function, in order to express the mutual dependence of two variable quantities. . . . The abstract theory of functions is the higher analysis. . . . The conception of a function has been slowly and hesitatingly evolved out of special and subordinate conceptions. It was Euler who first established it, making it the foundation of the entire analysis, and hereby he inaugurated a new period in mathematics " (p. 12, &c.)

[2] To Huygens, 16th September 1679 : "Je ne suis pas encor content de l'Algèbre, en ce qu'elle me donne ny les plus courtes voyes, ny les plus belles constructions de Géométrie. . . . Je croy qu'il nous faut encor une autre analyse proprement géométrique ou linéaire, qui nous exprime directement situm, comme l'Algèbre exprime magnitudinem. Et je croy d'en avoir le moyen, et qu'on pourroit représenter des figures et mesures des machines et mouvements en caractères, comme l'Algèbre représente les nombres ou grandeurs" (Leibniz, Mathem. Werke, ed. Gerhardt, vol. ii. p. 19).

the great success which attended Laplace's work, the elaboration of a system of the universe out of the principles of Newton, was largely due to the perfection which the analytical methods had gained in the hands of his predecessors, and to the skill with which he himself reduced the several problems to purely analytical questions.

But however much exact methods, learned societies, and regal endowments may do to promote the growth of the scientific spirit, experience has shown that popular favour and interest furnish a still more effective stimulus. Even the most abstract reasonings of the mathematician require to be brought into some connection with the general concerns of mankind, before they can attract talent from outside, or enter into that healthy action and reaction which are the soul of all mental progress. In this respect, also, France during the second half of the eighteenth century was far in advance of other countries. No other literature of that age can be compared with that of France, when we look at the influence or the expression which modern scientific views and interests had already attained in it; and no other country could at the end of the eighteenth century boast of such splendid means of scientific instruction as then existed in Paris. In two important departments—the popularisation and the teaching of science—France for a long period led the way.[1] A general inter-

14. Influence of science on French literature.

To Bodenhausen (about 1690) : " I am of opinion that in the problems of ordinary Geometry the *methodus Veterum* has certain advantages over *Analysin Algebraicam*, and I think I have remarked to you that there remains an *Analysis geometricæ propria, toto cœlo ab Algebra diversa et in multis longe Algebra compendio-* *sior utiliorque* " (ibid., vol. vii. p. 359). " It is certain that algebra, by reducing everything *a situ ad solam magnitudinem,* hereby very frequently complicates things very much " (p. 362).

[1] Perhaps it would be more correct to say that science was fashionable than that it was popular in the

est was thus created in the proceedings and debates of the Academy, and the discoveries of its illustrious members found their way into the lectures and text-books of the professors. Whatever eminence German science may have gained in this century, from a purely literary point of view, through the works of A. von Humboldt, or English science through those of Darwin, the history of both literatures during the eighteenth century can be written almost without any reference to science at all—so small was the direct influence of such giants as Newton and Leibniz on the popular mind. But who could exclude from a history of the elegant literature of France the names of Voltaire, of Buffon, of D'Alembert, or of Condorcet? These form a connecting link between science and general literature.[1] A study either of English or

---

eighteenth century in France. But it became popular through the influence of the great schools of Paris. Before becoming popular with the masses it became so in cultivated and literary circles. The result has been that science in France alone has attained to a perfect form of expression. Whereas in other countries the great models of original research and thought were written in the severe style handed down by the ancients (Newton's 'Principia' and Gauss's 'Disquisitiones Arithmeticæ'), the great work of Lagrange (the 'Mécanique analytique') is a model of literary style in the modern sense. Science in our age has become popular through its applications. It is the utilitarian spirit that has popularised science in Germany and England. In France alone science, before coming under the influence of the utilitarian, came under that of the literary spirit. It was the influence of

the academies that brought this about. See Maury, 'Les Académies d'autrefois,' vol. i. p. 178, &c. More than with Richelieu, the interest in science nowadays is unfortunately only too often purely "metallic" (quoted from Lord Chesterfield's Letters). See also on the literary as compared with the modern practical character of science, Maury, ibid., p. 161.

[1] "On érigeait même en principe la nécessité pour un philosophe de ne rester étranger à aucune science. 'L'esprit philosophique fait tant de progrès en France depuis quarante ans,' écrivait Voltaire à madame Du Châtelet, en lui dédiant sa tragédie d'Alzire, 'que si Boileau vivait encore, lui qui osait se moquer d'une femme de condition, parce qu'elle voyait en secret Roberval et Sauveur, il serait obligé de respecter et d'imiter celles qui profitent publiquement des lumières des Maupertuis, des Réaumur, des

of German eighteenth-century literature does not introduce one to the great controversies of science, but a
study of Voltaire leads one into the midst of the profound problems of the Newtonian and Cartesian philosophy, the disputes on the correct measure of force.[1]
Buffon's influence, also, by spreading a taste for the study
of nature and by making objects of natural history attractive, was probably much more important than his actual
contributions to the natural sciences themselves.[2]

For the growth and diffusion of the scientific spirit
itself, the great schools in Paris were even of greater
value than the popular writings of Voltaire and Buffon.
Most of the Academicians were trained in these schools,

Mairan, des Du Fay et des Clairault;
de tous ces véritables savants qui
n'ont pour objet qu'une science
utile, et qui, en la rendant agréable,
la rendent insensiblement néces-
saire à notre nation. Nous sommes
au temps, j'ose le dire, où il faut
qu'un poëte soit philosophe et où
une femme peut l'être hardiment.'
En parlant ainsi, Voltaire ne faisait
qu'exprimer l'opinion de son siècle,
et ambitieux lui-même de réunir le
titre de géomètre à celui de poëte et
d'historien, il s'était fait expliquer
par madame Du Châtelet la physique
de Newton" (Maury, 'Les Acad.
d'autrefois,' vol. i. p. 156).

[1] See Maury, vol. i. p. 157, &c.;
and Du Bois-Reymond, "Voltaire
als Naturforscher" in 'Gesammelte
Reden,' vol. i. p. 1.

[2] "Sans l'éloquence de Buffon,
la zoologie serait demeurée encore
longtemps le privilége d'un petit
nombre ; elle eut laissé indifférents
ceux que la nature émeut moins que
le charme de la parole. La vieille
éducation classique avait le tort
de nous laisser très-ignorants des
choses du monde créé. Buffon com-

muniqua aux sciences le charme des
lettres. La curiosité s'éveilla, et en
1760, Valmont de Bomare put ouv-
rir à Paris le premier cours d'histoire naturelle ; il fut assidûment
suivi" (Maury, vol. i. p. 283). A.
von Humboldt had a similar influence in Berlin seventy years later.
See Du Bois-Reymond, loc. cit.,
vol. i. p. 510. Guardia, 'Histoire
de la Médecine' (Paris, 1884), says
of Buffon, "Fontenelle avait rendu
la science aimable et accessible.
Buffon l'associa à la philosophie et
aux lettres et l'introduisit défini-
tivement dans la société" (p. 384).
What a contrast, when we read in
the 'Life of Sir W. R. Hamilton'
(by R. P. Graves, vol. ii. p. 196)
that Dr Buckland's communication at the Bristol meeting of the
British Association (1836) "was
apparently the first occasion of
bringing before the public mind in
England the geological doctrine of
the great antiquity of the earth;
for out of the expressly scientific
circles, very little—you [viz., Count
Adare] are aware—is known of
what scientific men are about"!

and many of them taught there for many years.[1]   It was
with a true insight into the higher intellectual needs of
the nation that the successive Governments of the Revo-

[1] Before the age of the Revolution, which did so much to promote higher scientific education,
Paris possessed already many great
schools. First in importance was
the Collège de France, founded in
1530 by Francis I. Gassendi and
Roberval taught there in the
seventeenth century, and about
the middle of the eighteenth century science began to be more extensively represented, Lalande and
Daubenton, occupying chairs. The
Collège et École de Chirurgie was an
ancient establishment. There was
the Jardin des Plantes, with Buffon,
Lemonnier, Daubenton, and Fourcroy ; the École royale des Mines,
founded in 1783, where Duhamel
taught metallurgy ; the École des
Ponts et Chaussées, founded by
Turgot in 1775. Daubenton, Fourcroy, and Vicq d'Azyr taught in
the École vétérinaire d'Alfort,
founded in 1766. Besides the
Académie des Sciences, the Académie royale de Chirurgie, founded
by Lapeyronie under Louis XV. in
1731, had a great influence on the
development of anatomy and surgery during the eighteenth century.
Tenon and Petit, as well as Quesnay
the economist, were amongst |its
members, and it kept up a lively
intercourse with anatomists all over
Europe. The Paris academies had
also their representatives and connections in the provinces. Independent academies of science were
affiliated with the Académie des Sciences—1716 at Bordeaux, 1706 at
Montpellier, 1746 at Toulouse, 1766
at Béziers. Before having received
their *lettres patentes*, which gave
their members certain privileges,
most of these academies had existed as independent societies. Other

provincial academies, such as Arles
(1668), Nîmes (1684), Soissons
(1674), Marseilles (1726), were affiliated with the Académie française.
Others, such as Caen (1705), Lyons
(1724), Dijon (1740), Rouen (1744),
Amiens and Nancy (1750), Besan-
çon (1757), Metz (1760), Clermont
(1780), Orléans (1786), were not
specially affiliated. These dates
show how very much earlier a
literary and scientific organisation
existed in France than in other
countries. The Protestant universities in Germany formed an organisation of a different kind, with
which I shall deal later on. The
academic system, so early developed
in France, was of great use to the
culture of the sciences. French
science is usually considered to be
almost entirely located in Paris.
M. Bouillier ('L'Institut et les
Académies de Province,' Paris,
1879) has drawn attention to the
great services of this network of
academies. Many of the most eminent writers belonged to these provincial centres, and worked for
them even after becoming members
of the more celebrated academies.
Montesquieu is connected with Bordeaux, Cassini and many eminent
doctors with Montpellier, Dijon has
the honour of bringing out Rousseau, and Toulouse gave prizes to
Bossut and Clairault. Robespierre's
name is connected with the Academy
of Arras, Marat discourses at Rouen
and Lyons on electricity and optics,
and Danton and Bonaparte compete
for the *prix Raynal* at Lyons.
" Mais," says M. Bouillier, " ce qui
nous semble le plus digne de
remarque et d'éloge, ce sont les
écoles gratuites de dessin, les cours
gratuits de physique, de chimie,

lution, in the midst of the more pressing problems of national safety and welfare, betook themselves to the solution of the great problem of national education and the instruction of all grades of society. "The Convention," says the historian of public instruction,[1] " affords us the strange and grand spectacle of an assembly, which on the one side seems to have no other mission than to crush in the name of public welfare everything that stands in the way of the triumph of the Republican State, and which can see no other way of attaining this than the most terrible and cruel of tyrannies; and which on the other side devotes itself, with a stoical calm and serenity, forming a surprising contrast to its acts, to the study, the examination, and the discussion of all the problems involved in public instruction, of all the measures conducive to the progress of science. It had the glory of creating institutions, some of which were carried away by the blast of the Revolution, but among which the most important still exist for the great honour of France, and bear proof of the loftiness of her ideas." [2]

17.
Promoted
by Govern-
ments of
Revolution.

d'histoire naturelle, d'anatomie, d'antiquités, fondés par un certain nombre d'académies et, entre autres, par Dijon, par Rouen, par Bordeaux, par Toulouse, par Montpellier, et dont les professeurs étaient des membres, non rétribués de ces académies. . . . A combien de jeunes talents les académies provinciales n'ont-elles pas donné l'essor, par leurs récompenses solennelles et leurs encouragements? Combien de leurs lauréats ne sont pas devenus des hommes célèbres?'' (p. 81, &c.) Besides Bouillier, consult on these matters the several articles, " Académie," " Collége," " École," in the ' Grande Encyclopédie.'

[1] C. Hippeau, 'L'Instruction publique en France pendant la Révolution,' 1e série, préface, p. xix.
[2] It appears nowadays a kind of paradox that, as M. Hippeau remarks, in the very year 1793, when " the Convention was labouring with a feverish ardour at the creation of schools of all degrees," this same Convention, on a report of the Committee of Public Instruction, voted on the 8th of August the suppression of all the academies of Paris and the provinces. On this M. Bouillier (' L'Institut et les Académies,' p. 95) remarks : " Bientôt il est vrai, les académies devaient renaître après la chute de la

It was of immense importance to the cause of science that in many of the discussions of that assembly a marked preference was shown for the scientific side of instruction. In this matter, as in many others, the successful constructive efforts of the Revolutionary Governments came from the side of those brought up in the

Montagne et du Comité de salut public. Nous n'ignorons pas que c'est encore la Convention qui, prise d'un tardif remords, la veille seulement du jour où elle devait faire place à un autre gouvernement moins despotique et moins cruel, décréta l'organisation de l'Institut. Mais la Convention du 3 brumaire an iv. n'était plus celle de 1793 ; c'était en réalité une autre Convention, épurée, décimée, renouvelée, animée d'un tout autre esprit," &c., &c. The idea of a national Institute for the advancement of letters, science, and arts was a very early one (see 'Rapport de Talleyrand Périgord,' September 1791, Hippeau, p. 102). The explanation how the same Government which was labouring at the problem of a national instruction, crowned by the higher teaching and research of an Institute, could begin by closing the existing academies and universities, lies in this, that the aim was to make education general and learning popular, not merely fashionable, as it had been. See, for instance, what Ducos said on the 18th December 1792 : " Les mœurs d'un peuple corrompu ne se régénèrent point par de légers adoucissements, mais par de vigoureuses et brusques institutions. Il faut opter ouvertement entre l'éducation domestique et la liberté ; car citoyens, tant que par une instruction commune vous n'aurez pas rapproché le pauvre du riche, le faible du puissant ; tant que, pour me servir des expressions de Plutarque, vous n'aurez pas acheminé à

une même trace, et moulé sur une même forme de vertu tous les enfants de la patrie, c'est en vain que vos lois proclameront la sainte égalité, la République sera toujours divisée en deux classes : les *citoyens* et les *messieurs*" (Hippeau, 2e série, p. 21). It was because the academies and colleges supported "les messieurs" that they were suppressed. In the end education must always begin from above, and before the people can be taught you must form their teachers. See Lakanal's Report on the Écoles normales, Hippeau, vol. i. p. 408. The academies and colleges of the eighteenth century were closed in order to make room for that uniform system of public instruction described by Talleyrand and Condorcet, but not without a frequently expressed admiration for the work which they had done. See the defence of the academies by Condorcet (Hippeau, *loc. cit.*, vol. i. p. 272), and the tribute to the "Collége de France," by Gilbert Romme (ibid., vol. i. p. 308). The arguments for radical change are summed up by that speaker as follows : "L'existence de ces corps privilégiés blesse tous nos principes républicains, attaque l'égalité et la liberté de penser et nuit aux progrès des arts. Mais si leur organisation est vicieuse, les éléments en sont bons, et nous serviront utilement dans l'organisation nouvelle de l'instruction publique que vous allez décréter" (p. 309).

school of Voltaire and the Encyclopædists, whilst the work of destruction had been performed by the followers of Rousseau. No one has expressed himself on the value of scientific study and knowledge in a clearer or more far-seeing manner than Condorcet. In his ' Report and Project of a Decree on the General Organisation of Public Instruction,' which he presented to the National Assembly in the name of the Committee of Public Instruction, he says : [1] "Many motives have brought about the kind of preference which is accorded to the mathematical and physical sciences. Firstly, for men who do not devote themselves to long meditations, who do not fathom any kind of knowledge—even the elementary study of these sciences is the surest means of developing their intellectual faculties, of teaching them to reason rightly and to analyse their ideas.[2] . . . It is because in the natural sciences the ideas are more simple, more rigorously circumscribed, it is because their language is more perfect, &c., &c. . . . These sciences offer a remedy for prejudice, for smallness of mind—a remedy, if not more certain, at least more universal, than philosophy itself.[3] . . . Those

[1] It was presented on the 20th and 21st April 1792. See Hippeau, 1ᵉ série, pp. 185-288. It was printed by order of the Convention, Paris, Imprimerie nationale, 1793.

[2] Ibid., p. 203.

[3] Ibid., p. 204. It is interesting to see how in all these reports the exact sciences are placed in the foreground. See, for instance, what Gilbert Romme says of the teaching of the proposed *instituts:* "Les sciences mathématiques et physiques, morales et politiques, l'agriculture et les arts. mécaniques, la littérature et les beaux-arts, com- poseront l'enseignement des instituts où l'on pourra suivre, dans leurs éléments, l'échelle entière des connaissances humaines" (vol. i. p. 322). "Les lycées seront l'école des gens instruits ; ils embrasseront les sciences, les arts et les lettres dans toute leur étendue." One is forcibly reminded that the most perfect realisation of this arrangement of studies is to be found a century later in the provincial science colleges of this country. The preference, however, is now given to science mainly for ultilitarian reasons : the difference is shown by

who follow their course, see the coming of an epoch
when the practical usefulness of their application will
reach greater dimensions than were ever hoped for, when
the progress of the physical sciences must produce a
fortunate revolution in the arts.   And lastly, we have
yielded to the general tendency of men's minds, which
in Europe seem to incline towards these sciences with
an ever-increasing ardour. . . . Literature has its limits,
the sciences of observation and calculation have none.
Below a certain degree of talent, the taste for literary
occupations produces either ridiculous pride or a mean
jealousy towards such talents as one cannot attain.   In
the sciences, on the contrary, it is not with the opinion
of men but with nature that we have to engage in a
contest, the triumph of which is nearly always certain,
where every victory predicts a new one." [1]

" It is," says Lakanal, in his report on the " Écoles centrales," 16th December 1794, " of great importance for
the nation to assure itself that the mathematical sciences
are cultivated and deepened, for they give the habit
of accuracy : without them astronomy and navigation
have no guide ; architecture, both civil and naval, has
no rule ; the sciences of artillery and of fortification have
no foundation." [2]   Gradually, under the pressure of exter-

19.
Lakanal.

---

the importance then attached to
mathematics as a training of the
intellect in precise thinking ; nowadays it is the mechanical side that
is favoured, and this is only too
often destructive of the truly scientific and exact spirit.

[1] Hippeau, *loc. cit.*, p. 258. Cf.
p. 261 : "Hâtons - nous . . . de
porter dans les sciences morales la

philosophie et la méthode des sciences physiques" (Condorcet).

[2] Hippeau, vol. i. p. 432. It is
interesting to see how the study and
teaching of the sciences in course of
the second half of the last century
in France undergo a development.
The literary interest predominates
in Fontenelle. Buffon and Voltaire
add to it the philosophical and

nal events, the exigencies of war and the defence of the country gain the upper hand, and a central establishment is founded to cultivate and teach the sciences and arts, "upon which depend the defence of the Republic by land and sea."[1] Few of the higher and philanthropic aims of the great educational leaders of the early years of the Revolution—of Mirabeau, of Talleyrand, of Condorcet— were realised; little was done for primary education; but science can boast of having been worthily represented and supported in the two great schools which still bear their original designation, and which can show a record of celebrated names and magnificent work superior probably to that of any other similar institution in Europe.

20.
École normale. École polytechnique.

They are the "École normale supérieure" and the "École centrale des Travaux publics," better known by the title "École polytechnique."[2] The founders of this

philanthropic, the Encyclopædists and Condorcet the educational ; the events of the Revolution and the discussions in the Assemblies bring out more and more the instructive, the utilitarian, and the economical aspects. The only creations which resulted were those in which the latter aims were predominant.

[1] Lakanal, see Hippeau, vol. i. p. 447.

[2] To these two great schools must be added as a third the "Muséum d'Histoire naturelle," "le plus magnifique établissement que les sciences aient possédé" (Cuvier, "Éloge de Fourcroy," part ii. of the 'Éloges historiques,' p. 44, Strasbourg, 1819). The foundation of the "École centrale des Travaux publics" was proposed by Barère on the 11th March 1794, and definitely organised on the report of Fourcroy (Hippeau, vol. i. p. 446) by a decree of 7th vendémiaire, an iv. (name changed to

École polytechnique, 15th fructidor). The opening of the courses was announced for the 10th frimaire following (Hippeau, vol. ii. pp. 139, 174, 175). The foundation of the "Écoles normales" was proposed by Barère (13th prairial, an ii.), and decreed on a report of Lakanal (Hippeau, vol. i. p. 423) on the 9th brumaire, an iii. (30th October 1794) (ibid., vol. ii. p. 179). The courses opened on the 1st pluviose. The work of the school was distributed as follows : Mathematics, Lagrange and Laplace ; physics, Haüy ; descriptive geometry, Monge ; natural history, Daubenton ; chemistry, Berthollet ; agriculture, Thouin ; geography, Buache and Mentelle ; history, Volney ; morals, Bernardin de St Pierre. (Hippeau, vol. ii. p. 180, where also will be found extracts from the 'Moniteur' of the 9th pluviose on the opening addresses.) The oldest pupil was Bougainville, the great

magnificent institution recognised " that, in spite of the diversity of applications, mathematics and physics are the indispensable basis of the studies in view." [1] Though the first period of the life of the École normale only counted four months,[2] we are indebted to it for the

traveller. The École polytechnique received an allocation of £12,000, and had 400 pupils to start with. On the 20th frimaire, an iii., the Convention, on a report of Thibaudeau, voted the necessary expenses for the enlargement of the Muséum d'Histoire naturelle (Hippeau, vol. ii. p. 196),—*viz.*, nearly £8000 for expenses, and £200 for each of the professors. The Museum had been originally destined for the culture of medicinal plants. Tournefort had given a great impetus to botanical, and Buffon, with Daubenton, to zoological studies. The Convention added several to the courses regularly held there on natural history, botany, mineralogy, and general chemistry. " Ces cours," says Thibaudeau, " fournissent 500 leçons par an, offrent l'ensemble le plus vaste et le plus complet d'enseignement sur toutes les branches d'histoire naturelle dont le plus grand nombre manquaient totalement à la France et dont quelques-unes manquent encore à l'Europe, l'application immédiate de toutes les sciences naturelles au commerce et aux arts."

Of other scientific and teaching institutions I must mention the "Bureau des Longitudes." This was organised by the Convention on a discourse by Grégoire, 7th messidor, an iii. (24th June 1795), in which he refers to the British Board of Longitude and the superiority of the British navy (Hippeau, vol. ii. p. 219). The appointments to this bureau were the *géomètres* Lagrange and Laplace, the *astronomes* Lalande, Cassini, Méchain, De-

lambre, one of whom had to deliver a course of astronomy, the travellers Borda, Bougainville, the *géographe* Buache, and the artist Carocher. It had charge of the observatory, which had already been reorganised by a decree promoted by Lakanal on the 31st August 1793 (Hippeau, vol. ii. p. 76), and published in the ' Connaissance des Temps.' There were, besides, several military schools and the medical schools, not to mention other foundations less connected with our subject but equally important, such as the School of Oriental Languages, established in the Bibliothèque nationale (germinal, an iii., Hippeau, vol. ii. p. 215); the Écoles de Santé, established 14th frimaire, an iii., on a report of Fourcroy, in Paris, Strasbourg, and Montpellier (Hippeau, vol. ii. p. 194).

[1] Ibid., vol. i. p. 450.

[2] The École normale was closed on the 30th floréal, an iii., on a decree of the Convention dated the 7th of that month. Danton explained that the school had not taken the line which the Convention had marked out—the courses in general having offered a direct teaching of the sciences rather than an exposition of the methods which are to be adopted in teaching (Hippeau, vol. ii. p. 215). It also seems that the eminent teachers of this institution had few pupils sufficiently prepared to follow them. The École normale was reopened in the year 1808 under the Empire, by the same decree of 17th March which organised the University of France.

21.
Monge's
'Descriptive
Geometry.'

foundation of a new branch of science—the 'Descriptive Geometry' of Monge, which was given to the world through shorthand notes [1] from his lectures delivered in that institution. They form the beginning of the new science, since developed by Poncelet, Steiner, and others, and known under the name of "projective geometry." [2]

Next to mathematics with its analytical and graphical application to physics and the arts, the subject most culti-vated in these higher educational establishments of Paris

22.
Science of
Chemistry.

at the end of the last century was the new science of chemistry. With some justice this science has been termed a French science,[3] not so much because even at that time

[1] See the account of the origin of this branch of mathematics in Bris-son's edition of the 'Géométrie de-scriptive,' Paris, 1847. In the pro-gramme prefixed to the treatise the three aspects of the new school— the national, the practical, and the educational—are well set forth : "Pour tirer la nation française de la dépendance où elle a été jusqu'à présent de l'industrie étrangère, il faut premièrement diriger l'éduca-tion nationale vers la connaissance des objets qui exigent de l'exacti-tude. . . . Il faut, en second lieu, rendre populaire la connaissance d'un grand nombre de phénomènes natu-rels. . . . La géométrie descriptive est un moyen de rechercher la vér-ité ; elle offre des exemples perpé-tuels du passage du connu à l'incon-nu ; et parcequ'elle est toujours ap-pliquée à des objets susceptibles de la plus grande évidence, il est néces-saire de la faire entrer dans le plan d'une éducation nationale." Monge generalised and placed on a scien-tific basis the methods used pre-viously by carpenters and stone-cutters, and partially dealt with geometrically by Courcier, Derand, Mathurin, Jousse, and Frezier. See

Montucla, 'Histoire des Mathéma-tiques,' vol. iii. p. 15.
[2] Monge taught also at the École polytechnique from the beginning. See the remarks of Chasles ('Rap-port sur les Progrès de la Géo-métrie,' Paris, 1870, p. 2) : "L'en-seignement théorique et profond qui a été la base de la première et judicieuse organisation de ce grand établissement était éminemment favorable aux progrès de la science, en même temps qu'il préparait séri-eusement les élèves à l'entrée dans les écoles d'application." The au-thor then refers with regret to the less scientific tone which had crept into the studies of that great school in the course of this century. See also p. 379.
[3] A. Wurtz ('Histoire des Doctrines chimiques,' Paris, 1868, p. 1) : "La chimie est une science française ; elle fut constituée par Lavoisier." Cf. Dumas ('Leçons sur la Philoso-phie chimique,' Paris, 1837, p. 137). Buckle ('History of Civilisation,' &c., 3 vols., vol. ii. p. 366, London, 1866) says : "That we owe to France the existence of chemistry as a science will be admitted by every one who uses the word science in the sense

chemistry was not indebted to illustrious foreigners [1] for some of its most important discoveries, as because the modern scientific spirit of accurate measurement first took hold of chemical phenomena on a large scale in the many important investigations which bear the name of Lavoisier and his followers, through whom the great reform of modern chemical knowledge and research was permanently established. It has been significantly pointed out [2] that it was the union of mathematical with empirical knowledge which, through men like Laplace, Meusnier, Monge, first

in which alone it ought to be understood, &c. . . . Until Lavoisier entered the field there were no generalisations wide enough to entitle chemistry to be called a science." The correctness of this view is fully and impartially examined by Hermann Kopp ('Die Entwickelung der Chemie in der neueren Zeit,' München, 1873, p. 89, &c.) He fully upholds the claims of Lavoisier to be called the father of modern chemistry (p. 145). See also what Liebig says.

[1] These were mainly, Black (discovered carbonic acid, called fixed air, in 1754), Cavendish (discovered hydrogen or inflammable air in 1767), and Priestley, who between 1771 and 1774 discovered oxygen (dephlogisticated air), nitrogen (phlogisticated air), and several of its compounds, among them ammonia (alkaline air). Of Priestley it is said by Cuvier that he may well be considered as one of the fathers of modern chemistry, "mais c'est un père qui ne voulut jamais reconnaître sa fille" ('Éloges,' vol. i. p. 208). Elsewhere ('Rapport historique sur les Progrès des Sciences naturelles,' Paris, 1810, p. 90) Cuvier dates the revolution in chemistry from the introduction of the mathematical spirit : "Il en est

une cause encore plus essentielle à laquelle même on doit à proprement parler, et cette théorie nouvelle, et les découvertes qui l'ont fait naître. . . . C'est l'esprit mathématique qui s'est introduit dans la science et la rigoureuse précision qu'on a portée dans l'examen de toutes ses opérations. . . . C'est dans le Traité élémentaire de Lavoisier que l'Europe vit pour la première fois avec étonnement le système entier de la nouvelle chimie," &c.

[2] Kopp, loc. cit., p. 202 : "Indeed, if we look at those who first worked together with Lavoisier or in his spirit, we shall find such as had devoted themselves principally to mathematics or mathematical physics, men like Laplace, Meusnier, Monge. Among chemists Lavoisier stood for a long time almost alone in his opinions." This view is also taken by Cuvier ('Rapport,' p. 91) : "Les nouveaux chimistes français . . . ont eu à se louer du concours de quelques-uns de nos géomètres les plus distingués," &c. ; and he attributes the next great step in chemical science to a similar introduction of a "rigueur toute mathématique" ('Rapport sur la Chimie lu à la Séance des 4 Acad.,' 23rd April 1826).

brought about the general recognition of Lavoisier's ideas; whereas the more exclusive representatives of chemistry, such as Berthollet and Guyton, held aloof for some considerable time. In the earlier syllabus of the École polytechnique, chemistry was brought into a similar proximity with the mathematical branches. And Berthollet's 'Statique chimique' denotes by its title alone the mathematical spirit in which the work was conceived.

23.
New mathematical sciences.

About that time also two new sciences were, if not invented, at least set on a firm basis, by which the use of mathematics was very largely extended, and by which great realms of interesting facts were made accessible to accurate measurements and exact reasoning. Both these sciences can be claimed by France as almost exclusively her own creations. They are the science of crystallography and the great theory of probabilities. The former was the work of the Abbé Haüy; the latter formed, next to the mechanics of the heavens, the main original contribution by which Laplace has perpetuated his name in the history of science. The theory of the Abbé Haüy, who first taught how crystals are built up from small particles of definite and regular geometrical forms, such as cubes, pyramids, &c., came to the aid of the mineralogists, who before him had vainly groped in the dark, searching for some method by which order and system could be introduced into the lifeless forms of nature as by the methods of Linnæus and Jussieu it had been introduced into the world of plants and animals. Before Haüy, the doctrines of mineralogy had been either attached to geology—especially in the celebrated school of Werner, or latterly, after the great developments in chemistry had

24.
Crystallography.

set in, to chemistry—especially by Bergmann.[1] Haüy established the science of minerals on an independent foundation by studying and systematising the forms of their crystallisation ; and he brought the science of mineralogy from Sweden and Germany into France, and gave it an independent position. Thus it came to form a connecting-link between the mathematical—*i.e.*, the measuring and calculating—and the purely descriptive sciences. " Mineralogy, though it is that part of natural science which deals with the least complicated objects, is nevertheless also that which lends itself least to a rational classification. The first observers named the minerals vaguely according to their external appearances and their use. It was not until the middle of the eighteenth century that it was attempted to subject them to those methods which had done service to geology and botany : the hope existed of establishing among them genera and

[1] See an account of the work of the chemical school, to which Cronsted (the inventor of the blow-pipe), Bergmann, Kirwan, and Klaproth belonged, in Cuvier's ' Rapport ' (p. 163). Also his " Éloge de Haüy " ('Éloges histor.,' vol. iii. p. 143, &c.) The beginnings of geometrical crystallography seem to go back to Linnæus ; but his view was discouraged in France by Buffon, who disliked Linnæus's writings. Whewell, who was himself an authority on crystallography, thinks Romé de l'Isle, who was not an Academician, had only scant justice done to him by Haüy and his friends (' Hist. of the Induct. Sciences,' 3rd ed., vol. iii. p. 176). More recent writers, such as Kobell (' Geschichte der Mineralogie,' München, 1864, p. 73, &c.) and Nicol (article "Crystallography," ' Ency. Brit.'), have done him justice. The 'Grande Encyclopédie ' thus summarises the work of Romé de l'Isle : " Il mesura mécaniquement [*viz.*, with Carangeot's goniometer] les angles et établit que ces angles ont toujours une valeur constante dans une même espèce minéralogique." That of Haüy is summarised in the two laws : " 1°, Tous les éléments semblables d'un cristal sont toujours semblablement et simultanément modifiés (loi de symétrie) ; 2°, toute facette modifiante intercepte sur les arêtes de la figure primitive des longueurs proportionelles à des multiples simples de la longueur de ces arêtes (loi de dérivation)" (Berthelot in 'Grande Encyclop.,' vol. xiii. p. 397).

species, as among organised beings, and it was forgotten that in mineralogy the principle is absent which had given birth to the idea of species—*viz.*, that of generation. The principle of individuality, such as it is conceived in the organic world—*viz.*, the unity of action of different organs which co-operate in the preservation of the same life—can scarcely be admitted in mineralogy."[1]

The Abbé Haüy, by founding the science of minerals on their regular forms of crystallisation, made mineralogy " as precise and methodical as astronomy ; in fact, we can say in one word that he was to Werner[2] and Romé de l'Isle, his predecessors, what Newton had been to Kepler and Copernicus." [3]

25.
Theory of
Probability.

From that well-defined province of science which deals in a precise and strict manner with the simple numerical relations which seem to underlie all forms of movement in nature, be they on a stupendous or on a minute scale

[1] Cuvier, " Éloge de Haüy" in 'Éloges historiques,' vol. iii. p. 155.

[2] The character of Werner (1750-1815) is nowhere better painted than by Cuvier in his "Éloge de Werner" (*loc. cit.*, vol. ii. p. 303, &c.) "Il commence l'époque la plus remarquable de la science de la terre, et même l'on peut dire qu'à lui seul il la remplit. . . . Il s'est formé des académies entières, qui ont pris un nom" (for instance, the Edinburgh Wernerian Society, founded by Jameson, 1808-1859), "comme si elles eussent voulu invoquer son génie et s'en faire un patron d'une espèce auparavant inconnue. Qui ne croirait, à entendre parler de succès si peu ordinaires, que ce fut quelqu'un de ces hommes ardens à propager leur doctrine, qui par des ouvrages nombreux et éloquens, ont subjugué leurs contemporains, ou qui se sont procuré des partisans par l'ascendant d'une grande richesse ou d'une position élevée dans l'ordre social? Rien de tout cela : confiné dans une petite ville de Saxe, sans autorité dans son pays, il n'avait aucune influence sur la fortune de ses disciples ; il n'entretenait point de liaisons avec des personnes en place : d'un naturel singulièrement timide, hésitant toujours à écrire, à peine subsiste-t-il de lui quelques feuilles d'impression. . . . C'est ainsi qu'en peu d'années la petite école de Freyberg, destinée seulement, dans le principe, à former quelques mineurs pour la Saxe, renouvela le spectacle des premières universités du moyen âge," &c., &c.

[3] Cuvier, ibid., p. 163.

—*i.e.*, from the province of mechanics and astronomy—
two different roads lead into those extensive domains in
which, not simplicity and regularity, but endless variety
and complication, seem to be the order and the rule of
Life.   Even a century ago the contrast must have been
striking between the 'Principia' of Newton and the 'Exposition du Système du Monde' of Laplace on the one
side, and the great array of volumes of Linnæus, Buffon,
Jussieu, Cuvier, and Lacépède on the other; though these
after all embraced only a small portion of the living forms
of nature which they attempted to classify or to describe.[1]
I have pointed out how the new and especially the
French methods of chemistry and crystallography con-
quered a large portion of intermediate ground, subjected
many tangled phenomena to exact treatment, and pushed
the mathematical method far into the dominion of natural
history.   It is that other history, not natural, but human
and often unnatural, which presents the opposite extreme
of the great panorama of world-life.   It is significant
that almost at the same time that mathematical reasoning found its way into natural history, conquering an extensive province of its vast territory, an entirely different
method was invented with the aim of dealing in a still
more vigorous manner with the phenomena of human
life and society.   This was the science of statistics, and

[1] Cuvier gives some figures as to
the increase of the known species
during his own lifetime. Lacépède
had described about 1200 or 1300
distinct species of fishes ; but when
Cuvier pronounced his Éloge in
1826, the Cabinet du Roi contained
already more than 5000 species
('Éloges historiques,' vol. iii. p. 317).

Linnæus had counted in 1778 about
8000 species of plants. Cuvier in
1824 estimates the number as
50,000 or more (see 'Éloges,' vol. iii.
p. 469, &c., where he also gives some
idea of the numbers of known
species in the different classes of
animals).

connected with it the doctrine of averages and the mathematical theory of probabilities.[1]   The same great mind

[1] The beginnings of the science and theory of probabilities are not subject to controversy, as were those of the infinitesimal calculus. Pascal and Fermat about the middle of the seventeenth century entered into a correspondence relative to a question in a game of chance, propounded by the Chevalier de Méré, a noted gambler. They agreed in their answer, but could not convince their friend, who moreover made this the occasion of denouncing the results of science and arithmetic. But this comparatively insignificant problem — so different from the great cosmical problems which led to the invention of the infinitesimal calculus about the same time — was the origin of a series of investigations and discussions in which the greatest mathematicians, such as Huygens, James and Daniel Bernoulli, De Moivre, D'Alembert, and Condorcet joined. Most of them did not escape the errors and misstatements which creep in an insidious manner into the discussion and vitiate the conclusions. In fact, the science advanced through the influence of those who depreciated it like D'Alembert, and those who exaggerated its importance like Condorcet. At length, under the hands of Laplace, who defined it as common-sense put into figures and attributed to it a high educational value, it assumed a state wellnigh approaching to that perfection which Euclid gave to geometry and Aristotle to logic. Since the publication of Laplace's celebrated 'Théorie analytique des Probabilités' (Paris, 1812) writers on the subject have found ample occupation in commenting on the theorems or recasting the proofs given in that work, which holds a similar position to that occupied in

another department of mathematics by the 'Disquisitiones Arithmeticæ' of Gauss (1801). Up to the present day there exist differences of opinion as to the value of the science, the two opposite views being represented in this country by Mill ('Logic,' 5th ed., vol. ii. p. 62) and Jevons ('Principles of Science,' vol. i.), the latter summing up his opinion as follows : "In spite of its immense difficulties of application, and the aspersions which have been mistakenly cast upon it, the theory of probabilities is the noblest, as it will in course of time prove perhaps the most fruitful, branch of mathematical science. It is the very guide of life, and hardly can we take a step or make a decision of any kind without correctly or incorrectly making an estimation of probability" (1st ed., p. 248). A similar opinion seems to have been held by James Clerk Maxwell (see Life by Campbell and Garnett, p. 143), who called the calculus of probabilities "Mathematics for practical men."   In this country A. de Morgan and Todhunter, the former in a popular essay in the 'Cabinet Cyclopædia' and in a profound treatise in the 'Encyclopædia Metropolitana,' the latter in his well-known History (London and Cambridge, 1865), have done a great deal to make this subject better understood.   The applications of the theory have gradually increased through numerous mortality and insurance calculations ; as also in the estimations of error in astronomical and physical observations, where the well-known method of least squares (first employed by Gauss in 1795, see Gauss, Werke, vol. vii. p. 242 ; first published by Legendre in 1806, and then proved by Laplace in his 'Théorie,'

which elaborated the principles of Newton into a system of the universe, and attacked the intricate mathematical problem which this system presented, gave to the world likewise the first complete treatise on that calculus which comes into play if we eliminate from the apparently most arbitrary region of phenomena, that of human life and history, all regard for final or efficient causes, for providential design and freewill, for human error, human malice and benevolence—in fact, all notice of that element which from another and equally important point of view forms the subject of greatest interest—the inner life of the individual.   It was proposed, and it has since been carried out, to look upon human beings and human events not as things possessed of an inner world of thought and freewill, but as lifeless units, more uniform and regular than the balls thrown into the urn at an election, or the counters in a game of chance.   By overstepping with one bound the great field of human activity, full of so much confusion and so much interest, it was proposed to investigate what knowledge would result from a purely mathematical inspection, in which human beings figured merely as units and symbols.[1]   This attempt, which has since

&c., 1812) is now extensively employed. Of this branch of mathematics Bertrand says : "Les plus grands géomètres ont écrit sur le calcul des probabilités ; presque tous ont commis des erreurs : la cause en est, le plus souvent, au désir d'appliquer des principes à des problèmes qui par leur nature échappent à la science."   In the hands of Clerk Maxwell the calculus has acquired an additional interest and importance through the distinction which he made between what he termed the "histori-

cal" and the "statistical method" of treating phenomena, and the application of the latter to the kinetic theory of gases (see Life, pp. 438, 562). This subject will occupy our attention in a special chapter.

[1] The beginnings of the science of statistics belong likewise to the age that produced the higher mathematics. More extensive "countings" seem to have been contemporaneous with more refined calculations. Hermann Conring, professor at Helmstädt, a friend of Leibniz (see Leib-

led to such interesting results, and which has furnished almost all the knowledge upon which a judicious regulation and government of society depends, was the work of Laplace, and was produced in an age and in a nation which seemed to have set at naught all ideas of order and method in human affairs, which defied all authority and all tradition, and trusted its fate to the most radical revolution which civilised society ever witnessed.[1]

It is curious to read the criticism which the first Napoleon, that wayward child of the Revolution, passed on the author of the mechanics of the heavens and the theory of probability. Laplace, like so many other men of science, had been called by the Emperor to assist in the labours of administration, but, according to his judgment, proved himself a poor administrator, being unable

niz's 'Philosophische Schriften,' ed. Gerhardt, vol. i. p. 155), lectured about 1660 on subjects now comprised under the term "Statistics," and about the same time John Graunt of London published 'Natural and Political Annotations made upon the Bills of Mortality' (1666). Sir William Petty, one of the founders of the Royal Society, published in 1683 'Five Essays in Political Arithmetick.' The newly discovered calculus of probabilities induced mathematicians to take an interest in the subject, and to urge the desirability of gaining data for their calculations. Many of these turned upon questions of mortality and the ravages of diseases, such as the smallpox. But though undoubtedly the fact that during the French Revolution mathematicians for the first time had a great influence in administrative and governmental matters contributed enormously to the introduction of statistical methods, the great epoch

in this science is allied with the name of the Belgian Quetelet (1796-1874), of whom more later on.

[1] Cantor ('Historische Notizen über die Wahrscheinlichkeitsrechnung,' Halle, 1874, p. 6) says: "The tendency of thought which prepared the Revolution, and which is marked by an unsparing and destructive criticism of the conditions of society in state and family, could not dispense with an instrument which, more than any other, enables one to subject to general views the most different factors of civilisation. It belonged to the favourite ideas of that age, that the calculus of probabilities should be among the most important subjects of public instruction; for it was said to be the calculus of common-sense, through which alone the influence of hope, fear, and emotion on our judgment could be destroyed, and prejudice and superstition removed from the decisions of social life."

to grasp practical issues, and always descending into infinitesimals.   It is hardly to be doubted now, after the
lapse of a century, that the infinitesimals of Laplace play
a more important part in problems of administration and
government than the ideas of Napoleon.   Laplace, unlike some other great scientific thinkers, attached great
value to a popular exposition of the principles of his discoveries.   Descartes required a Fontenelle and Newton a
Voltaire to make their ideas accessible and useful to the
mass of students.   Laplace was his own Fontenelle and
Voltaire.   " Few works," says Sir John Herschel, " have
been more extensively read, or more generally appreciated,
than Laplace's ' Essai philosophique sur les Probabilités,'
and that on the ' Système du Monde ' by the same author.
It is not, perhaps, too much to say that were all the
literature of Europe to perish, these two essays excepted,
they would suffice to convey to the latest posterity an
impression of the intellectual greatness of the age which
could produce them, surpassing that afforded by all the
monuments antiquity has left us.   Previous to the publication of the ' Essai philosophique,' few, except professed
mathematicians or persons conversant with assurances
and similar commercial risks, possessed any knowledge of
the principles of this calculus, or troubled themselves
about its conclusions, regarding them as merely curious
and perhaps not altogether harmless speculations.   Thence-
forward, however, apathy was speedily exchanged for a
lively and increasing desire to know something of a system
of reasoning which for the first time seemed to afford a
handle for some kind of exact inquiry into matters no one
had ever expected to see reduced to calculation, and bear-

ing on the most important concerns of life. Men began to hear with surprise, not unmingled with some vague hope of ultimate benefit, that not only births, deaths, and marriages, but the decisions of tribunals, the results of popular elections, the influence of punishments in checking crime, the comparative value of medical remedies and different modes of treatment of diseases, the probable limits of error in numerical results in every department of physical inquiry, the detection of causes, physical, social, and moral—nay, even the weight of evidence and the validity of logical argument—might come to be surveyed with that lynx-eyed scrutiny of a dispassionate analysis, which, if not at once leading to the discovery of positive truth, would at least secure the detection and proscription of many mischievous and besetting fallacies."

Both ways of approaching the intricate phenomena of nature and history, that of mechanics dealing with the general laws of motion and of lifeless masses, and that of statistics dealing with the arithmetical properties of large numbers of units, leave out of consideration that hidden and mysterious phenomenon to which alone is attached, if not order and method, yet certainly all that commands interest in the created world: the factor of life—the existence of individuality. The view which Laplace took of the universe or of human affairs is an attempt to see how far science and reasoning can go while disregarding the principle of individuality.[1] The

26.
Laplace gained his results by disregarding the principle of individuality.

---

[1] See Clerk Maxwell on 'Science and Freewill' (Life by Campbell and Garnett, p. 438): "Two kinds of knowledge, which we may call for convenience dynamical and statistical. The statistical method of investigating social questions has Laplace for its most scientific and Buckle for its most popular expounder. Persons are grouped according to some characteristic, and the number of persons forming

method has been most fruitful, and, far from being exhausted, promises undreamt of results in the future.   It was probably more from the desire to keep his view clear and his method simple, than with any necessarily sceptical tendency, that when Laplace was questioned by Napoleon how it was that in the great volumes of the 'Mécanique céleste' the name of God did not appear, he replied, " Sire, je n'ai pas besoin de cette hypothèse."

But French science did not leave that great field of research uncultivated, which is the very playground of individual life.   Its cultivation was the work of that other great representative of French science—the contemporary of Laplace—Georges Cuvier.[1]   Linnæus had

27. Individuality the centre of interest in the sciences of life.

the group is set down under that characteristic.   This is the raw material from which the statist endeavours to deduce general theorems in sociology.   Other students of human nature proceed on a different plan.   They observe individual men, ascertain their history, analyse their motives, and compare their expectation of what they will do with their actual conduct.   This may be called the dynamical method of study as applied to man.   However imperfect the dynamical study of man may be in practice, it evidently is the only perfect method in principle, and its shortcomings arise from the limitation of our powers rather than from a faulty method of procedure.   If we betake ourselves to the statistical method, we do so confessing that we are unable to follow the details of each individual case, and expecting that the effects of widespread causes, though very different in each individual, will produce an average result on the whole nation, from a study of which we may estimate the character and propensities of

an imaginary being called the Mean Man."

[1] It is not necessary here to explain the reasons which have induced me to confine myself mainly to the two great names of Laplace and Cuvier as the great representatives of the exact scientific spirit, as it first asserted its supremacy in France, and from there gradually fought its way all over Europe.   To me it seems that nowhere has this modern scientific spirit been represented in greater completeness and greater purity. This is so much the more remarkable, as other influences and temptations were not wanting in that age and country which might have interfered with the application of the purely scientific method.   The scientific spirit is in danger of being contaminated by two interests which are essentially foreign to it : the one is the practical, the other the philosophical.   Frequently they are united ; and when united their influence on the progress of science has frequently been disastrous.   In no department of knowledge has this

begun the work of natural history by inventing a system
of classification and a technical language or nomenclature.
Buffon in his brilliant and elegant portraits had cast around
it the charms of poetry and romance. Jussieu had imported botany from Sweden into France, and in the garden
of Trianon had given a living model of the arrangement
of plants; botanising had become popular through the

union of the practical and philosophical spirit been more marked
than in the medical sciences. Essentially interested as it is in the immediate application of scientific discoveries to the needs of suffering
mankind, we witness in the course
of the seventeenth and eighteenth
centuries a one-sided alliance of the
art of healing with chemistry (Sylvi-
us, 1614-1672), with physics (Borelli,
1608-1679), and with mechanics (Pit-
cairn, 1652-1713), and the reaction
of the animists (Stahl, 1660-1734,
and Hoffmann, 1660-1742), and the
vitalists (Bordeu, 1722-1776, and
Barthez, 1734-1806). A large portion of the history of medicine (see
Haeser, 'Geschichte der Medicin,'
Jena, 1881, vol. ii., and Guardia,
'Histoire de la Médecine,' Paris,
1884) consists in the account of the
opposition to premature generalisations, adopted from other sciences,
or still more dangerously from metaphysics. As examples of the metaphysical tendency we have the Scotch
systems of Cullen and Brown, and
the German "Philosophy of Nature."
The reasons why philosophy has so
frequently allied itself with medicine, thus preventing the purely
scientific spirit from gaining admission, are twofold. "Young
men," says Cuvier, "adopt these
theories with enthusiasm, because
they seem to abridge their studies
and to give a thread in an almost
inextricable labyrinth" ('Rapport,'
p. 333). The other reason is that
the art of healing has as much a

psychological as a physical side,
and a philanthropic as much as
a scientific interest. In respect of
this it is well to note that the age
and country which gave to Europe
the great models of purely scientific
research in Laplace and Cuvier was
rich also in great thinkers who
applied themselves in a philosophical spirit to the advancement of
scientific and practical medicine, to
the reform of hospitals, to the care
of the insane, to the education of
the deaf and dumb. The whole
school of the ideologues, headed by
Condorcet, Cabanis, and Destutt
de Tracy, was closely allied with
the medical profession. But however important this side of French
thought may have been, its influence on the rest of Europe at
that time cannot be compared
with that of the purely scientific
writings belonging to mathematics
and natural science. Such names
as Cabanis and Bichat belong to
a different current of European
thought, which I purposely separate
from the exact or purely scientific.
And this separation is justified his-
torically by the fact that in the
Académie des Sciences for a considerable time medical science was
only meagerly represented, whilst
philosophy during the period of the
suppression of the Académie des
Sciences morales et politiques, from
1803-1832, had no academic representation at all. The great
name of Bichat is not among the
Academicians, and Cuvier himself

writings of Rousseau; gardening and the study of plant-life had become a royal pastime, and a favourite recreation for those oppressed with the troubles of the State or the sorrows of private life. Cuvier, while asking the reason why other portions of natural history had not shared the same attention, breaks out into the following eloquent words: " The study of animals presents diffi-

explains the exclusive attitude of the Academy to the medical profession in his Éloges of Hallé, Corvisart, and Pinel ('Éloges,' vol. iii. p. 339, &c.) See also Maury (p. 304): " Les sciences physiques, chimiques et naturelles avaient pris une telle extension dans les travaux de l'Académie, qu'a la fin du dix-huitième siècle, la médecine, qui n'y avait jamais été au reste bien largement représentée, fut de plus en plus reléguée à l'arrière plan ; ce n'était plus que de loin en loin que les médecins, les chirurgiens de la Compagnie, . . . y présentaient des observations sur des points médicaux. . . . La médecine, qui, selon la juste observation de Cabanis, tend aux hypothèses par la nature même du sujet auquelelles'applique, n'offrait point assez de constance dans ses principes et d'évidence dans ses démonstrations pour satisfaire des esprits qui se détachaient tous les jours davantage des vieilles spéculations de l'école. C'est ce qui explique le peu de faveur qu'elle rencontrait à l'Académie." To what extent this rigid demarcation, according to which " observations relatives aux dispositions morales et intellectuelles des individus n'entrent assurément dans les attributions d'aucune académie des sciences " ('Mémoires de l'Institut,' vol. ix. p. 110), was beneficial to medical science is an important question. In the organisation of the Institute of the 3rd brumaire, an iv. (25th October 1795), there are awarded out of 60 members only 6 to medicine and surgery combined, and in the " nouvelle organisation " of 3rd pluviose, an xi. (23rd January 1803), there are 6 members out of 63. This section is given as the last, even after " économie rurale et art vétérinaire"(see Aucoc, 'L'Institut,' p. 3, &c.) It is interesting to note how in contrast to this the medical profession occupied for a long period a foremost place in the Royal Society of London, so much so that frequently opposition was made to the admission of new members belonging to it (see Weld, ' History of the Royal Society,' vol. i. chap. 4 ; vol. ii. p.153). Of 5336 papers contained in the ' Philosophical Transactions ' from 1665 to 1848, 1020, the largest number in any department, belonged to anatomy, physiology, and medicine (ibid., vol. ii. p. 565). Babbage complained of the influence of the Colleges of Physicians and Surgeons in the Royal Society, as occasionally filling the pages of the 'Transactions ' with medical papers of very moderate merit ; and also because the preponderance of the medical interest introduces into the Society some of the jealousies of that profession ('Decline of Science in England,' 1830, p. 188). In the foundation of the British Association this union with the medical interest was dropped ; though the older "Versammlung deutscher Naturforscher und Ärzte," after which it was modelled, established and maintained that union.

culties which only great zeal can surmount; we have
to subject them to torments in order to appreciate their
physical powers; their innermost energies only reveal
themselves to the dissecting-knife—only by living among
corpses can we discover them.   Among them we find the
same spectacle as in the world, whatever moralists may
say : they are hardly less wicked or less unhappy than
we are; the arrogance of the strong, the meanness of
the weak, vile rapacity, short pleasures bought by great
efforts—death brought on by long suffering—that is the
rule among animals as much as among men.   With
plants existence is not surrounded by pain—no sad
image tarnishes their splendour before our eyes, nothing
reminds us of our passions, our cares, our misfortunes—
love is there without jealousy, beauty without vanity,
force without tyranny, death without anguish—nothing
resembles human nature." [1]

**28.
Into this
centre
Cuvier car-
ried exact
research.**
Into the centre of individual and organised life—the
life of the animal and human creation—Cuvier carried
exact research, grounding it on the science of comparative anatomy. [2]   At the same time, he marked out as the
principal problem, around which all investigations must
turn, and upon which all classification must depend,

[1] 'Éloges historiques,' vol. i. p. 91.
[2] Cuvier, in the Introduction to
'Le Règne animal, distribué d'après
son organisation, pour servir de base
à l'histoire naturelle des animaux
et d'introduction à l'anatomie comparée' (Paris, 1817), says that for
thirty years he had devoted to comparative anatomy all his time (p.
v), that the first results had appeared in 1795, his 'Leçons d'Anatomie comparée' in 1800 (p. vii),
that he has made anatomy and zoology march side by side (p. vi).   He
compares natural history as a science
with other sciences, stating that
dynamics is become a science almost
entirely of calculation, that chemistry is still a science altogether of
experiments, that natural history
will for a long time to come remain
in most of its parts a science of observation (p. 5); he maintains that
geometry is a study of syllogisms,
natural history a study of method
(p. xviii).

the phenomenon of individual life, that great vortex into which agencies, processes, and the elements of inorganic nature are continually drawn, from which they are continually ejected, preserving not the unity of substance but, among changing events, the unity of form.[1]

"It is not," he says, "in the substance that in plants and animals the identity of the species is manifested, it is in the form. There are probably not two men, two oaks, two rose-trees, which have the compound elements of their bodies in the same proportion—and even these elements change without end, they circulate rather than reside in that abstract and figured space which we call the form; in a few years probably there is not left one atom of that which constitutes our body to-day—only the form is persistent; the form alone perpetuates in multiplying itself; transmitted by the mysterious operation which we call generation to an endless series of individuals, it will attract successively to itself numberless molecules of different matter, all of them merely transient."[2]

[1] "La vie est donc un tourbillon plus ou moins rapide, plus ou moins compliqué, dont la direction est constante, et qui entraîne toujours des molécules de mêmes sortes, mais où les molécules individuelles entrent et d'où elles sortent continuellement, de manière que la forme du corps vivant lui est plus essentielle que la matière" ('Règne animal,' p. 13, &c.) "Il vient sans cesse des éléments du dehors en dedans : il s'en échappe du dedans au dehors : toutes les parties sont dans un tourbillon continuel, qui est une condition essentielle du phénomène, et que nous ne pouvons suspendre longtemps sans l'arrêter pour jamais. Les branches les plus simples de l'histoire naturelle participent déjà à cette complication et à ce mouvement perpétuel, qui rendent si difficile l'application des sciences générales" ('Rapport,' p. 150, &c.) "Dans les corps vivans chaque partie a sa composition propre et distincte ; aucune de leurs molécules ne reste en place ; toutes entrent et sortent successivement : la vie est un tourbillon continuel, dont la direction, toute compliquée qu'elle est, demeure constante, ainsi que l'espèce des molécules qui y sont entraînées, mais non les molécules individuelles elles-mêmes. . . . Ainsi la forme de ces corps leur est plus essentielle que leur matière," &c. (ibid., p. 200).

[2] 'Éloges historiques,' vol. iii. p. 156.

Keeping this unity of form, this absorbing vortex of life, the totality of organisation, always before him, Cuvier, in surveying the whole region of animated nature,[1] fixes finally for the purposes of classification and division on that system of organs which expresses most truly the peculiarity of each of the great branches into which he divides the animal world—namely, the nervous system.[2] But rather than follow him at present into the

[1] "La partie anatomique du problème général de la vie est résolue depuis longtemps pour les animaux, au moins pour ceux d'entre eux qui nous intéressent le plus. Les voies que les substances y parcourent, sont connues ; . . . il aperçoit aussi comment ces routes, si compliquées dans l'homme, se simplifient par degrés dans les animaux inférieurs, et finissent par se réduire à une spongiosité uniforme. Les recherches de M. Cuvier—dans les leçons d'anatomie comparée—ont achevé d'assigner à chaque animal sa place dans la grande échelle des complications de structure" ('Rapport,' p. 202, &c.)

[2] It is not my object here to give an account of the views of Cuvier, still less of his contributions to natural history, which—in spite of the special theories and laws which he and his followers established (see especially Flourens, 'Histoire des Travaux de Georges Cuvier,' 3me éd., 1858)—remained in his hands to the last pre-eminently a science of observation. It has been pointed out that Cuvier only gradually (probably about 1812) arrived at the final principle of division—viz., the nervous system—and that he adopted it from others (notably Virey and De Blainville), that before 1812 he had successively used the organs of generation (1795), of nutrition, and of circulation as principles of classification. In his Report of 1808,

in mentioning his own labours, he says : " M. Cuvier, en étudiant la physiologie des animaux vertébrés, a trouvé dans la quantité respective de leur respiration, la raison de leur quantité de mouvemens, et par conséquent de l'espèce de ces mouvemens. . . . En effet, M. Cuvier, ayant examiné les modifications qu' éprouvent dans les animaux sans vertébres les organes de la circulation, de la respiration, et des sensations, et ayant calculé les résultats nécessaires de ces modifications, en a déduit une division nouvelle où ces animaux sont rangés suivant leurs véritables rapports" ('Rapport,' p. 311, &c.) Compare also Carus, 'Geschichte der Zoologie,' München, 1872, p. 602 ; Flourens, "Éloge de Cuvier," in his 'Éloges historiques,' 3me série, Paris, 1862, p. 122, &c. ; Hahn in the 'Grande Encyclopédie,' article "Cuvier." See also the Introduction to the 'Règne animal,' which proposes to arrange living beings according to their " organisation," by investigating their " structure," their "internal as well as external conformation." Cuvier here states that no one before had tried to arrange the classes and orders according to the " ensemble de la structure" (p. vi). He is thus led to the law of the " subordination des caractères, . . . ayant soin d'établir toujours la correspondance des formes extérieures et intérieures qui, les unes comme les

details of his natural history, his comparative anatomy, or his palæontology, of which latter sciences he is the creator, it serves our present purpose better to learn how he viewed the object of natural science in general—how he defined its task. As the first step in civilisation was the creation of a language possessing definite rules, so the first step in the growth of a science is that taken by Linnæus, who was not terrified by this enormous work, that of giving names, of framing a nomenclature.[1] " But," says Cuvier, " to name well, you must know well. These

autres, font partie intégrante de l'essence de chaque animal " (p. xiv). He opposes former artificial classifications, such as the principle that living beings can be arranged " de manière à former des êtres une seule ligne " (p. xx). "Un être organisé est un tout unique, un ensemble de parties qui réagissent les unes sur les autres pour produire un effet commun. Nulle de ses parties ne peut donc être modifiée essentiellement sans que toutes les autres ne s'en ressentent " ('Éloges,' vol. ii. p. 279).

[1] The formation of a nomenclature or a terminology is one of the most important steps in the beginning and the progress of science. Cuvier refers frequently to this: " Nos livres saints, à leur début, nous représentent le Créateur faisant passer ses ouvrages sous les yeux du premier homme, et lui ordonnant de leur imposer des noms. . . . Ces noms, qu'il est prescrit à l'homme d'imposer, ne sont pas des signes incohérens appliqués au hasard à quelques objets isolés. Pour qu'ils deviennent réguliers et significatifs, ils exigent, comme il est dit, que les êtres aient passé devant le nomenclateur " ('Éloges,' vol. iii. pp. 450, 452). Nowhere is terminology more important than in chemistry. " L'un des moyens qui ont le plus puissamment contribué à faciliter l'enseignement de la science en général, et à préparer l'adoption universelle de la théorie nouvelle, c'est la nomenclature créée par cette société de chimistes français. . . . Donner aux élémens des noms simples ; en dériver, pour les combinaisons, des noms, qui exprimassent l'espèce et la proportion des élémens qui les constituent, c'était offrir d'avance à l'esprit le tableau abrégé des résultats de la science, c'était fournir à la mémoire le moyen de rappeler par les noms la nature même des objets. C'est ce que M. Guyton de Morveau proposa le premier dès 1781, et ce qui fut complètement exécuté par lui et par ses collègues en 1787 " ('Rapport,' p. 88, &c.) Cf. ' Éloges,' vol. iii. pp. 194, 482, 496. Cuvier ('Éloges,' vol. iii. p. 302) mentions " cette antipathie pour les méthodes et pour une nomenclature précise à laquelle Buffon s'est laissé aller en tant d'endroits " ; he speaks of Pinel " qui avait cherché d'abord à former pour les descriptions des maladies un langage précis, modelé sur celui que Linnæus avait introduit en botanique " (ibid., vol. iii. p. 386).

beings and their parts which are to be known are to be counted by the million; it is not enough to know them singly, for they are submitted to an order, to mutual relations, which must likewise be appreciated, for it is according to this order that each has its part to play, that each disappears at its time, that they reappear similarly made, always in the same proportions, and armed with the necessary forces and faculties for the maintenance of these proportions, and of the whole of this perpetual vortex. Not only is each being an organism, the whole universe is one, but many million times more complicated; and that which the anatomist does for a single animal—for the microcosm—the naturalist is to do for the macrocosm, for the universal animal, for the play of this alarming aggregation of partial organisms."[1]

It was this sustained regard for the value of detailed research and minute observation, coupled with an equal appreciation of the unity of all regions of existence, and all branches of learning, that elevated Cuvier to the height of the science of his age and his country, and made him a true exponent of the modern scientific spirit. The works of Newton and Laplace may contain more formulæ of lasting value, more instruments of permanent scientific use—they may, for all time, have traced a few lines of the enwoven cipher of the all-pervading mechanism of nature; it is, however, well to note that he only who keeps in steadfast view the life rather than the mechanism of existence, approaches the great secret of nature, and gauges rightly the value of each component

[1] Cuvier, 'Éloges historiques,' vol. iii. p. 453.

part, or the worth of each human effort.[1] In this respect the nineteenth century knows no greater figure than Cuvier; not even Humboldt, great and comprehensive as was his scientific view. The advantages also of Cuvier's position as permanent Secretary of the French Academy of Sciences were exceptional, and well fitted to bring out his extraordinary talents. We can say that in him science has become fully conscious of its true methods, its usefulness, its most becoming style, its inherent dignity, its past errors, its present triumphs, the endless career which lies before it, and the limits which it cannot transgress.

Educated in Germany, at the same school as Schiller and Dannecker,[2] imbued by early experience and by

29. Cuvier's training.

---

[1] "C'est la continuation de ce commandement de voir et de nommer, par où s'ouvre la vie de notre espèce, c'est la voie qui devait nous conduire soit à des contemplations plus hautes, soit seulement à des inventions utiles. En effet l'histoire naturelle ne fait aucun pas sans que la physiologie et la philosophie générale marchent d'un pas égal, et sans que la société reçoive leur tribut commun" ('Éloges,' vol. iii. p. 474).

[2] Cuvier has himself written an account of his early life and studies. It is given by Flourens, 'Éloges,' vol. i. pp. 167-193. He was born in 1769, of a Protestant stock, at Montbéliard, the capital of a small principality, situated in the Jura, and then belonging to Würtemberg. The autocratic Duke Charles (1737-1793) had founded a military academy in Stuttgart, his capital, where 400 youths were at his expense housed and educated according to a strict rule, but under the guidance of enlightened masters, and in a thoroughly modern spirit. The institution was a kind of opposition to the Protestant Church rule, which had very early spread a system of popular and compulsory education, throughout the country. It is a chapter of history well worth reading. The great problems of popular education as against higher instruction, Protestant discipline in the lower as against military discipline in the higher schools, the democratic as against the aristocratic spirit, the independence as against the State - regulation of University teaching, were fought out by the dukes and the Estates of Würtemberg in a prolonged warfare, a sample of similar movements all over Germany, and well told by Perthes in his 'Politische Zustände und Personen in Deutschland zur Zeit der französischen Herrschaft' (Gotha, 1862, pp. 501-548). Cuvier evidently saw the better side of the system, for he entered after the imperious character of the duke had been subdued by the victorious estates. Forced to change his ways, which he conscientiously did, the duke laid by for his country, as a local historian says, "a fund of in-

personal contact with that spirit of general education
and universal training which then animated the German-
speaking nations of the Continent, thoroughly grounded
in classics and mathematics, with a cosmopolitan knowledge of languages and literature, which fitted him to
understand the merits of different nations, he became
the great exponent of that peculiar system of higher
culture which since the time of Colbert the French had
elaborated—the academic system.[1] The centre of this

telligence and acquisitions by which
we have benefited up to modern
times" (Perthes, p. 510). We know
the other and older side of the
picture from the 'Life of Schiller'
(see, *inter alia*, Carlyle, 'Life of
Schiller,' collected works, library
edition, vol. v. p. 258). Cuvier
gives a long description of the "Karl-
schule " : " C'était un établissement vraiment magnifique. Envi-
ron quatre cents boursiers et pen-
sionnaires, logés dans un édifice tel
qu'il n'y en a aucun d'approchant
en Europe (parmi ceux qui sont
consacrés à l'instruction de la jeun-
esse), vêtus d'un bel uniforme, con-
duits par des officiers et des sous-
officiers tirés des régiments du duc,
reçevaient des leçons de tout genre
de plus de quatre-vingts maîtres ou
professeurs. On a beaucoup parlé
de l'esprit de despotisme avec lequel
le duc disposait de leurs personnes
et choisissait pour chacun d'eux
l'état qu'il devait embrasser, et je
crois en effet qu'il en était ainsi
dans l'origine de l'établissement ;
mais de mon temps, je n'ai rien
vu de semblable, et ce qui est certain, c'est que personne ne prétendit
même me donner de conseil à cet
égard. Il y avait cinq facultés
supérieures, droit, médecine, administration, militaire et commerce "
(Flourens, *loc. cit.*, p. 171).

[1] The first great representative

of this academic spirit and culture
was Fontenelle, who, living during
a hundred years, from 1657 to 1757,
was Secretary of the Académie des
Sciences during forty - two years,
from 1699 (the year of the recon-
stitution of the Academy) to 1741.
Among his successors were men like
Condorcet, Delambre, Cuvier, and
Arago.   Fontenelle gave to scientific subjects a dignified popularity,
separated the departments of science
and metaphysics, kept the scientific
interest free from the commercial,
and through his connection with the
Académie française did probably
more than any other writer to establish that superiority of style and
diction for which the great French
men of science are so remarkable and
so superior to those of other countries. Bertrand, himself a successor
of Fontenelle, says of him : "Prêtant
aux travaux de ses confrères la
finesse de ses aperçus et la vivacité
ingénieuse de son style, il a su dans
leurs portraits, qui sont des chefs-
d'œuvre, plus encore que dans l'analyse de leurs découvertes, donner
aux plus humbles et aux plus
modestes une célébrité imprévue
et durable, et le juste et sérieux
hommage qu'il rend au vrai mérite
fait aimer et respecter tout à la fois
les savants et la science " ('L'Académie des Sciences et les Académiciens,' p. 113).   See also Voltaire's

system was the old Academy of Sciences, which, with a short interruption during the storm of the Revolution, survived,[1] and formed the principal feature in the Institute. Allied with this institution, and directly inspired by its spirit, were the great schools of natural science, the great collections of natural objects, latterly also the great medical institutions of Paris. It professed to protect scientific studies in a royal and generous manner, attracted talent from outside, rewarded foreign as well as French research,[2] and tried to keep the scientific spirit of inquiry, as well as the form in which it found expression, pure and undefiled.[3] It favoured the co-

'Siècle de Louis XIV.'; Cabanis, 'Révolutions de la Médecine' (Œuvres, Paris, 1823, vol. i. p. 200); Flourens, 'Éloges historiques,' vol. iii. p. 31, &c.; Maury, 'Les Académies d'autrefois,' vol. i. p. 153, 163 et passim; Bouillier, 'Éloges de Fontenelle,' Introduction.

[1] "Tandis que tout a été renouvelé dans la politique et les mœurs publiques . . . la vie scientifique et littéraire a sensiblement gardé sa constitution. . . . Le Collège de France, l'Académie française, l'Académie des Inscriptions et Belles-lettres, l'Académie des Sciences, la Bibliothèque impériale, l'Observatoire, le Muséum d'Histoire naturelle, subsistent encore, comme au siècle dernier, et dans nos provinces, une foule d'académies sont d'une création antérieure à 1789" (Maury, loc. cit., p. 1).

[2] "Euler fut quatre fois couronné pour des questions de physique et de mathématiques. . . . Daniel Bernoulli obtint le prix dix fois" (Maury, p. 171). Among the celebrated Éloges by Fontenelle there are those of Leibniz, of Peter the Great, of Newton, of Marsigli, of Boerhaave; among those by Con-

dorcet there are those of Haller, Linnæus, Hunter, and Euler; among Cuvier's there are those of Gilbert, Priestley, De Saussure, Cavendish, Pallas, Rumford, Werner, Banks, and Davy.

[3] "Jusqu'à présent," says Fontenelle in 1699, "l'Académie des Sciences ne prend la nature que par petites parcelles. Nul système général, de peur de tomber dans l'inconvénient des systèmes précipités dont l'impatience de l'esprit humain ne s'accommode que trop bien, et qui, étant une fois établis, s'opposent aux vérités qui surviennent" (quoted by Flourens, 'Éloges,' vol. iii. p. 19). "L'esprit de l'Académie des Sciences a donc toujours été l'esprit d'expérience, d'étude directe, d'observation précise, l'amour de la certitude. D'abord cartésienne, elle devint ensuite Newtonienne," &c. (ibid., p. 21). Fontenelle contrasts the "philosophie des mots et celle des choses, de l'École et de l'Académie" ('Éloge de Du Hamel' in Bouillier, p. 10). "Fontenelle se plaît à multiplier les exemples de cette incapacité chez les savants de faire fortune et de ce noble désintéressement." "Il aimait mieux

operation of many minds in rearing the great edifice of
science, and found a place for the minutest research, as
well as a field for the development and sway of great and
governing ideas. Of the best form of this spirit and
system—the Académie—Cuvier was the greatest representative. Through several dozen Éloges which he pronounced on the decease of a number of the most illustrious scientific men of Europe, as well as through
several Reports, in which he summed up the labours and
progress of his age, and the peculiar features of his period,
he affords to the student of history an insight into that
distinctive phase which scientific thought had entered in
France at the end of the eighteenth century. This he
allows us to contrast with other phases of thought, such
as the philosophical or individual, which obtained in other
ages or countries, and suggests as well as gives the means of
answering the question, to what extent the scientific ideal

30.
Cuvier the
greatest
representa-
tive of the
Academic
system.

étudier que subsister," he said of
one of the Academicians (Bouillier,
pp. ix, xii). Cuvier was very watchful over the Academy in keeping
out the speculative spirit. See
what he says in the joint Report
on geology with Haüy and Lelièvre
('Mém. de l'Institut,' vol. viii. 1607,
p. 136). " Que doivent donc faire
les corps savans pour procurer à une
science aussi intéressante et aussi
utile, les accroissemens dont elle est
susceptible ? . . . Ils doivent tenir
la conduite, qu'ils ont tenue depuis
leur établissement, à l'égard de
toutes les autres sciences : encour-
ager de leurs éloges ceux qui con-
statent des faits positifs et garder
un silence absolu sur les systèmes
qui se succèdent." Compare with
this what he says about the use of
the principle of "vital force," always referring to Newton's method

('Mém. de l'Inst.,' vol. vii. p. 77,
&c.), further in his analysis of Gall
and Spurzheim's Mémoire ('Mém.
de l'Inst.,' vol. ix. p. 65): "Les
commissaires de la classe . . . ont
donné leur assentiment à presque
toutes les propositions de MM. G.
& S., qui ne dépendent que de
l'inspection anatomique, &c. . . .
les commissaires ont cru également-
ment de leur devoir de prévenir le
public, qu'il n'y a aucun rapport
direct, aucune liaison necessaire
entre ces découvertes et le doctrine
enseignée par MM. G. & S., &c. . . .
Toutes ces matières sont encore trop
étrangères aux attributions de la
classe, elles tiennent aux faits sensibles d'une manière trop lâche,
elles prêtent à trop de discussions
vagues, pour qu'un corps tel que
le nôtre doive s'en occuper" (p.
159).

of the end of this century agrees with or differs from that of its beginning. Upholding the Newtonian rather than the Baconian and Leibnizian standard in the mathematical and physical sciences,[1] he has marked that line which our whole century has contributed to trace out more distinctly ; whilst, as regards the purely natural sciences, his continued emphasising of the great problem of organisation, and his later controversy with Geoffroy de Saint-Hilaire, mark that point in which this century has most distinctly departed from the prevailing ideas of its early years.[2] He also recognised earlier than any other mind of similar eminence what our century increasingly realises, how, without a system of condensation, contained in reports, statistics, and figures, aided by classifications and systems, the growing bulk of accumulated knowledge becomes chaotic and unmanageable.[3]

[1] Cuvier was not brought up in the school of the Encyclopædists, and I cannot find that he attached the great importance to the writings of Bacon which that school commonly did. As to Newton and Leibniz, he contrasts their methods, considering them " comme les chefs et les représentans des deux méthodes opposées qui se sont disputé l'empire de la science " ('Histoire des Sciences naturelles,' publiée par Magdeleine de Saint-Agy, Paris, 1841, vol. iii. p. 19, &c.) See also in his joint Report with Haüy and Lelièvre on the Science of Geology ('Mém. de l'Institut,' 1807, p. 133) : "On vit renaître dans cette partie de l'histoire naturelle la méthode systématique de Descartes, que Newton semblait avoir bannie pour jamais de toutes les sciences physiques, . . . et lorsqu'on songe que Leibniz et Buffon sont au nombre

des philosophes dont je parle ici," &c.

[2] A future chapter will deal specially with this subject. Cuvier, as is well known, maintained the fixity of species, and opposed the theories of St Hilaire and Lamarck, in which a later generation recognises the beginnings of the Darwinian doctrine of the transmutation of species. "On est obligé d'admettre certaines formes, qui se sont perpétuées depuis l'origine des choses, sans excéder ces limites ; et tous les êtres appartenans à l'une de ces formes constituent ce que l'on appelle une espèce" ('Règne animal,' vol. i. p. 20).

[3] Cuvier was the first great scientific writer who undertook to give a historical survey of the position of the different natural sciences, with a view of ascertaining what had been achieved and what remained to be done. He did what

Cuvier had also a true historical sense, which enabled him to trace the connection of science with political history, with literature, with the fine and useful arts. And he helps to answer a question which to us is of paramount interest, How did science fare during the great cataclysm of the Revolution ? how under the reactionary despotism of the First Empire ? Before attempting to reply to these questions in the light of subsequent and general European history, I will select a few passages from Cuvier which throw light upon these points : [1]—

31. On the fortunes of science during the Revolution and the First Empire.

" There is always a revolution required in order to change habits which have become general, and the most necessary revolutions do not take place without some circumstance, which is sometimes long delayed. We have been able to see how in such a case everything furthers the sciences, even the delays and contrarieties which they seem to suffer under.

" The events which disturbed the world, and which for natural science temporarily dried up the sources of its riches,[2] obliged it to return to itself, and to make a new study of what it possessed, more fruitful than the most

a generation later the British Association undertook to do, and what in Germany the many " Jahresberichte " do nowadays. See his " Analyse des Travaux," &c., ' Mém. de l'Institut,' vol. ix. p. 53, and his celebrated ' Rapport historique sur le Progrès des Sciences naturelles depuis 1789,' Paris, 1810.

[1] ' Éloges historiques,' vol. iii. p. 456, 1824.

[2] This refers to the isolation of France during the war and the Continental blockade, which deprived it of foreign imports and the scientific collections of foreign specimens ; see also ' Éloges,' vol. i. p. 9 ; vol. iii. p. 202 : " Quand la jalousie des peuples nous privait des produits étrangers, la chimie les faisait éclore de notre sol." " Le conseil des mines établi en 1793, lorsque l'interruption de tout rapport avec l'étranger fit sentir le besoin de tirer parti de notre territoire a donné à ces sortes de recherches une impulsion toute nouvelle" (' Rapport,' p. 178).

fortunate departures could have been. During this apparent rest, all the different parts of method were deepened; the interior of natural objects was studied; even minerals were dissected and reduced to their mechanical elements; a still more intimate analysis was made by a perfected chemistry; the earth itself was, during this interval, if the expression is allowable, dissected by the geologists; its depths were sounded; the order and layers of rock which form its shell were recognised.[1] In the absence of foreign contributions the interior of the soil on which we walk became tributary to science. The beings of which it contains the remains came to light, and revealed a natural history anterior to that of to-day, different in its forms, and nevertheless subject to similar laws, thus giving to these laws a sanction which no one expected. The botanists did not gather so many plants in their collections, but with the lens in hand they demonstrated more and more the intimate structure of the fruit, the seed, the various relations which connect the parts of the flower, and the indications which these relations furnish for a natural division. The most delicate forms of organic tissues were exhibited; medicine

[1] Cuvier refers here to the investigation of the fossils in the Paris basin, which he undertook during the years 1804 to 1808: "La singularité des animaux dont je découvrais les ossements à Montmartre me fit désirer de connaître plus en détail la composition géologique des environs de Paris. Mon ami Brongniart s'associa à moi pour ce travail; nous fîmes ensemble et séparément beaucoup de courses. . . . Ces recherches ont donné une face toute nouvelle à la géologie, et ont occasionné toutes celles qu'ont faites ensuite en Angleterre MM. Webster, Buckland, Labêche et autres" (Cuvier, "Mém. sur sa Vie" in Flourens, 'Eloges,' vol. iii. p. 188). This was the beginning of the Science of Palæontology, a term which Cuvier did not use himself (Flourens, 'Travaux de Cuvier,' p. 147). See also Cuvier, 'Recherches sur les Ossemens fossils de Quadrupèdes,' &c., 1st ed., 1812, 3rd ed., 1825, in the Introduction.

and chemistry united their efforts to appreciate in the
minutest detail the action of external elements on the
living organism.[1] The different combinations of organs,
or what we call the different classes, the different genera,
were not less studied than general theories. There were
no animals, ever so small, the inner parts of which,
unveiled by anatomy, did not become known as well
as our own. Every organic system was likewise submitted to a special examination. The brain, marking
the degree of intellectual power; the teeth, signs of
the nature and energy of the digestive forces; the bony
system, above all, which is the support of all others,
and which determines the connected forms of animals,
—all these were followed into the smallest species and
into the minutest parts. We see how, after such studies,
there could be no more talk of superficial or artificial
methods. The old natural history had ceased to rule.
It was not that old natural history any more, but a
science full of life and youth, armed with quite novel
ways and means, which beheld the world reopened by
the Peace."[2]

In an earlier passage,[3] speaking of the reopening of
academies and schools by the Government of the Revolu-

---

[1] Compare with this the 'Rapport' of the year 1808, p. 201, &c.
The above remarks refer mainly to
Bichat. "Bichat a donné à l'anatomie un grand intérêt, par l'opposition de structure et de forme qu'il
a développée, entre les organes de
la vie animale, c'est-à-dire, du sentiment et du mouvement, et ceux de
la vie purement végétative. . . .
L'attention particulière donnée par
Bichat au tissu et aux fonctions des
diverses membranes, et l'analogie

qu'il a établie entre celles de parties
très éloignées, ont jeté aussi des
lumières nouvelles sur l'anatomie,
principalement dans ses rapports
avec la médecine" ('Rapport,' p.
218).

[2] This refers to the peace which
concluded the Napoleonic wars, and
re-established the free intercourse
of France with the rest of the world.

[3] In the 'Éloge of Fourcroy,"
of the year 1811 ('Éloges,' vol. ii.
p. 40, &c.)

tion, Cuvier remarks: " It was not merely a question of
isolated discoveries, but of institutions, which, in assuring
the conservation of the sciences, would multiply their
progress indefinitely. What was needed was no longer a
simple experimenter, master of his subject and his instruments, it was a man obliged to battle against all kinds of
obstacles, and to benefit his fellow-citizens, mostly in spite
of themselves. The Convention had destroyed academies,
colleges, universities; nobody would have dared to ask
boldly for their restitution; but soon the effects of their
suppression showed themselves in the most susceptible
point; the armies were without doctors and surgeons,
and these could not be created without schools.[1] But
who would believe that time was required to give courage
enough to call them schools of medicine. Doctor and
surgeon were titles too contrary to equality, apparently
because there is no authority over the patient more necessary than that of the doctor; therefore the odd term
" schools of health " was used, and there was no question
of either examination or diploma for the students. In
spite of this, a penetrating glance reveals, in the regulations which were carried, the intentions of him (Fourcroy)
who drew them up. The three great schools founded at

[1] See 'Éloges,' vol. i. p. 353.
"Cependant les gens qui avaient
fait toutes ces suppressions eurent
promptement lieu de s'apercevoir
que, s'il était à la rigueur superflu
d'apprendre toute autre chose, on
ne pouvait guère se dispenser d'apprendre la médecine. Toute la
France se précipitait aux frontières,
et, après des prodiges inouis de
dévouement et de valeur, les défen-
seurs de la patrie ne trouvaient
aucun secours pour leurs blessures
et pour leurs maladies. On com-
mença donc par l'érection des écoles
de médecine cette longue suite de
restaurations, que l'établissement
de l'université vient de couronner
et de lier en un ensemble aussi
imposant par l'étendue de son plan
que par la vigueur de son organisation." See also 'Rapport,' &c., p.
360.

this epoch,[1] received an abundance of means, of which up to that time there was no idea in France, and which still form the finest ornament of the University."

Similar passages might be collected in which Cuvier enlarges on the influence of war and revolutions, of the Continental blockade and the isolation of the country; on the reconstruction of hospitals and the admission of medical science into the Academy; on the creation of new industries; on the development of the mining and mineral wealth of the country; on the scientific value of colonies and travels, and many other interesting topics. In confining myself more closely to the history of thought and the growth of the modern scientific spirit, I will make some reflections which his remarks force upon us.

32.
France has done more than other countries to popularise science.

I have noted above how France more than any other country worked for the popularisation of science, how her polite literature alone during the eighteenth century bears the strong impress of modern scientific ideas; no other country has a Fontenelle, a Voltaire, a Buffon. This peculiarity must be recognised as a very powerful and valuable stimulus to the growth of the scientific spirit. It emanates largely, if not exclusively, from the peculiar position of the old Academy of Science. It must, however, not be forgotten that it was not a popularisation of the kind we witness nowadays.

33.
Difference between the literary and the national popularisation.

The class of literature which in our age spreads broadcast the discoveries or ideas of science; the endless number of magazines, reviews, and daily papers; the small treatises, the cheap primers, the compact text-books, did

[1] They were the three "Écoles de Santé" at Paris, Strasbourg, and Montpellier (see Hippeau, 'L'Instruction publique en France,' vol. ii. p. 194).

not then exist.[1]   Science was not a subject of general, still
less of popular, instruction.   It was an occupation of the
few, who, privileged by fortune or talent, or gifted with
inordinate perseverance, forced their way into the *salons*
of society[2] or the rooms of the Academy.   The first public
course of natural history was opened in Paris by Valmont
de Bomare in 1760.[3]   Science still stood far out of the reach
of the practical man or the poor man; it had not yet
become an element of education or an instrument for
industry.   It was a fashionable pursuit, a luxury of the
great, a key that occasionally opened the door of the
palace; but it was not a thing of immediate use, except
in adding glory and renown to its royal protectors, or
to the rare genius which could make new discoveries.
Almost the only application made of it was in navigation, and in the construction of instruments connected
therewith.   This essentially literary — not national —
popularisation of science had also its great dangers.
No ideas lend themselves to such easy, but likewise to
such shallow, generalisations as those of science.   Once
let out of the hand which uses them, in the strict and
cautious manner by which alone they lead to valuable
results, they are apt to work mischief.   Because the tool
is so sharp, the object to which it is applied seems to be

34.
Dangers of
the merely
literary pop-
ularisation.

---

[1] Cuvier, in his 'Rapport,' &c., p.
361, mentions the elementary works
published by some of the medical
professors at the beginning of the
century, but says also that "En
Allemagne, surtout, où l'usage des
livres élémentaires est plus commun
que chez nous, il n'est presque
aucune université, dont les professeurs n'en aient publié d'excel-
lens."

[2] See Maury, p. 182, &c.   Also Cuvier, 'Rapport,' vol. ii. p. 427 : "En
France la réputation des ouvrages
dépend, pour l'ordinaire, des femmes
et de quelques gens de lettres, qui
croient pouvoir juger des sciences
positives, parce qu'ils ont combiné
quelques idées générales de méta-
physique."
[3] See Maury, 'L'ancienne Académie des Sciences,' p. 283.

so easily handled. The correct use of scientific ideas is only learned by patient training, and should be governed by the not easily acquired habit of self-restraint. It is well known how the fundamental notions of a mechanical science, let loose into literature by Fontenelle, by D'Alembert, by Condorcet, or absorbed by Voltaire and Diderot, were expanded into a system of materialistic philosophy in 'L'Homme Machine,' the 'Système de la Nature,' and other works, the extreme views of which the great scientific thinkers could hardly approve of.[1] These hasty but

[1] As a great deal of confusion existed for a long time in European literature as to the exact succession in time of the different works which assisted to spread mechanical views of the world and of life, I put down the main dates :—

Fontenelle (1657-1757) published his Eloges of the great Academicians, in which the principles of the philosophy of Descartes, Leibniz, and Newton were popularly expounded and discussed, from 1700 onward. His 'Pluralité des Mondes' had appeared already in 1686 ; it had popularised Cartesian ideas.

Voltaire (1694-1778) published his 'Élémens de la Philosophie de Newton' in 1738.

La Mettrie (1709-51) published his 'Histoire naturelle de l'Âme' in 1745, and his 'L'Homme Machine' in 1748.

D'Alembert and Diderot published the first volume of the 'Encyclopédie' in 1751.

Buffon (1707-88) published, 1749, his 'Théorie de la Terre,' being the first portion of the 'Histoire naturelle.'

Holbach (1723-89) published under the name of Mirabaud, 1770, the 'Système de la Nature.'

Of these works, the three which created the greatest popular sensation — viz., Voltaire's 'Élémens,' La Mettrie's 'L'Homme Machine,' and Holbach's 'Système'—were all published in Holland. Voltaire, D'Alembert, and Diderot appear to have approached philosophical problems mainly from the position of Newton's natural philosophy, La Mettrie from the teachings of the great Boerhaave, Holbach principally from a study of chemistry. It is unnecessary to say that none of them had the sanction of their great masters for the applications they made of principles which had been established and used for special scientific purposes. And the same may be said with reference to the influence of Locke, which in almost all the instances mentioned was combined with that of the great naturalists. But this does not belong to the line of thought in which we are interested at present. For the sake of completeness only I mention that Locke's teachings as well as Newton's were made popularly known in France by Voltaire's "Lettres sur les Anglais' (burnt by order of the Parliament of Paris in 1734), whereas Condillac's (1714-80) more systematic treatise, entitled 'Essai sur l'Origine des Connaissances humaines,' appeared in 1746. It is

brilliant generalisations, expressed frequently in the most perfect language, did no good to the truly scientific cause ; they did not spread the genuine scientific spirit.   Much of the good done by Fontenelle, by Voltaire, by Buffon, was spoiled or neutralised by premature and ill-founded theories.   How much, or how little, they contributed (either directly or by a kind of reaction which set in against them, of which Rousseau may be regarded as the centre) to bring about the Revolution is a matter of much controversy ; certain it is that the Revolution broke their sway, and destroyed their immediate influence.[1]   To the purely literary the Revolution added

35
The Revolution added the modern practical popularisation of science.

important, in dealing with the extreme materialistic writings which French literature produced between 1745 and 1770, to keep distinct the different origins from which they started, and the different influences which combined to produce them : the mathematical and mechanical principles borrowed from Newton, the physiological and medical emanating from Linnæus and Boerhaave, and the psychological coming from Locke and Shaftesbury.   Lange, in his ' History of Materialism ' (transl. by Thomas, London, 1880, 3 vols.), was the first to point out clearly the correct chronology and succession of these writings (see especially vol. ii. pp. 49-123), and to dispel the misconceptions which, since the appearance of Hegel's ' Geschichte der Philosophie' in 1833-36, had passed through nearly all historical works published in Germany.   From his exhaustive references, it is evident that the extreme views of La Mettrie, Diderot, and Holbach cannot be fathered on any of the great scientists or philosophers, but were an attempt to apply scientific principles to the solution of philosophical, ethical, or religious questions, frequently for practical and political purposes.

[1] It would probably be more correct to say that these daring attempts to deal with the general problems of knowing and being, with the nature of the soul and the conduct of life, were discarded as premature, and that the followers of Condillac and Locke betook themselves to a more patient study of the facts of the inner life, as the followers of Buffon forsook his brilliant generalisations for the more patient and fruitful study of all the forms of physical nature.   And in this respect the Government of the Revolution took a memorable step when it founded on the 3rd brumaire, an iv. (25th October 1795), on a Report of Daunou, based mainly on ideas expounded by Condorcet, the "Académie des Sciences morales et politiques."   It was the intention to abandon metaphysical generalisations, and to combine the scientific and historical spirit in the study of mental, moral, and social phenomena, drawing extensively on the assistance of the medical sciences, or a knowledge of human nature in its nor-

something different—*viz.*, the modern practical popular-isation of science: it established its educational and its technical importance. Science was to be not an elegant amusement, or a refined luxury, nor even exclusively the serious occupation of the rare genius: it was to be the basis of a national instruction, and the foundation of the greatness and wealth of the nation. The Memoirs of the Academy were cleansed of all dangerous general-isations which might have brought them into touch with political controversy; the language was confined to the measured and concise statement of facts, or to theories capable of mathematical verification and treatment; con-jectural matter was carefully excluded, and a standard of scientific excellence, both in matter and form, was raised, to which we still look up with admiration.[1] At the same time, this lofty and dignified spirit enlivened the courses

mal and diseased conditions. This organisation produced, during its short existence of only seven years, some memorable works; but its position was for various reasons secondary only: it was eclipsed by the European renown which the "Académie des Sciences" possessed, owing to its historical antecedents and its brilliant discoveries and the practical usefulness of its labours. But the idea of including ethical and political studies under the term "Science," due probably to Con-dorcet, was fixed by this organisa-tion, and has in the course of the century acquired increasing influ-ence. From these beginnings we shall have to study its career in an-other portion of the present work.

[1] According to Cuvier, "la langue naturelle de l'Académie des Sci-ences" is "la langue des chiffres" ('Éloges,' vol. i. p. 24); "l'Acadé-mie a toujours eu pour principe de ne se rendre qu'à des calculs ou à des expériences positives" (vol. iii. p. 12). Compare also 'Mém. de l'Institut,' vol. vii. p. 77, where he speaks of the method of Newton, showing how little the employment of a principle like that of "vital force" in physiology can be compared with that of gravitation, employed by Newton to explain the movement of the heavenly bodies; again, vol. viii. p. 139, where he refers to the great service rendered by the Aca-demy, "s'il parvenait à diriger les esprits vers des recherches positives, mais longues et pénibles." And vol. ix. p. 61: "On aime toujours à voir se multiplier dans les sciences expérimentales les moyens simples d'arriver à la précision et de se rapprocher des sciences mathéma-tiques," and other passages quoted above, p. 115 and p. 128. See also his remarks on the Philosophy of Nature, 'Rapport,' p. 335.

of lectures delivered in the great schools by the first men
of the nation, and became, through them, the habit of a
large number of ardent pupils, who were to carry it further into more popular teaching, or into the applications
of art and industry.[1] The results of both are well known.
We still live, at the end of the century, under their immediate influence. If now we continually appeal to scientific authorities for aid in the solution of practical problems, it is well to remember that nothing helped more to
raise science to the eminence of a great social power than
the action of the Revolutionary Government in 1793.
Whilst it guillotined Lavoisier, Bailly, and Cousin; drove
Condorcet to suicide, and others like Vicq-d'Azyr and
Dionis du Séjour into premature death;[2] it had to ap-

---

[1] See Cuvier, "Réflexions sur les Sciences," 1816, in 'Éloges,' &c., vol. i. p. 24, &c.: "Que l'on re- cherche, ce qu'ont valu à la France depuis vingt ans les inventions pratiques dérivées des découvertes de MM. Berthollet, Chaptal, Vau- quelin, Thénard, &c., dans la seule chimie minérale, dans cette branche assez bornée des sciences physiques; l'extraction de la soude, la fabrica- tion de l'alun, du sel ammoniac, des oxydes de plomb, des acides miné- raux, toutes substances que nous tirions de l'étranger; l'épuration des fers, la cémentation de l'acier et enfin le développement des arts qui emploient ces matières premi- ères : il est clair que c'est par cen- taines de millions qu'il faudra cal- culer." Also, vol. iii. p. 202 : "Les applications de la science à la pra- tique avaient fait de M. Berthollet, lorsque la guerre de la révolution éclata, le chimiste le plus connu du public, après Lavoisier; et il était presque impossible que l'on ne re- courût pas à lui au moment où la chimie devint pour la guerre un auxiliaire de première necessité, et lorsqu'il fallut demander à notre sol le salpêtre, la potasse et jus- qu'aux matières colorantes; qu'il fallut apprendre à faire en quelques jours toutes les opérations des arts. Chacun se souvient de cette prodi- gieuse et subite activité qui étonna l'Europe, et arracha des éloges même aux ennemis qu'elle arrêta. M. Berthollet et son ami M. Monge en furent l'âme."

[2] Vicq-d'Azyr (1748-94), the great forerunner of Cuvier in the new science of comparative anatomy, "au sortir d'une de ces parodies sinistres décorées du nom de fête nationale, était saisi d'un mal qui l'enlevait en quelques instants dans le délire de la peur. Dionis du Séjour (1734-94), après deux années d'effroi et de misère, ne trouvait plus assez de force pour goûter les temps moins malheureux amenés par la chute de Robespierre" (Maury, 'Les Académies d'autre- fois,' vol. i. p. 332).

peal for its most necessary requirements to the society of scientific authorities, which it professed not to need. "Everything," says the historian of the Academy,[1] "was wanting for the defence of the country—powder, cannons, provisions. The arsenals were empty, steel was no longer imported from abroad, saltpetre came not from India. It was exactly those men whose labours had been proscribed who could give to France what she wanted. Fourcroy, assisted by researches begun by Lavoisier, taught the methods of extracting and refining saltpetre; Guyton de Morveau and Berthollet made known a new method of manufacturing gunpowder, and studied the making of iron and steel; Monge explained the art of casting and boring cannons of brass for land use, and cast-iron cannons for the navy. On the 6th of August 1793 the Convention had again to appeal to the Academy in order to know what advantage it would be to refine as much as possible the coins of the Republic?" In the space of a few years science had become a necessity to society at large.[2] In the Constitution of the regenerated Academies it was placed at the head, as the most important department of knowledge.

[1] Maury, *loc. cit.*, vol. i. p. 329. See also Biot's 'Essai sur l'Histoire générale des Sciences pendant la Révolution française.' Paris, 1803.

[2] The last entry in the record of the "procès-verbaux de l'Académie" before the suspension was a Report by Borda, Laplace, and Lagrange, in answer to a demand of the Convention, dated 19th January 1793, for advice on the new system of weights and measures which the Republic should adopt. And so necessary had the assistance of men of science become to the Government, that even during the suspension, which lasted from the 8th August 1793 till the 22nd August 1795, Lakanal had succeeded in procuring the following decree from the Government of the Convention: "La Convention nationale décrète que les membres de la ci-devant Académie des Sciences continueront de s'assembler dans le lieu ordinaire de leurs séances, pour s'occuper spécialement des objets qui leur auront été ou pourront leur être renvoyés par la Convention nationale" (Maury, *loc. cit.*, p. 331; Aucoc, 'L'Institut de France,' p. ccvii, &c.)

The influence of the first Napoleon on science is naturally a matter of as much controversy as his merit in almost every branch of administration. The reports [1]

36.
Influence of
the first
Napoleon
on science

[1] According to a decree of the Government, dated 13th ventôse, an x. (4th March 1802), the Institute, then consisting of three classes— the "Académie des Sciences physiques et mathématiques," the "Académie des Sciences morales et politiques," and the "Académie de Littérature et Beaux-arts"— was ordered to furnish "un tableau de l'état et des progrès des sciences, des lettres et des arts, depuis 1789 jusqu'au 1ʳᵉ vendémiaire an x." This "tableau" was to be divided into three parts according to the three classes of the Institute. These Reports were to be repeated every five years. The first (and only) Reports were not presented before February and March 1808. The Republican Government had then been superseded by the Empire, and by a decree of the 3rd pluviôse, an xi. (23rd January 1803), the Institute had been reorganised. There were now four classes : 1. Des Sciences physiques et mathématiques (corresponding to the old Académie des Sciences). 2. De la langue et de la littérature françaises (corresponding to the old Académie française). 3. D'histoire et de littérature ancienne (corresponding to the "Académie d'Inscriptions et de Belles-lettres"). 4. Des beaux-arts. "On supprima la classe des sciences morales et politiques qui existait dans l'organisation du 3 brumaire, an iv. Ce fut un trait caractéristique de la répugnance du premier Consul pour la discussion des matières politiques et leur enseignement" (Thibaudeau, 'Le Consulat et l'Empire,' Paris, 1835-37, vol. iii. p. 396). Accordingly there were prepared four, or rather five, Reports, the first in two parts by Delambre and Cuvier on the progress of the Mathematical and Physical Sciences; the second by Marie-Joseph Chénier on the progress of Literature ; the third by Dacier on the progress of History and Classical Literature ; the fourth by Le Breton on Fine Arts. Of these the two Reports of Delambre and Cuvier gave great satisfaction, that of Dacier gave less satisfaction ; Chénier, who himself admired the eighteenth - century philosophy, had an embarrassing task to perform, of which, however, he acquitted himself worthily (Thibaudeau, loc. cit., vol. vi. p. 557). The Report of Chénier has been several times reprinted. The new science which was founded by Condillac, Turgot, Condorcet, and others, and which aimed at introducing the truly scientific spirit into psychology, psycho-physical researches, and questions of society and legislation, received no recognition, as it had also lost its representation in the suspended "Académie des Sciences morales et politiques." After the re-establishment of this section of the Institute in 1832, a royal decree of 22nd March 1840 ordered a Report on the progress of the Moral and Political Sciences from 1789 to 1832. The task was so great that it could not be accomplished before the Revolution of 1848, and was therefore abandoned (Aucoc, 'L'Institut de France,' pp. 62 note, 300). Some reference to the subject is contained in the introduction to Chénier's Report, and in the last chapter of Dacier's, which was written by De Gérando. The true history of the new science has been recently written by F. Picavet, 'Les Idéologues,' Paris, 1891.

which Delambre and Cuvier drew up at his request, touching the progress of science during the twenty years which followed the outbreak of the Revolution, have become classical as monuments of the achievements of a great age,[1] and as examples of the best style in which to treat such a subject.   Written immediately under his eye, they cannot be considered quite impartial, so far as the tone is concerned in which they refer to his personal favours and protection.[2]   There can, however, be no doubt that he recognised scientific merit, and drew many eminent men of science into the service of the Government.   The institutions on which he prided himself so much,—the École Normale, the École Polytechnique, and the unfinished scheme of a great centralised Institution of Learning and Education, descending from the heights of the Institute, through the various branches of the higher and secondary into a multitude of primary schools, bearing the name of the " University,"—had either existed, or been planned before him.[3]

[1] Napoleon in discussing at the council meeting the decree which ordered the several reports, said to Regnaud : "Soignez bien cette rédaction, car elle sera examinée par les pédagogues de toute l'Europe" (Thibaudeau, *loc. cit.*, vol. ii. p. 496).

[2] See what Cuvier himself says on this subject (Mémoires, &c., in Flourens, ' Éloges,' vol. iii. p. 187): " Un rapport sur le progrès des sciences devait être présenté aux consuls en fructidor an xi. . . . Ou ne fut prêt qu'à la fin de 1807 : ce n'était plus aux consuls mais à l'empereur que l'on avait à présenter le travail. Il le reçut avec un grand appareil dans la séance du conseil d'État.   M. Delambre et moi présentâmes le nôtre les pre-

miers ; le 3 févr. 1808, accompagnés de Bougainville, président, et des doyens de toutes les sections. La cérémonie fut solennelle ; l'empereur fit une belle réponse, qui est imprimée à la fin du rapport. Je sus le lendemain, par M. de Ségur et d'autres conseillers d'État, qu'il avait exprimé une grande satisfaction de mon rapport en particulier : ' Il m'a loué comme j'aime à l'être, dit-il.'   Cependant je m'étais borné à l'inviter à imiter Alexandre et à faire tourner sa puissance au profit de l'histoire naturelle."

[3] Regarding the University, see ' Code Universitaire ou Lois, Statuts et Règlemens de l'Université Royale de France, mis en ordre par M. Ambroise Rendu,' Paris, 1835.   In

It will therefore always remain a matter of doubt to what extent he originated ideas, or merely adopted those of others before and around him. He favoured the mathematical sciences, and created great prizes for physical, notably electrical, discoveries, partly because these pursuits promised to surround his Government with glory, partly because he recognised their practical importance for the purposes of the state and nation; partly also, because he himself had had a mathematical training.[1] During his

37.
Napoleon favoured the mathematical sciences.

the Introduction we read as follows : "Bonaparte passait à Turin. Un jour qu'il parcourait le palais de l'Université fondée en 1771 par Charles Emmanuel III., il se fit représenter les statuts qui régissaient cette institution. Il y vit quelque chose de grand et de fort qui le frappa. . . . Tout ce plan d'éducation établi sur la base antique et impérissable de la foi chrétienne, tout cela lui plut, et il en garda la mémoire jusqu'au sein de ses triomphes en Italie et en Allemagne. Rassasié enfin de gloire militaire, et songeant aux générations futures, après avoir solidement établi l'administration civile, après avoir relevé les autels et promulgué le Code Napoléon, après avoir par différentes lois, substitué les Lycées aux Écoles Centrales, régénéré les Écoles de Médecine, et créé les Écoles de Droit, il voulut fonder aussi pour la France un système entier d'instruction et d'éducation publique. Il se souvenait de l'université de Turin et l'agrandissant comme tout ce qu'il touchait, dans la double proportion de son empire et de son génie, il fit l'Université impériale."

[1] Among many references relating to this subject, I select one from Villemain, 'Souvenirs contemporains d'Histoire et de Littérature,' which in the first volume (9ᵐᵉ éd.,

Paris, 1874, p. 137) contains the description of a visit to the École Normale in 1812, and a discussion with Narbonne, to whom the Emperor had fully expressed his aims regarding education and learning. "L'Empereur n'est inquiet que d'une chose dans le monde, les gens qui parlent, et à leur défaut les gens qui pensent. . . . Il veut, et il me l'a dit vingt fois, que son règne soit signalé par de grands travaux d'esprit, de grands ouvrages littéraires. Être loué comme inspirateur de la science et des arts, être le chef éclatant d'une époque glorieuse pour l'esprit humain, c'est l'idée qui le flatte le plus ; c'est ce qu'il a cherché par des Prix Décennaux. . . . Il veut (à l'École Normale) des études fortement classiques, l'antiquité et le siècle de Louis XIV. ; puis quelques éléments de sciences mathématiques et plus tard la haute géométrie, qui est, dit-il, le sublime abstrait, comme la grande poésie, la grande éloquence est le sublime sensible." Napoleon said to Narbonne: "J'aime les sciences mathématiques et physiques ; chacune d'elles, l'algèbre, la chimie, la botanique, est une belle application partielle de l'esprit humain ; les lettres, c'est l'esprit humain lui-même. . . . Aussi, j'ai deux ambitions : élever la France au plus haut degré de la puissance

campaigns in Italy and Germany, and on his expeditions
to Egypt and the East, he surrounded himself with some
of the greatest scientific authorities, such as Berthollet
and Monge.   From political as well as personal motives,

38.
He discoun-
tenanced the
contempor-
ary repre-
sentation of
philosophy.

he discountenanced the once fashionable sensualistic philosophy.   This philosophy has now fallen to the second
rank, though still represented by eminent thinkers, such
as Cabanis, Destutt de Tracy, Daunou and Garat.   It
was these thinkers of whom Napoleon sneeringly spoke
under the designation of " Idéologues." [1]

After all that has been said by admirers to magnify,
and by opponents to minimise, Napoleon's merits in promoting the cause of science, and in spreading the modern
scientific spirit, I cannot but recognise that he was, amongst
the great heroes and statesmen of his age, the first and
foremost, if not the only one, who seemed thoroughly to
realise the part which science was destined to play in

guerrière et de la conquête affermie,
puis y développer, y exciter tous
les travaux de la pensée sur une
échelle qu'on n'a pas vue depuis
Louis XIV. C'était le but de mes
Prix Décennaux qu'on m'a gâtés par
de petites intrigues d'*idéologues*, et
de couronnements ridicules, comme
celui du catéchisme de Saint-
Lambert."

[1] A full account of these authors,
their influence and their aims, will
be found in F. Picavet, 'Les Idéologues, Essai sur l'histoire des idées
et des théories scientifiques, philo-
sophiques, religieuses, &c., en France
depuis 1789,' Paris, 1891.

Thibaudeau, 'Le Consulat et
l'Empire,' gives many details regarding Napoleon's connection with
science, with literature, and with
the growing industries of France.
Among the latter see especially

the great efforts made to supersede
colonial and foreign goods by home
productions. Prizes and encouragements of all sorts were given ;
technical schools and colleges were
established ; exhibitions were promoted. Sheep were imported from
Spain, sugar was made from raisins
and beetroot, saltpetre and soda by
chemical processes, the *garance* or
madder root and the *kermès* were to
take the place of *cochenille ;* the *pas-
tel* the place of the imported indigo.
That an enormous impetus was
thus given to chemistry cannot be
denied. (See Thibaudeau, *passim*,
and especially vol. v. p. 248, &c.)
See also Cuvier's 'Rapport,' &c.,
for an account of applications of
science, especially chemistry, pp.
376-386, and Delambre, 'Rapport,'
&c., pp. 326-362.

the immediate future. This part, as we know, it has played both by entirely changing the external face of things, and by running out into endless applications; and we have seen the importance of that statistical spirit of numbering, measuring, and registering, by which alone a survey of complicated phenomena is possible. Of the statistical method Napoleon himself made use on an extensive scale: perhaps he was the first among rulers to do so.[1] That the great leader of men has to recognise not only the inductive philosophy of statistics and averages, but likewise governing ideas of a different class, Napoleon was well aware, and his ultimate failure may be traced to the fact that, however great as a general and as a calculator, his soul had no room for those high, religious, and unselfish motives of which he himself said to Fontanes, that they in the end always decide the fate of nations.[2] Yet he belongs to the small company of great military figures in history—a company which includes Alexander the Great, Cæsar, and Peter the Great

39.
He himself made extensive use of the statistical method.

[1] See Delambre, 'Rapport,' &c., p. 222. "Depuis le peu de temps qu'on s'en [i.e., with statistics] occupe en France, elle y a fait les plus grands progrès, au moyen de l'attention particulière et des secours que le Gouvernement françois donne à tous les travaux utiles. Les préfets des départemens ont été invités à recueillir et à transmettre au Ministre de l'intérieur les renseignemens les plus précis sur toutes les questions qui sont du ressort de la statistique."

[2] See 'Œuvres littéraires de Napoléon Bonaparte,' vol. iii. p. 5 ; Conversation avec Fontanes, Saint Cloud, 19 Sept. 1808 : "Fontanes, savez-vous ce que j'admire le plus dans le monde ? C'est l'impuis-

sance de la force pour organiser quelque chose. Il n'y a que deux puissances dans le monde : le sabre et l'esprit. J'entends par l'esprit les institutions civiles et religieuses. À la longue, le sabre est toujours battu par l'esprit." Also vol. iv. p. 423 : "Les vraies conquêtes, les seules qui ne donnent aucun regret, sont ceux que l'on fait sur l'ignorance. L'occupation la plus honorable comme la plus utile pour les nations, c'est de contribuer à l'extension des idées humaines. La vraie puissance de la République française doit consister désormais à ne pas permettre qu'il existe une seule idée nouvelle, qui ne lui appartienne."

—who have succeeded in permanently inscribing their names in the annals of science beside those of its true and great representatives. Some of the glory of Laplace and Cuvier falls upon him. Except for this Napoleon has scarcely a place in the history of thought. In it those who were Napoleon's servants are rulers and lawgivers; it is they who enlighten our century. They were the first great exponents of the scientific spirit, nursed under the influence of the academic system. This was peculiarly a product of the French mind and culture. It is well to recall in the words of Cuvier what the scientific spirit is. At the end of the report which he presented in the year 1808 he says:[1] "These are the principal physical discoveries which have lighted up our period, and which open the century of Napoleon. What hopes do they not raise! how much does not the general spirit signify, which has brought them about, and which promises so much more for the future! All those hypotheses, all those suppositions, more or less ingenious, which had still so much sway in the first half of the last century, are now discarded by true men of science: they do not even procure for their authors a passing renown. Experiments alone, experiments that are precise, made with weights, measures, and calculation, by comparison of all substances employed and all substances obtained: this to-day is the only legitimate way of reasoning and demonstration. Thus, though the natural sciences escape the application of the calculus, they glory in being subject to the mathematical spirit, and by the wise course which they have invariably adopted, they do not expose them-

40.
His scienti-
fic glory is
mainly deri-
vative.

[1] 'Rapport,' &c., p. 389.

selves to the risk of taking a backward step; all their
propositions are established with certainty, and become
so many solid foundations for that which remains to be
built." [1]

Nor can we look upon the great prominence which
Cuvier gives to French names in the course of his survey
as unjust or partial.   He was well aware of the contributions of other nations : no one has spoken in more generous and correct terms of Priestley and Cavendish, of
Banks and Rumford, of Pallas, Werner, and Humboldt.
We must admit the correctness of the remark, " that
even in those departments where chance has willed that
Frenchmen should not make the principal discoveries,
the manner in which they have received, examined, and
developed them, and followed them out into all their
consequences, places their names next to those of the
real inventors, and gives them in many ways the right
to share in the honour." [2]

In the first decades of this century the home of the
scientific spirit was France : for though not born there,
it was nevertheless there nursed into full growth and
vigour.   But it soon set out on its wanderings through

41.
Deserved
prominence
given to
French
names by
Cuvier.

[1] Compare also the "Réflexions
sur la marche actuelle des Sciences," being the introduction to
the ' Éloges historiques,' vol. i. p.
1, &c.

[2] 'Rapport,' p. 391. It is also
remarkable how clearly Cuvier here
announces the defects which the
teaching of science was still labouring under.   Whilst he rightly
praises the great Paris institutions,
the medical schools, the mathematical, physical, and polytechnic
establishments, the new schools of
technology and agriculture, as unequalled organisations for higher
instruction, he draws attention to
the absence of equally efficient elementary schools and to the neglect
of those provincial institutions
which before that age had already
done so much to disseminate knowledge and learning.   At the end of
our century both France and Great
Britain have still only very partially
supplied the wants which Cuvier so
clearly defines in the beginning.

other lands and nations. At the end of our century—
nay, even during the whole of the second half—we find
this spirit naturalised in Italy, in Germany, in England,
in the north and east of Europe. There is now no science
which can be named pre-eminently after one nation. All
nations have contributed their share to the cosmopolitan
power and influence which science possesses. They have
enlarged and deepened the scientific spirit and widened
its career. Thus far it has been the growth of the
scientific spirit which has occupied us; we must now
proceed to study its diffusion, and learn to recognise the
peculiar features which Germany and England have on
their part contributed. In doing so, we must turn away
for a moment from the academic system with which we
have been specially occupied.

CHAPTER II.

THE SCIENTIFIC SPIRIT IN GERMANY.

"No Augustan epoch flowered,
No Lorenzo favours showered
Ever German Art upon ;
She was not by glory nourished
And her blossom never flourished
In the rays of Royal sun." [1]

Perhaps with more correctness Schiller might, early in the century, have applied these lines to German science than to German art. If art and poetry were only slightly indebted to princely protection, German science was still less so.[2] Leibniz's scientific labours languished while he

---

[1] Schiller, "Die deutsche Muse."

[2] Astronomy was the only science that enjoyed some little princely favour. William IV., surnamed "the Wise," son of Philip the Magnanimous of Hesse and himself Elector, was an astronomer of some note, and stood in intimate relations with Mercator, Tycho, and other astronomers. In 1561 he built himself an observatory at Cassel and appointed Rothmann to be his "Mathematicus." Frederick II. of Denmark gave Tycho a magnificent observatory, called "Uranienburg," where he laboured from 1576 to 1597, but which was subsequently destroyed. Tycho was then employed by the Emperor Rudolf II., and inaugurated the observatory in Prague (1599-1601) ; he made Kepler his assistant, and enabled the latter by the use of his observations to find and prove his three celebrated laws ("Astronomia nova," Prague, 1609 ; "Harmonices mundi," Linz, 1619 ; "Tabulæ Rudolphinæ," 1627). Full details will be found in Rudolf Wolf, 'Geschichte der Astronomie,' München, 1877, p. 266, &c.

occupied the position of historiographer and diplomatist
at the Court of Brunswick,[1] and Tobias Mayer's valuable
observations were only published with the aid of English
money.[2]   But if the German princes did little or nothing

1.
Foundation
of German
universities.

directly for the development of science, they indirectly

[1] Leibniz (1646 - 1716) entered,
1676, the service of John Frederick,
Duke of Hanover, as librarian and
councillor.   The Duke died 1679,
and Ernest Augustus, who in 1692
was made Elector of Hanover, succeeded him.   Leibniz's time was
taken up with diplomatic and legal
researches and negotiations referring to the position of the House
of Hanover, and the reunion of the
Protestant and Roman Catholic
Churches ; latterly with genealogi-
cal and antiquarian studies referring to the history of the House of
Brunswick.   He wrote the 'Annales
imperii occidentis Brunsvicenses,'
beginning with the year 768, the
date of the accession of Charles the
Great, from whom Leibniz proved
that the House of Brunswick de-
scended through the Italian House
of Este.   He carried the history
down to the year 1005, closing a
few days before his death with the
words "quos ex tenebris eruendos
aliorum diligentiæ relinquo."   The
work was not printed till 1843,
when G. H. Pertz, the first editor
of the celebrated 'Monumenta
Germaniæ' founded by the great
Stein, published it with an elaborate preface.   Of the annoyances to
which Leibniz was subjected in the
course of his studies, see an account
in the correspondence with the
Minister von Bernstorff (1705-16),
published by Doebner, Hanover,
1882, introduction. See also Guh-
rauer, 'Leibnitz, eine Biographie,'
2 vols., 2nd ed., Breslau, 1846.
Considering   the   greatness   of
Leibniz in so many different
directions, his motto is note-

worthy : "Didici in mathematicis
ingenio, in natura experimentis, in
legibus divinis humanisque auctori-
tate, in historia testimoniis niten-
dum esse."
[2] Tobias Mayer (1723-62), born
at Marbach, the birthplace of
Schiller, from 1751 Professor of
Economics and Mathematics at
Göttingen.   To use the words of
Karsten Niebuhr, "Though he
had never seen a big ship, he
taught the English how to determine the longitude on the open
sea."   He competed for the great
prize of £20,000 offered in 1713 by
the Board of Longitude for a method
of determining the longitude at
sea within $\frac{1}{2}°$ accurately ; smaller
prizes being offered for an accuracy
of $\frac{2}{3}°$ and 1°.   The prize of £5000,
and subsequently of £10,000, was
awarded to Harrison in 1758 and
1764 for his chronometers.   Euler
and Mayer laboured in a different
direction at the same subject, by
publishing lunar tables and perfecting the lunar theory.   After
repeated revisions, Mayer sent his
tables, 1755, to London, where they
were submitted to Bradley, who reported favourably on them.   After
further corrections, and after also
submitting his theory, Mayer's
widow received, in 1765, £5000,
Euler £3000, and the work was
published, 1770, by order of the
Board of Longitude, under the
title 'Tabulæ motuum solis et
lunæ novæ et correctæ, auctore
Tob.   Mayer : Quibus accedit
methodus longitudinum promota
eodem auctore.'

furthered her cause most powerfully by founding that great institution of culture, which more than anything else is characteristic of the German mind, in which it has found its most perfect expression, and where it can be most exhaustively studied—the system of the German universities.

"There is no people," says Mr James Bryce, "which has given so much thought and pains to the development of its university system as the Germans have done—none which has profited so much by the services universities render—none where they play so large a part in the national life." [1] If it is correct to say that this system owed its foundation to the German princes, it is equally true that its development is the work of the German people. [2] It may be doubtful whether, without the

2.
Development of the universities by the people.

[1] See James Bryce's preface to the English translation of Conrad's valuable book, 'The German Universities for the last Fifty Years,' Glasgow, 1885, p. xiii.

[2] A great deal has been written about the German universities: For the purposes of a History of Thought, I confine myself to a reference to the valuable writings of F. Paulsen, 'Geschichte des gelehrten Unterrichts auf den deutschen Schulen und Universitäten,' Leipzig, 1885, and two essays in the 45th volume of Von Sybel's 'Historische Zeitschrift,' 1881. The succeeding phases of mediæval and modern, of Roman Catholic and Protestant, of the thought of the Church, the Renaissance, the classical and the modern ideals, are all reflected in the foundation and reform of the universities and high schools of Germany and the surrounding countries. The *first* foundations, in imitation of the universities of Paris and of Italy, were Prague 1348, Vienna 1365, Heidelberg 1386, Cologne 1388, Erfurt 1392, Würzburg 1402, Leipsic 1409, Rostock 1419. A *second* epoch—under the influence of the humanistic studies—begins in the middle of the fifteenth century and adds eight new foundations—Greifswald 1456, Freiburg 1457, Trier 1457, Basel 1459, Ingolstadt 1472, Tübingen 1477, Mainz 1477, Wittenberg 1502, Frankfort on the Oder 1506 (Paulsen, 'Geschichte,' p. 14). A *third* epoch begins with the Reformation. The first Protestant university is Marburg, founded by Philip of Hesse, 1524. Melanchthon's influence is everywhere decisive. Tübingen is reconstituted by Duke Ulrich 1535; Leipsic by Duke George 1539. Basel, after three years' suspension, is reopened 1532. Frankfort on the Oder is reopened by Joachim of Brandenburg 1537, who also founds the new University of Königsberg 1541. Greifswald is

individual influence of the former, without the divided interests of the dismembered empire, without the conflicting religious views, the political and personal rivalry of the many states and sovereigns,[1] so many scattered centres of culture and learning would have sprung so early into existence; but it is not doubtful that it is owing to the common interests of the nation, to the uniting tie of the same language, the same thought, and the same aspirations, that these scattered centres have been in course of time united into a great network,[2] a vast organisation for the higher intellectual work of the nation and of mankind. The German nation may pride itself on possessing at the present moment the most

reconstituted on a Protestant foundation 1539; Rostock in 1540-50; Heidelberg by the Elector Frederick II. in 1544. Jena is founded 1558 by John Frederick, Helmstädt by Julius of Brunswick in 1568; Giessen followed in 1607; Rinteln in 1621; Altdorf in 1662. Of the greatest influence on German culture were the Dutch Protestant universities—Leyden 1575, Franeker 1585, Utrecht 1634, Harderwyk 1648; they were for a long time—as formerly the Italian universities—the goal of the young scholar's wanderings (Paulsen, p. 179). They—as well as Geneva—held a similar position to the Scotch universities (see Sir A. Grant, 'Story of the University of Edinburgh,' vol. i. pp. 21, 126, 188, 213, 229, 233, 263, 274, 283, 297, &c., vol. ii. p. 263). A *fourth* epoch begins with the foundation of Halle 1694, the first really modern university (Paulsen, p. 353). The spirit of Bacon and Leibniz, represented by Thomasius, is the leading power; it is not by any means irreligious, since Francke

(the so-called "pietist") is as important a factor as Thomasius. German is substituted for Latin. Other universities follow the reform, thus Königsberg 1735, Leipsic, Wittenberg, Helmstädt, Kiel, Tübingen, &c. A *fifth* epoch —the evolution of the ideal of science in the German sense, *Wissenschaft*—begins with the foundation of Göttingen in 1737. Of this more in the text.

[1] Conrad, *loc. cit.*, p. 2 : "There is scarcely a stronger bond of connection between the various parts of Germany than that supplied by the universities, and in no other respect have the barriers that separated State from State been so long broken down. . . . The historical development cannot be accurately traced unless the growing extent in which the south German universities are attended by students from the north be kept in view."

[2] See especially Paulsen's remarks referring to the foundation of Göttingen under George II. ('Geschichte des gelehrten Unterrichts,' p. 425).

powerful and best equipped army. But this is only the creation of the present age. With greater pride it may boast of having trained in the course of centuries the largest and most efficient intellectual army, ready at any moment to take up and carry to a successful issue great scientific undertakings demanding the intense thought and labour of a few secluded students, or the combined efforts of a large number of ready workers. This army is scattered through the length and breadth of the land, and even beyond its frontiers in neighbouring countries, wherever universities and high schools are situated.[1] It is not a stationary power, but is continually on the move from south to north, from west to east, to and fro, exchanging and recruiting its forces, bringing heterogeneous elements into close contact, spreading everywhere the seed of new ideas and discoveries, and preparing new land for still more extended cultivation.

[1] The extent of the German university system cannot be estimated by the twenty universities marked on the map attached to the translation of Conrad's book, as these represent only the existing universities of the present German empire; nor yet by the forty-three universities given in the appendix, p. 290, as they contain only some of the Austrian, but none of the Swiss universities; nor even by taking up Ascherson's valuable 'Deutscher Universitäts-Kalender,' which contains the German-speaking universities — thirty-four in number in 1887 — but of course does not contain the names of those which have been suppressed. There are also the universities of Denmark, Norway, and Sweden, which have exchanged many important professors with Germany, and those of Holland in older, of Belgium in modern times, which have done the same thing. The Russian universities also were largely organised on German models, though since the reforms of 1863 they aim at a more national character. Brandis founded the University of Athens on German lines in 1837. The Russian University at Kasan, that "ultima musarum Thule," was founded in 1804, and Göttingen supplied its first professors. From there and from the hardly less remote Transylvanian town, Maros Vásárhely, there issued the revolution of our fundamental notions in geometry, and there is reason to believe that both Lobachévsky's and Bolyai's theories are ultimately connected with the speculations of Gauss. See Prof. A. Vasiliev's Address on Lobachévsky, translated by Halsted, p. 5 *sqq.*

It is not my intention to dwell on the history of the
German universities, on the gradual growth of the university system; though every stage in that history is interesting and important if we wish to understand the inner working and usefulness of this great organisation. Neither do
I wish to do more than just mention, as an equally impor-

3.
Geographi-
cal distribu-
tion of the
German uni-
versities.
tant subject, the geography of the German universities;
how through nearly fifty larger or smaller towns, in the
course of six centuries, learning and higher education have
been spread over the German-speaking countries of Europe.
These figures alone suggest the intricacy of the subject,
the many springs, the continual ebb and flow of the rising
tides of ideas, the many courses of thought, the many
schools of learning, the internal conflicts, the unavoidable
friction, the healthy competition and rivalry, the republican spirit, the impossibility of any creeping stagnation
of life, the absence of any lengthened tyranny of doctrine,
of an oppressive hierarchy, or of idols of opinion and
belief. I leave it to my readers to indulge in comparisons
easily suggested by these different aspects, to fasten upon
the strong and upon the weak points of this great system
of the German universities.[1]   What I wish to emphasise

[1] The migration of students as
well as of eminent professors from
one university to another is one of
the most important features of
German academic life. Thus we
find the imaginative tendencies of
the southern intellect represented
by Hegel and Schelling in philosophy transplanted into the midst
of the encyclopædic and logical
sciences of the North, or into the
centre of industrial Switzerland in
the person of Vischer; the theological criticism of the Tübingen
school wandering northward to
Marburg and Berlin in Zeller; and
the philological criticism of Gottfried Herrmann locating itself in
Zürich in his celebrated pupil and
biographer Köchly, and in Bavaria
through Thiersch. Jacobi came from
the lower Rhine to Munich, where
also Liebig formed a centre of modern scientific celebrities. Savigny
in Berlin and Thibaud in Heidelberg represent the historical and
philosophical schools of German
jurisprudence. Vienna for a long
time was the most celebrated German training-school of practical

very strongly here is the existence in the midst of European life, all through our century, of this vast organisation for intellectual work, this great engine of thought; and to assign to it one of the foremost places among the great agencies with which we shall have to deal.

The beginning of the present century found this great institution of university education in full swing among all the German-speaking nations.[1]   The eighteenth century brought it to that state of perfection in which we have been accustomed to see it.   In the course of that century it outgrew its earlier and more limited phases of existence, its period of more restricted usefulness; it emancipated itself from Court and personal favouritism, from ecclesias-

4.
Full development of the German university system.

medicine and surgery, whereas Berlin concentrated the great representatives of the more recent scientific developments. In the course of the last hundred years no one university has been allowed to retain for any length of time the supremacy in any single branch. The light has quickly been diffused all over the country, when once kindled at one point. How will the future compare in this respect?

[1] This is not quite the case as regards Switzerland. The city of Basel, which before the Reformation was the seat of much learning, the names of Sebastian Brandt, Reuchlin, and Erasmus being intimately connected with it, had a university from 1459. The antagonism to classical and polite literature which characterised a large section of the Reformers (see Paulsen, p. 128 *sqq.*) destroyed many flourishing centres of culture; amongst them the University of Basel, which was suspended in 1529, when the city accepted the Reformation, but reopened three years later in 1532.

Geneva, though this is outside of the German-speaking area and presents a culture quite peculiar to itself, had an academy from 1559, with many celebrated professors and numerous students of theology from all countries of Europe. Lausanne, Bern, and Zürich had colleges or high schools in the seventeenth century. But down to the nineteenth century Basel remained the only university in the Continental sense. The reasons why Switzerland developed her university system so late are discussed in Tholuck, 'Das akademische Leben des 17ten Jahrhunderts,' vol. ii. p. 314, &c., where also minute information is given on the several high schools of Switzerland. The question is interesting, seeing that the greatest in many branches of science—such as Bernoulli, Euler, Haller, Cuvier, Steiner—have come from Switzerland, and that by reason of the names of Rousseau and Pestalozzi it has become the centre of modern ideas on education.

tical protection and influence; it acquired through the
statutes of governments or special foundations larger and
better secured means of subsistence; it substituted the
vernacular for the Latin tongue. The circle of studies,
though from early times professedly all-embracing, did
not become worthily filled up and cultivated with equal

**5.
The philo-
sophical
faculty.**

and impartial care till the fourth faculty, the *philosophical faculty,* was properly developed. Theology, law,
and medicine conduct their studies for practical ends
and purposes; the two former especially were frequently
liable to be used merely for the ends of the Church or the
State; but the philosophical faculty embraces all those
studies which aim at establishing truth, be this defined
as merely formal or as real, as belonging to method or
to knowledge. We can assign a definite date to the
firm establishment of the " libertas philosophandi," and
the professed introduction of the " libertas docendi " in
the university programme [1]—namely, the opening (in

**6.
The Univer-
sity of Göt-
tingen.**

1734) of the University of Göttingen (inaugurated in
1737). " The foundation stone," says Professor Paulsen,
" of the academic constitution is the ' libertas docendi.'
On this point Von Münchhausen, whom we may call the
real founder of the university, and his two advisers,
Mosheim, the theologian of Helmstädt, and Böhmer, the
jurist of Halle, were agreed. All 'inquisitiones,' so writes
the former, choke the powers ' ingeniorum,' and spoil the
beginnings of a learned society. He advises above all
that the greatest care should be used in the equipment
of the theological faculty. Accordingly Münchhausen
laid his eye upon men whose teaching led neither to

[1] Paulsen, ' Geschichte des gelehrten Unterrichts,' p. 424, &c.

' Atheismo' nor 'Naturalismo,' who neither attack the 'articulos fundamentales religionis evangelicæ,' nor introduce enthusiasm, nor yet evangelical popedom. Likewise the jurists received full freedom for teaching and for the expression of legal opinions, whereas at Halle, following the common rule, the Prussian interest, at least in matters of public law, was the measure of things. At Göttingen the chief stress was laid on the culture of the essentially modern sciences. In the foremost rank stood the administrative and historico-political branches where Pütter, Achenbach, Schlözer, Gatterer, Heeren, gave to the university her world-wide fame; the mathematical and scientific branches are marked by the brilliant names of Haller, Lichtenberg, Blumenbach, Kästner; the philological branches by Gesner, Heyne, Michaelis. The university met the demand for encyclopædic discourses. Münchhausen arranged in 1756 that a member of each faculty should deliver a public course on the whole field of the sciences taught there; in the philosophical faculty Gesner treated philologico-historical, Kästner physico-mathematical subjects. An ' Index Lectionum' of the year 1737 shows nine professorships: 1. Politics and Morals. 2. History of Literature. 3. History. 4. Elocution and Poetry. 5. Logic and Metaphysics. 6. Oriental Languages. 7. Mathematics and Physics. 8. Administrative Sciences; to which is added, lastly, a professorship of Philosophy without special definition." [1]

It is evident that, owing to their constitution, as well

[1] The original endowment of Göttingen was fixed at 16,000 thalers, equal to £2400. This was more than double the endowment of Halle. (Paulsen, p. 425.)

as to their number, the German universities were destined to become the most powerful organisation for the diffusion of knowledge. Further, they have been in the course of the present century more closely linked with many hundreds of high schools, and with the growing number of technical schools.[1] For both of these they had to train the teaching staff, and from the ranks of these they again largely filled their own chairs. Thus they not only combined in themselves the spirit of research and the profession of teaching, but they infused into the widely scattered teaching staff of many hundreds of

*7.
Relation of
universities
and high
schools.*

---

[1] The technical schools in Germany and Switzerland are a creation of modern times. We can distinguish three classes. (1) The "Realschule." This stands in a kind of opposition to the "Latin school." The name (according to Paulsen, p. 483) occurs first in Halle, where the archdeacon Semler established in 1706 a mathematical and mechanical "Realschule." J. J. Hecker established at Berlin in 1739 an "economico-mathematical Realschule." The object of these schools was to teach "Realia," to introduce practical rather than learned information. A special development was the "philanthropinism" of Basedow, well known even to English readers from Lewes's Life of Goethe (see vol. i. p. 276, &c.) (2) A second class embraces the "Gewerbeschulen," which may be rendered "Schools of industry." Karl Schmidt ('Geschichte der Pädagogik,' vol. iv. p. 163) calls Beuth the founder of them in Prussia, 1817, and gives the school of Aachen as the first. They form a kind of bifurcation with the higher classes of the Gymnasia (or learned schools). They may be more specially commercial, agricul-

tural, or military. (3) Out of these a third class — answering to the growing demand for the practical application of the higher mathematical sciences — has grown up, named polytechnic schools. The celebrated École Polytechnique of Paris has been the model. The first of this class in Germany was established at Vienna in 1816. Then followed Munich, Hanover, Karlsruhe, Stuttgart, Nürnberg, Augsburg, Darmstadt, Zürich, Aachen, latterly also Berlin (Reichsanstalt) and Brunswick (Carolinum). In many ways they equal the universities in the scientific spirit of their teaching. What is wanting is the philosophical, the historical, the encyclopædic treatment. In this respect they form in their best examples a contrast to the Göttingen programme. To many serious-thinking minds they indicate the gradual dissipation of the German ideal of *Wissenschaft*, the narrowing down of *Wissenschaft* to science in the English and French meaning of the word. Their danger lies in the direction of being contented with practical usefulness, as the danger of the German type of university lay in being contented with erudition.

schools the same habit—almost absent in other countries —of looking upon private study and research as a necessary qualification of the lecturer and teacher. The educational organisation of the combined universities and higher schools has thus become an equally powerful organisation for research, and for increasing knowledge. Wherever the progress of learning and science requires a large amount of detailed study inspired by a few leading ideas, or subservient to some common design and plan, the German universities and higher schools supply a well-trained army of workers, standing under the intellectual generalship of a few great leading minds. Thus it is that no nation in modern times has so many *schools of thought* and learning as Germany, and none can boast of having started and carried through such a large number of gigantic enterprises, requiring the co-operation and collective application of a numerous and well-trained staff.[1] The university system, in one word, not only teaches knowledge, but above all it teaches *research*. This is its pride and the foundation of its fame.

8.
The university a training-school of research.

[1] The editions of the ancient classics brought out by Tauchnitz, Weidmann, and Teubner are well known. The collections of the Histories of all countries, begun by Heeren and Ukert and continued in this century by the publishing firm of Salomon Hirzel of Leipsic; the 'Jahresberichte,' started by Berzelius for chemistry, and now separately conducted for all the different sciences; contain summaries of the labours of the whole world systematically arranged. There is the geographical establishment of Petermann at Gotha; not to speak of publications specifically national, such as the 'Monumenta Germaniæ,' as other countries possess similar undertakings. Von Zach was the first to establish a regular international organ for astronomical observations. It was started in 1798, and soon became the "living organ of astronomy," equally appreciated by Lalande and Gauss. This "monthly" was soon succeeded by Schumacher's "weekly," the 'Astronomische Nachrichten.' See Wolf, 'Geschichte der Astronomie,' p. 764, &c. Humboldt's and Gauss's scheme for a network of magnetic observations all over the world was taken up by English men of science.

It is a useful and interesting task to trace intellectual developments and habits to their external causes. The centralisation of the powers and resources of a whole nation into one capital, as was the case in Rome and in Paris, may explain the brilliancy of their literatures; the more scattered and diffused culture of Greece and of Germany is likewise reflected in their many schools of thought and learning; the insular position of England has impressed its advantages and disadvantages upon her history, and has influenced her mental life. These influences have frequently been pointed out and examined. The historian of thought has another and more difficult task to perform. Habits of thought and intellectual qualities never become the property of a large number of persons unless they assume a definite form; through this they become a marketable article which can be communicated and transmitted, and in which those also can participate from whom the deeper motives and higher aims remain hidden. Every school has its watchword, in which its leading thought, its ideal, is embodied. The widely scattered and yet closely connected community of intellectual workers represented by the German university system, which covers with its network of universities and high schools the German-speaking countries of Europe, has during the period of its greatest influence developed its own special ideal, and it has expressed this in a special

9.
The ideal
of *Wissenschaft*.

word—namely, the word *Wissenschaft*. Neither the French nor the English application of the word science [1] corresponds to the use or gives the meaning of the word *Wissenschaft*. This meaning cannot be defined by any

---

[1] Compare the notes at the beginning of the last chapter, p. 89, &c.

single word in the English language. Expressions such as "student of science" or "science tripos" have a meaning in English, but they would have none if translated into German. In each case the word *Wissenschaft* would require a qualification. An "Académie des Sciences" could not according to German usage exist separately beside an "Académie française" or an "Académie des Inscriptions," for it would include them.[1] Scientific treatment in England means the exact experimental or mathematical treatment of a subject: no one ever calls Bentley[2] or Gibbon[3] a great scientific writer, though in

[1] The two older academies in Paris, the "Académie des Sciences" and the "Académie des Inscriptions et Belles Lettres," covered very nearly the same ground as the modern Berlin "Academie der Wissenschaften und Künste," which is divided into two classes, the "mathematisch-naturwissenschaftliche" and the "philosophisch-historische Classe," the two sides being equally comprised under the term *Wissenschaften*. A similar division exists in the learned societies of Vienna, Leipsic, Munich, and Göttingen.

[2] Richard Bentley (1662-1742), popularly known in England mainly through his Boyle Lectures, his controversy about the Epistles of Phalaris, and his thirty years' feud as Master of Trinity College, Cambridge, with the dons of his college, but hardly known "as the first, perhaps the only, Englishman who can be ranked with the great heroes of classical learning" (Mark Pattison, 'Ency. Brit.'), was from the first recognised as a consummate genius by the scholars of Germany, by Grævius and Spanheim, who welcomed him as "novum et lucidum Britanniæ sidus," as "splendidissimum Britanniæ lu-

men." The many beginnings which he had laid for subsequent critical research among the ancient classical authors were taken up abroad by men like Heyne, Reiz, F. A. Wolf, Gottfried Hermann, and Friedrich Ritschl, in whose hands they have developed into a special school of philology, counting probably over a hundred representatives, many of whom have openly avowed their indebtedness to Bentley. (See Köchly, 'Gottfried Hermann,' Heidelberg, 1874, pp. 115 *sqq.*, 142, 189. Ribbeck, 'Friedr. Wilh. Ritschl,' 2 vols., Leipzig, 1879 and 1881, vol. i. p. 229; vol. ii. pp. 111, 176, &c., 418, 429.)

[3] Gibbon (1737-94) gave a new impetus to the study of the history of Roman law through the celebrated 44th chapter of his 'Decline and Fall of the Roman Empire.' It was translated by Professor Hugo of Göttingen and Professor Warnkönig of Liège, and has been used as the text-book on Civil Law in some of the foreign universities. See Smith's edition of Gibbon's History with the Notes of Milman and Guizot, chap. xliv., note. Herder, Savigny, and Niebuhr stand all under the immediate influence of Gibbon, and Lessing saw

Germany each stands at the head, and forms the beginning, of a definite scientific movement. The distinction between scientific and philosophical thought which I have explained in the Introduction would be unintelligible if science were translated simply by *Wissenschaft;* the word *Wissenschaft* is not opposed to, but embraces, the word philosophy : Fichte, whose whole doctrine was, according to French and English ideas, almost the reverse of scientific, uses the word *Wissenschaftslehre* to denote and characterise his system.[1]   In fact the German word for science has a much wider meaning than *science* has in French or English; it applies alike to all the studies which are cultivated under the roof of " alma mater "; it is an idea specially evolved out of the German university system, where theology, jurisprudence, medicine, and the special philosophical studies are all held to be treated "scientifically," and to form together the universal, all-embracing edifice of human knowledge.[2]   Such an

10.
Has been
developed
under the
German
university
system.

[1] Fichte (1762-1814) begins his first philosophical work, published in 1794, with the words, " Philosophy is a science," and he then proceeds to give to his philosophy the term *Wissenschaftslehre*, or general doctrine or theory of science. A further definition which he gives is as follows: " A science has a systematic form; all propositions in it hang together in one single fundamental proposition, and are united by it into a whole." It is evident that whoever approached Fichte's writings with the ideal of science, as it was established by the labours of Lavoisier and the great French academicians, would

not accept these first sentences of Fichte's book. He would admit that the sciences as cultivated by the great Frenchmen had a unity of method, the exact method, the method of observation, measurement, and calculation, but not necessarily a unity of system, or a highest all-embracing proposition. It is evident that science means to Fichte something more than it meant to the Académie des Sciences : it meant *Wissenschaft*, not merely methodical, but systematic, unified knowledge.

[2] It would be an interesting task to trace in German literature from the time of Leibniz the gradual evolution of the idea of *Wissenschaft*, to see how the word has grown in pregnancy and significance till it became firmly estab-

idea, the use of such a term, could only be born and developed where the different faculties, the various branches of knowledge, lived habitually, for many ages, under the same roof, coming into continual contact, and learning to regard each other as members of one family, as integral parts of one whole. The German university

lished as denoting a moral as much as an intellectual ideal, which it was the duty of the German university to uphold and to realise. Such an investigation would have to show how the encyclopædic view is represented by Leibniz, how Winckelmann applied the term to the studies of antiquity, how Lessing taught method and clearness, how Herder widened and deepened the view, extending it to the elemental forces as well as to the finished forms of human culture, how it was finally raised as the standard of German university teaching by F. A. Wolf and W. von Humboldt, finding an eloquent exposition in Fichte's lectures on the "Nature of the Scholar" ('Vorlesungen über das Wesen des Gelehrten,' Erlangen, 1805), and a practical realisation in the foundation of the University of Berlin in 1809, during the period of Germany's greatest degradation. The following words of Fichte have reverberated in the soul of many a German scholar to whom Fichte's philosophy was unknown or distasteful, and this same spirit has leavened and united studies which stand apparently in no connection with each other. "The scholar" (and specifically the teacher of scholars) "shows his respect for science [*Wissenschaft*] as such and because it is science, for science generally as one and the same divine Idea in all the various branches and forms in which it appears." Of one who may be seduced into overestimat-

ing his own branch, Fichte says: "It becomes evident that he has never conceived science as One, that he has not comprehended his own branch as coming out of this One, that he thus does not himself love his branch as science but only as a trade; this love of a trade may otherwise be quite laudable, but in science it excludes at once from the name of a scholar. . . . In the academic teacher science is to speak, not the teacher himself," he is to speak to "his hearers not as his hearers but as future servants of science," he is to represent the dignity of science to coming generations (Fichte, Werke, vol. vi. p. 436, &c.) I have myself heard expressions similiar to these from the mouth of one who represented what we should now consider the very opposite phase of nineteenth-century thought, from one of the earliest representatives in Germany of exact research, Wilhelm Weber of Göttingen. Driven into a corner by the questionings of devoted friends as to his own discoveries and contributions, which he was modestly fond of tracing to Gauss, and unable to deny his own part, he would warmly exclaim, "But is it not possible that science could do something herself?" Professor Adamson has pointed out ('Fichte,' in "Philos. Classics," p. 79) how the fundamental idea in these writings of Fichte has been made familiar to English readers through the teaching of England's greatest modern moralist, Carlyle.

system has the merit of having elaborated the widest conception of science, of having fixed the highest and most general scientific standards.   Opposed to science is that which is unscientific, dilettante, popular; that which is not a vocation, but a handicraft; that which grows and lives outside of the great university system, including in this the innumerable learned schools which form its base, and the academy which forms its summit.

11.
In France
and England
"Science"
means "Exact Science."
What France and England have elaborated and termed Science, is called in Germany Exact Science; but it is opposed to the German ideal of science to hold that the exact method is the only method which deserves to be called scientific.[1]

[1] This is perhaps not quite correct. No doubt the term "exact Sciences" is used frequently during the last half - century to denote the mathematical and experimental sciences; very much in the same sense as we see them defined by Cuvier in the beginning of the century, and described as the ground covered by the labours of the "Académie des Sciences." There exists, however, in Germany another school of thought, very influential throughout this century, and one that has exerted a very wide and wholesome influence, which stands in no connection whatever with the mathematical sciences, though it applies the word "exact" to its methods and researches.   This is the school which maintains that the real introduction to the study of antiquity lies in a knowledge of the ancient, preeminently the classical, languages, as exact and precise as any mathematical knowledge could be, and sees in an acquisition of such precise knowledge the training necessary for success in philological and his-

torical research, just as familiarity with mathematical formulæ and measuring instruments has long been considered quite indispensable training to success in the natural sciences.   Of this view Gottfried Hermann may be considered as a somewhat one-sided, Friedrich Ritschl as a more profound and far - seeing, but equally energetic representative.   It is Ritschl who was the most influential.   Without at present entering into the controversies which existed between what were termed the "Sprach-philologen" and the "Sach-philologen," I desire here to refer to the fact that such very different representatives of thought as Fichte, Weber, and Ritschl, than whom no men could be more dissimilar in cast of mind, all find their ideal expressed in the word *Wissenschaft*. I have quoted Fichte, the speculative generaliser, and Weber, the exact mathematical physicist.   I will add what Ritschl, the critical philologist, says.   He trusted, as his biographer reports, "in the indestructible magnetic force of

Before the methods of exact science were introduced into Germany under English and French influences, the Germans possessed many scientific methods. There was the science of philosophical criticism, established by Kant; the science of historical criticism, of Biblical criticism; the science of philology: all these professed to have methods as definite, aims as lofty, and a style as pure, as the exact sciences brought with them.

At present a tendency of thought may exist in Germany, akin to the positive philosophy in France and England, which aims at introducing the methods of the natural sciences so as to cover the whole ground of research, and to allow of no other methods. Should it succeed, it will destroy the essential features of the German university system, and with it the ideal of *Wissenschaft* as it has existed in all the leading minds of Germany during the last hundred years.

I intend to come back to this subject later on, and to define more clearly what the German ideal of science —what *Wissenschaft*—is. That which we are occupied with at present is the diffusion of the scientific spirit, in the narrower sense, as it was firmly established in France through the great mathematicians and scientists at the

the studies of classical antiquity"; he maintained that philology, as science, not the barren training of a pedagogic seminary, is the only right thing for future masters. "The good teacher must, even for teaching purposes, have and know, both in quantity and quality, more than he requires for immediate progress; the portion he requires for immediate communication, for practical teaching purposes, must be delivered out of the fulness and the depth of knowledge; it must, even in its circumscribed nature, contain the germs of further mental development. Such depth, such fructifying power, comes only from science" (*Wissenschaft*). See Ribbeck, 'Leben Ritschl's,' vol. ii. p. 277. And as every mode of thought, if clearly felt and active, finds its expression in language, so Ritschl was fond of characterising his scientific method by the word ἀκρίβεια.

beginning of this century, as it is summed up in their works and in the Memoirs of the Institute. What reception did it find in Germany? How has it thriven under the German university system? These are the questions which interest us at present.

12. Reception of Exact Science in Germany.

The general recognition of the purely scientific studies conducted on a large scale by the French Academy of Science, as an integral portion of the German university syllabus, belongs to the beginning of the present century. During the first forty years of the century complaints were continually heard that some of the most important sciences were not worthily represented.[1]   The eighteenth

[1] One of the latest instances of such complaint is to be found in J. Liebig's paper "On the state of Chemistry in Austria" ('Annalen der Pharmacie,' 1838, vol. xxv. p. 339). This was followed by the highly interesting pamphlet 'On the state of Chemistry in Prussia' (Braunschweig, 1840). According to the eminent author, chemistry was the science which was the latest to attain a worthy domicile and an independent footing in the great universities of Germany. Mathematical physics had a centre at Königsberg, physiology had been established as an independent science at Berlin through the appointment of Johannes Müller in 1833, chemistry was still only taught in Prussia in connection with other branches of science, with medicine, with technology, with mineralogy. There were no chemical laboratories to be found in Prussia. Men like Rose, Rammelsberg, Mitscherlich, received none or only the scantiest support in their practical courses of chemistry. It is interesting to note how Liebig, whilst pointing to the enormous importance which chemistry possesses from an economic and political point of view by reason of its working great changes and revolutions, industrial and other, insists on the necessity of teaching chemistry scientifically, and not with an immediate practical bias. In this respect he is as much a representative of the scientific spirit in the wider sense as the great men mentioned in the note to p. 171. The following passage (p. 39) may still be read with interest and profit: "I have found among all who frequent this laboratory [Giessen] for technical purposes a prominent inclination to occupy themselves with applied chemistry. They usually follow hesitatingly and with some suspicion my advice to leave alone all this time-absorbing drudgery, and simply to become acquainted with the necessary ways and means of solving purely scientific questions. By following this advice their minds learn easily and quickly how to find the best means; they themselves adapt them to circumstances and modify them; all operations, all analyses, which serve to ascertain a certain state, which must be made in order to find the conditions

century produced in Germany men of great scientific importance; but their position was irregular and uncertain, and they undoubtedly do not wholly or exclusively belong to the history of the university system.   Leibniz, Euler, Haller, Werner, Markgraf, Tobias Mayer, Lambert, and Humboldt are all intimately connected with the growth of modern science : their position and sphere of action were in each case different.[1]   Leibniz was a courtier, Euler an

for the solution of the problem, have a definite sense ; each of them possesses a certain charm which dispels fatigue, and if the question is really answered, then they know the ways and means of attaining similar ends. I know many who are now at the head of soda-, vitriol-, sugar-factories, of colour-works and other establishments. Without ever having had anything to do with them beforehand, they were in the first half-hour acquainted with the processes, the second already brought a number of appropriate improvements, &c., &c." Similarly Helmholtz in 1862 ('Reden,' vol. i. p. 142): "He who in the cultivation of the sciences aims at immediate practical usefulness, may be pretty sure that he will miss his aim. Science [*Wissenschaft*] can aspire only to a perfect knowledge and a complete understanding of the sway of physical and mental forces. The individual worker must find his reward in the joy over new discoveries, as new victories of mind over matter, in the æsthetical beauty which an orderly display of knowledge affords, &c., &c." How little do our modern colleges of science correspond with this view of *Wissenschaft!*

[1] On Leibniz (1646-1716), see p. 158 ; Werner (1750-1817), p. 118 ; and Tobias Mayer (1723-62), p. 158. A. von Humboldt (1769-1859) is well known to English readers.

Leonhard Euler (1707-83), a native of Basel, passed the greater part of his life at St Petersburg as a member of the Academy, a portion of it (1741-66) as an Academician at Berlin. He has been termed the father of pure mathematics, inasmuch as he freed mathematical analysis from geometrical conceptions, established the notion of function or mathematical dependence, and did much to make the theory of numbers an independent branch of science. His memoirs are said to number nearly a thousand ; his works, if all printed, would fill 60 to 80 quartos (see Hankel, 'Die Entwicklung der Mathematik,' Tübingen, 1884, p. 12). Andreas Sigismund Markgraf (1709-82) was born and lived at Berlin, a member of the Academy. On his various chemical researches see Kopp, 'Geschichte der Chemie,' vol. i. p. 208. Albrecht von Haller (1708-77) was a native of Bern. He was, next to Leibniz, perhaps the most encyclopædic mind of modern times, equally celebrated as botanist, physiologist, and poet. He has been termed the father of physiology. Brought up under the celebrated Boerhaave, he accepted a chair at the newly founded University of Göttingen in 1736, and taught there for seventeen years anatomy, botany, medicine, and surgery.

academician, Werner the head of a great mining school, Humboldt a traveller, Markgraf a private gentleman. Haller, indeed, shone as a great light in the University of Göttingen, where he did more than any other to place scientific studies on a level with classical ones, and to create for them a permanent abode within the pale of "alma mater." He founded in 1751, in close connection with the university, the *Göttingen Society*, which from 1753 published the celebrated 'Göttinger Gelehrte Anzeigen.'[1] Tobias Mayer and Lambert[2] can hardly be said to have got much help either from the university, to which the former belonged, or from the Academy, of which the latter was a member; their celebrity rests on works produced by private and unaided effort. Humboldt also depended upon his personal means and upon his connection with the Paris Academy, and only attained late in life, and in the course of the present century, his eminent position as the head and patron of German science. Von Zach and Olbers, who together with Tobias Mayer and Lambert raised German astronomy during the eighteenth century to the level of English and French science, stood outside the university system. Von Zach was indebted to personal connections, and ultimately to Duke Ernest II. of Gotha, for the position which

[1] The 'Göttinger Gelehrte Anzeigen' had existed since 1739.

[2] Joh. Heinrich Lambert (1728-77), a very extraordinary man, was a native of Mühlhausen, Alsace, which then belonged to Switzerland. He was received as a member of the Berlin Academy, and associated there with Euler and Lagrange. He is celebrated through his 'Photometry' (1760) and 'Pyrometry' (1779), his equation referring to the orbits of comets, employed by Olbers in his method for calculating them (Weimar, 1797, republished by Encke, 1847), and his prophetic prediction of the proper motion of the sun (in his Cosmological Letters, 1761). This motion was actually calculated by Sir William Herschel in his paper "On the proper Motion of the Sun and Solar System" ('Philos. Trans.,' 1783).

he held as a kind of corresponding centre of European astronomy, and as the leader of a large school of German astronomers of this century.[1] Olbers was a practising physician at Bremen,[2] where he followed astronomical studies as a recreation, making himself eminent by great services to science, among them by his method of calculating the orbit of a comet : as the greatest of his services he counted the fact of having discovered, trained, and appreciated the rising genius of Bessel.[3]

[1] Franz Xaver von Zach (1754-1832) was a native of Pesth. After having served in the Austrian artillery, and taken to astronomy as a favourite study, he spent some time in Paris and London, and became acquainted with Lalande, Laplace, Herschel, Maskelyne, Ramsden, and others. He was engaged by Duke Ernest II. of Gotha in 1786 to erect an observatory on the Seeberg near Gotha. This was completed in 1791. Here he trained a number of younger astronomers, and was the first to establish and maintain a periodical specially devoted to astronomy. It was first (1798) published under the title ' Geographische Ephemeriden,' then (1800-13) as ' Monatliche Correspondenz zur Beförderung der Erd- und Himmelskunde.' Lalande and Gauss both testified to the usefulness of this international publication, without which Piazzi's discovery (see p. 182, note 1) would probably have been lost. See Wolf, ' Gesch. d. Astronomie,' p. 764.

[2] Heinr. Wilh. Mat. Olbers (1758-1840) was born near Bremen. He followed astronomy as a private study. He is mainly known by his rediscovery of the first of the smaller planets (see p. 182, note 1), by his theory, once generally accepted, of the origin of the smaller

planets through the disruption of a primitive large planet, and by his ' Abhandlung über die leichteste und bequemste Methode die Bahn eines Cometen aus einigen Beobachtungen zu berechnen ' (1797). In this work, by using Lambert's equation, he succeeded in perfecting the methods of Newton and his successors so as actually to calculate the elements of several comets. This method is still in general use (see Wolf, loc. cit., p. 519).

[3] Friedr. Wilh. Bessel (1784-1846) attracted the attention of Olbers by his mathematical abilities whilst employed as clerk in a shipping office at Bremen. If Tobias Mayer's lunar tables were remunerated and published with English money, Germany repaid the debt by the industry of Bessel, who calculated and reduced the observations made by Bradley (1692-1762, Astronomer Royal from 1742) at Greenwich during the years 1750 to 1761. They had been neglected and remained unpublished till 1798, when Olbers induced Bessel to make them useful to science. This he did by calculating from them some of the most important and fundamental data of astronomy. After many years of labour he brought out his ' Fundamenta Astronomiæ pro A. 1755 deducta ex observationibus viri incomparabilis James

13.
Science not
yet domi-
ciled at the
German uni-
versities
during the
eighteenth
century.

The general impression we receive from a perusal of the histories of science and learning in Germany at the close of the eighteenth century is, that the university system had, so far as philosophical and classical studies were concerned, attained almost to the eminence which it has held during this century, but that it had not—with the exception perhaps of Göttingen—received into its pale the modern spirit of exact research, such as it had been developed by the great French Academicians. Eminent students of science lived outside of the universities, belonging wholly or largely to the international Republic which had its centre in Paris, exerting little influence on higher German education through the universities, and hardly any on German literature, which had meanwhile ripened into the age of Classicism. This scattered condition of German science gave it on the one side a character which was foreign to the general tendencies of German thought, since this had come under the excessive influence of the speculative spirit without that wholesome check which exact research has always exerted.[1]

Bradley in specula astronomica Grenoviænsi per A. 1750-62 institutis' (1818). By his determination (1838-40) of the parallax of the star 61 Cygni he made the first accurate calculation of the distance of a fixed star, which he computed at 12 billion astronomical miles.

[1] It was the age of the *Naturphilosophie*, which, through the influence of Schelling in the south and Hegel in the north of Germany, filled the chairs in the universities, and penetrated into the learned societies. This philosophy of nature had the effect of frequently replacing induction by speculation, the patient work of the calculator, the observer, the experimenter, and the dissector by general theories, such as, applied to literary, historical, and poetical subjects, had acquired a certain importance, and a semblance of veracity and usefulness. In France the whole spirit of the Academy of Sciences opposed this form of learning. Cuvier denounced it or regarded it with suspicion, in England it remained unknown, and in Germany itself individual great minds opposed it, or did their work outside of its influence. Such were notably A. von Humboldt and Gauss. Younger men, such as Liebig and Joh. Müller,

On the other side, we find in the wide domain of general literature valuable beginnings and foreshadowings of later scientific thought, as in Georg Forster [1] and in

came temporarily under its influence. As regards its harmful effect on the natural and medical sciences, the popular addresses of Helmholtz and Du Bois-Reymond may be consulted. Its philosophical value will frequently occupy us in later chapters of this work. Its period can be approximately fixed by the publication in 1797 of Schelling's 'Ideen zu einer Philosophie der Natur.' The death of Hegel in 1831, and Humboldt's Berlin lectures during the years 1827 and 1828, may be considered as marking approximately the end of the generation which came under the one-sided influence of the *Naturphilosophie.* We shall have ample occasion later on to notice how many valuable leading ideas connected with this phase of thought were temporarily abandoned and have since come prominently before the scientific world. The year 1830 marked the victory of Cuvier's ideas over those of his great contemporary Geoffroy St-Hilaire in the French Academy, and with it the temporary defeat of the valuable suggestions contained in the writings of Lamarck and Goethe.

[1] Georg Forster (1753-94) was one of those unique men in the history of literature and science who combine the artistic with the scientific spirit, promoting equally the interests of poetry and of exact knowledge by a loving study of Nature, leading to new views of art as well as to deeper conceptions in science. He may be classed with White of Selborne and other naturalists of England among the small number of those who quietly and unostentatiously prepared the healthier forms

of Naturalism which permeate the poetical and scientific thought of our century, culminating in the great names of Wordsworth and Goethe, of Humboldt and Darwin, of Wallace and Haeckel. His life presented many interesting and some unhappy episodes; it introduces us into the political aspirations of the early French Revolution, to which he sacrificed himself. It has been written by Moleschott, the naturalist, by Heinrich König, the novelist ('G. Forster in Haus und Welt,' Leipzig, 1858, 2 vols.), by Klein ('Georg Forster in Mainz'). Fr. Schlegel ('Charakteristiken und Kritiken,' vol. i.), Gervinus (Introduction to the 7th vol. of 'Georg Forster's Werke'), and Hettner ('Literatur des 18ten Jahrhunderts,' vol. iii.) have written appreciative essays on him. A. von Humboldt calls him his master ('Kosmos,' vol. i. p. 345), and Herder (Preface to Georg Forster's translation of 'Sakuntala') prophesies his lasting fame against the opinion of his less appreciative contemporaries. He has a place in the classical literature both of England and Germany through his beautiful description of Captain Cook's second voyage round the world — his father, Joh. Reinhold Forster, having been selected as the naturalist on that voyage (London, 1777, 2 vols. 4to), German edition, 1779. Richard Garnett has said of him : "His account of Cook's voyage is almost the first example of the glowing yet faithful description of natural phenomena which has since made a knowledge of them the common property of the educated world. . . . As an author he stands very high ; he is almost the first

Goethe;[1] but they could hardly be encouraged and developed sufficiently without that strict training which is acquired through the routine of the class-room, or under the eye of a recognised authority.

14.
Scientific
periodicals.

The want of academic union and organisation, and the scattered situation of the many small centres of learning and culture in Germany, led, however, to the early development of those scientific periodicals which form such a characteristic feature in German literature. They were the medium for the exchange of ideas, and the collecting-ground for researches, in an age when exact science was not systematically taught at the Universities, and when such researches otherwise would have run the risk of being lost in obscurity or oblivion.

At the end of the eighteenth century Germany,

and almost the best of that valuable class of writers who have made science and art familiar by representing them in their essential spirit, unencumbered with technical details " ('Ency. Brit.,' vol. ix. p. 419). Forster lived in the period of transition from the thought of the eighteenth century to that of the nineteenth, and a study of his Life, Works, and Correspondence is a very good introduction to nearly all the great problems which then, especially on the Continent, troubled the minds of the greatest men. If he may be accused of want of patriotism, he is certainly to be admired for his freedom from national narrow-mindedness.

[1] It has taken nearly a century before the real value of Goethe's scientific ideas has been correctly gauged. His non-academic surroundings, his unscientific style, his antagonism to Newton, his mission as a poet—supposed in those days to be less realistic than we have since become accustomed to consider it—all these circumstances contributed to the result that Goethe's scientific writings were not taken au sérieux by the naturalists of his age. Then came a period when men of science began to sift the wheat from the chaff ; but even they have only tardily recognised that, more than in special discoveries or suggestions, his greatness lies in that general conception of Nature which was so foreign to his age, and which nevertheless is becoming more and more familiar and necessary to ours. See especially Helmholtz's valuable essays on Goethe as naturalist from the years 1853 and 1892 ('Vorträge,' vol. i., and address delivered at the meeting of the Goethe Society at Weimar, 1892), and the remarkable progress of his own views on this subject contained therein. We shall have ample opportunity of reverting to this subject.

though not by its universities, was already an important power in the Republic of exact science which then had its centre in Paris. Just at the beginning of the nineteenth century two events happened which foreboded for the highest branches of the mathematical sciences a revival of the glory which in this department Kepler and Leibniz had already given to their country. These two events are both coupled with the name of Carl Friedrich Gauss. They added greatly to the reputation of the University of Göttingen, with which this remarkable man was connected for half a century.[1] The *first* was the publication of the ' Disquisitiones Arithmeticæ' in Latin in 1801—a work by which Gauss placed himself on a level with the great mathematicians, Euler, Lagrange, and Legendre.[2] The

15.
Gauss's
mathematical researches.

[1] Carl Friedrich Gauss (1777-1855), a native of Brunswick, called by Laplace the first mathematician of Europe, may be considered as the first and foremost representative of the modern mathematical school, of which we shall have to treat later on. Unlike most of the great mathematicians of the Continent, he was self-taught, and followed in his earliest works quite independent lines of thought; resembling in this the great isolated thinkers of Britain whose ideas take a generation or more to penetrate into the text-books of the school. Gauss had the highest opinion of the dignity of pure science, and it almost appears as if, among the moderns, only Newton had come up to his ideal. For him alone he reserves the adjective " summus," and he adopts his synthetic and classical methods of exposition, removing, as has been said, the scaffoldings by the aid of which he had erected his monumental works.

Gauss trained few mathematicians ; but among the few who penetrated the secret of his ideas are such original thinkers as the Hungarian Bolyai (1775-1856), the geometers Möbius (1790-1868) and Von Staudt (1798-1867), who all mark quite independent lines of research. On Gauss see Sartorius, 'Gauss zum Gedächtniss,' Leipzig, 1856 ; Hänselmann, 'K. F. Gauss,' Leipzig, 1878 ; E. Schering, 'C. F. Gauss,' Göttingen, 1887.

[2] It appears that Gauss, to whom the arithmetical discoveries of Fermat and the proofs of Euler, Lagrange, and Legendre remained for a long time unknown (see his Works, edited by Schering, vol. i. p. 6 ; vol. ii. p. 444), had independently, in his eighteenth year, as a student at Göttingen, already arrived at a great number of propositions referring to the properties of numbers, and had then also found methods of geometrically constructing the regular polygon of seventeen sides.

second was the invention of a new and shorter method of calculating the orbit of a planet from a limited number of contiguous observations.[1] This method was communi-

The latter was the first addition made after 2000 years to the knowledge of this matter possessed by the ancients. (See 'Disquis. Arithm.,' sec. 365 : "Magnopere sane est mirandum, quod, quum jam Euclidis temporibus circuli divisibilitas geometrica in tres et quinque partes nota fuerit, nihil his inventis intervallo 2000 annorum adjectum sit," &c. ; and his manuscript note to this passage, given by Schering, vol. i. p. 176 : "Circulum in 17 partes divisibilem esse geometrice, deteximus 1796, Mart. 30.") It is probably owing to the independent manner in which Gauss approached the subject that he early found the necessity of treating subjects of higher arithmetic (*i.e.*, of the theory of numbers or "discrete magnitudes" as distinguished from algebra, which is the theory of "continuous magnitudes") by an independent method, for which he invented a language and an algorithm. He thus raised this part of mathematics into an independent science, on which the 'Disquisitiones Arithmeticæ' is the first elaborate and systematic treatise. Legendre's 'Traité des nombres' (1799) is a complete thesaurus of all that was at that time known and of what was added by him, but it does not attempt to establish the science on a new basis.

[1] On the 1st January 1801 Piazzi at Palermo had found a movable star of 8th magnitude, RA. 57° 47', ND. 16° 8', which he announced to Bode at Berlin as a comet on the 24th January ; but a few days later he concluded it must be a planet, and named it "Ceres Ferdinandea." No one be-

sides Piazzi could find the star, but several astronomers, Piazzi himself, Olbers at Bremen, and Burckhardt at Paris, tried to calculate the orbit from the observations of the discoverer, which were contained within only 9 degrees. The attempt to do so under the supposition of either a circular or a parabolic or an elliptic orbit failed, and Olbers expressed the fear that with the circular or elliptic elements which had been published in Zach's periodical, it might prove impossible to find the star when it should again become visible. Very near the expected time, as late as the beginning of December, Gauss communicated his elements to Von Zach, who published them at once, recommending astronomers to follow Dr Gauss's figures and look 6° to 7° more eastward than the positions of Burckhardt, Piazzi, and Olbers indicated. And actually on the 7th December 1801 Zach himself, and on the 1st January 1802 Olbers, succeeded in finding the star, "like a grain of sand on the sea-shore," very near the positions calculated by Gauss. These results, followed soon by the discovery of other planets by Olbers and Harding, gave a great impetus to the study of astronomy. Gauss's methods were published *in extenso* in the now celebrated 'Theoria motus corporum cœlestium' in 1809. Two problems are herein treated in a novel and complete manner. The first was to calculate by a simple and accurate method from the necessary number of observations the orbit of a planet or comet on the assumption of Newton's law of gravitation, but without any other special conditions.

eated to Von Zach in the course of the year 1801, and enabled him and Olbers to rediscover the first of the small planets, Ceres, which Piazzi had observed on the 1st of January 1801 at Palermo, and afterwards lost as it approached the region of the sun's light. Through this Gauss placed himself on a level with the great French astronomers Laplace, Lalande, and others. The new professor of mathematics and director of the observatory of Göttingen was admitted into the august company of the Paris academicians, who then ruled, and since the death of Euler had almost monopolised, the mathematical studies of the world. Although Gauss thus introduced the higher and abstract branches of exact science into the programme of a German university, and established a link between Paris and Germany in mathematics, as Humboldt had done shortly before in the natural sciences, fully a quarter of a century was to elapse before the spirit of exact research, and of the higher mathematics, really began to leaven the German universities. It then at length entered the field as a third and equally important agent by the side of the

16.
Scientific
spirit enters
the univer-
sities in the
second quar-
ter of the
century.

This was achieved to perfection, a proof of the usefulness of the method being the fact that Gauss succeeded in finishing in one hour a calculation which had taken Euler three days, and had resulted in his blindness. The second problem arises from the fact that the number of observations is always in excess of the number mathematically necessary, and that, owing to the unavoidable inaccuracies, different sets of observations give slightly different orbits. How are these to be used so as to give the most correct average result? This involves a question in probabilities. As early as 1795 Gauss was in possession of the so-called method of least squares, which occurred to him so naturally that he suspected that Tobias Mayer must have already known about it. It also occurred independently to Legendre, who was the first to publish it, in 1806, in his 'Nouvelles méthodes pour la détermination des orbites des comètes.' See Sartorius, 'Gauss zum Gedächtniss,' p. 41 *sqq.*

philosophical and classical spirit. During these twenty-five years Gauss lived and soared in solitary height—a name only to the German student, as Euler had been before him. Probably he was better known to the younger astronomers whom he trained, and the elder ones with whom he corresponded. But astronomy was not then within the pale of the universities. To what extent the character of Gauss's own genius was the cause of this it is difficult to say.[1] He himself had not come under the influence of any great teachers such as Paris then possessed; he was self-taught, and had early imbibed a great admiration for the methods of Euclid, Archimedes, and Newton; he wrote in the classical style fitted for all times, but not for uninitiated beginners.[2]   It is certain,

[1] Bjerknes, in his most interesting memoir on Abel, refers frequently to the awe in which Gauss was held by younger mathematicians.

[2] In this Gauss resembled Newton. He was therefore, like Newton, frequently forestalled by others, who published his new methods and ideas in an unfinished and fragmentary form; whereby it is not suggested that these simultaneous discoveries or inventions were not quite independent. Two examples of this may be added to those given above. When Gauss published the 'Disquis. Arith.' in 1801, he left out the last or eighth section, which was to treat of the residues of the higher orders. He had already nearly completed the theory of biquadratic residues. In dealing with this subject he had found it necessary to extend the conception of number beyond the limits then in use. If we confine ourselves to integers, the only extension which then existed of the notion of number was in the use of negative numbers.

These were counted on a straight line backward, as positive (or ordinary) numbers were counted forward. Gauss conceived the idea of counting numbers laterally from the straight line which represented the ordinary—positive and negative—numbers. He called numbers which were thus located in the plane "complex numbers," as they had to be counted by the use of two units, the ordinary unit 1 and a new unit i. He also showed that this new unit i stood in such relations to the ordinary unit 1 as were algebraically defined by the mysterious imaginary symbol $\sqrt{-1}$. The complete exposition of this new or complex system of counting was not explained by Gauss till the year 1831, when he published the 'Theoria residuorum biquadraticorum.' In the meantime the geometrical representation of imaginary quantities had been devised and published by Argand (1806), but not being employed for such important researches, it had re-

however, that the spirit of exact and specially mathematical research owed its right of domicile within the universities to others who came after him, and to circumstances with which he was hardly connected.

The man to whom Germany owes its first great school of mathematicians was Jacobi. He was self-taught like Gauss; but whilst Gauss followed in the footsteps of Newton and the ancients, Jacobi followed in those of Euler, Lagrange, and Laplace. The style and methods of these mathematicians, being more suited for didactic purposes than the classical style of Euclid, Newton, and Gauss, was probably more congenial to the mind of Jacobi, who from his twenty-first year (1825) developed a great activity as an academic teacher.[1]   He was first

17.
Jacobi's
mathematical school.

mained unknown and unnoticed. See on the history of the subject, Hankel, 'Theorie der complexen Zahlensysteme,' 1867, pp. 71, 82. Gauss, through hiding his researches on this subject so long, lost the claim to the priority of the invention, though not of the effectual use of it. In another instance he allowed others to appropriate the merit of cultivating a large new field which had been familiar to him many years before. It was known all through the first half of the century that Gauss was in possession of valuable discoveries in what he termed the "new transcendent functions." References in the 'Disquisitiones,' § 335, in his correspondence with Schumacher, Bessel, Olbers, and Crelle, had made his friends curious to see the "amplum opus" which he had promised. It appears, however, that, independently of him, Jacobi and Abel (1802-29) following the investigations of Legendre (whose labours began in 1786 and culminated in

his great work 'Traité des fonctions elliptiques, &c.,' 1825-28, 2 vols. and 3 supplements), succeeded in developing the theory very much on the same lines as Gauss had taken nearly a generation earlier. Eminent mathematicians who, since the publication of Gauss's posthumous papers, have fully investigated the subject, assign to Jacobi and Abel the undisputed priority of publishing, but to Gauss that of discovering, the fundamental properties of the "doubly periodical" functions. Full details will be found in the historical introduction to Enneper's 'Elliptische Functionen,' 2nd ed., Halle, 1890. See also Gauss's Werke, vol. iii. p. 491-496; Dirichlet's Discourse on Jacobi in Jacobi's Werke, vol. i. p. 11; C. A. Bjerknes, 'N. H. Abel,' Paris, 1885; Koenigsberger, 'Zur Geschichte der Theorie der elliptischen Transcendenten,' Leipzig, 1879.

[1] Carl Gustav Jacob Jacobi (born at Potsdam 1804, died at Berlin 1851) was the first great mathe-

at Berlin, then at Königsberg; these two universities having become through him and Bessel the German teaching centres of the higher mathematics, both pure and applied. They have up to the present day fully maintained this pre-eminent position. They were teaching centres in the sense defined above—not only as regards mathematical knowledge and method, but likewise as regards mathematical research. For this purpose—as in the philological sciences—the lecture-room was not sufficient; there was also wanted a repository for the independent and original contributions of the school. Like the École polytechnique thirty years before in Paris, the Berlin school of mathematicians started with an important periodical. This was known as Crelle's Journal. Together with the Memoirs of the Paris Academy and the Journal de l'École polytechnique, it forms the principal repository for the higher mathematical work of the first half of the century.[1] It was also through

matical teacher of Germany. Of him Lejeune Dirichlet says : " It was not his business to communicate what was finished and what had been communicated before ; his lectures all treated of subjects which lay outside of the field of the text-books, and covered only those parts of science in which he had himself been creative. With him this meant that they exhibited the greatest variety. His lectures were not remarkable for that kind of clearness which is characteristic of intellectual poverty, but for a clearness of a higher kind. He tried primarily to show the leading ideas which underlay any theory, and whilst he removed everything that had an artificial appearance, the solution of problems presented itself so easily to his hearers that they could hope to do something similar. . . . The success of this unusual method was truly remarkable. If in Germany the knowledge of the methods of analysis is now spread to a degree unknown to former times, if numerous mathematicians extend the science in every direction, this gratifying result is principally owing to Jacobi. Nearly all have been his pupils," &c. (Dirichlet's Discourse in the Academy of Berlin, 1852, Jacobi's Werke, vol. i. p. 21.)

[1] The two mathematicians on whom A. L. Crelle (1780-1855) relied mainly for contributions when he started the ' Journal für die reine und angewandte Mathematik ' in 1826 were Abel and Steiner. For originality of thought they stand quite alone. Both extended

Jacobi, and still more through his contemporary Lejeune
Dirichlet (born 1804 at Düren, of French extraction,
and trained in Paris under Laplace, Legendre, Fourier,

the field of research which they
cultivated by fundamentally new
ideas of such breadth that fully
half a century was required before they were thoroughly appreciated by mathematicians. Abel
(a Norwegian by birth) died in
1829 when only twenty - seven
years old, having during the four
years which embrace his published
memoirs extended the limits of
algebra and laid the foundations
for a more comprehensive treatment of the higher or transcendent
functions, or forms of mathematical
dependence. Mathematicians before him had tried to solve algebraically equations beyond the fourth
degree, but had failed. Abel proved
that the problem as then conceived
could not be generally solved. Legendre had through his unaided
labours, extending over thirty
years, established the theory of
elliptic integrals as far as was
possible on the lines then adopted.
Abel—and simultaneously Jacobi—
treated the subject from an entirely
novel point of view, and by doing
so opened out quite a new field of
research, the extent and importance
of which Abel fully recognised when
he presented to the French Academy his memoir of 1826, in which
he dealt with functions of which
those studied by Legendre and
Jacobi were only special cases.
This memoir, containing Abel's
celebrated theorem, which he had
already discovered in 1825, and
which was published in a brief article in Crelle's Journal in 1829, remained unnoticed, being, as Legendre explained to Jacobi, almost un-
readable. See Enneper, 'Elliptische
Functionen,' 2nd ed., p. 192; Jacobi's Werke, vol. i. p. 439, &c. Abel

has been called the greatest mathematical genius that has yet existed
(Oltramare in ' La grande Encyclopédie,' art. " Abel "); his fellow-
worker, Jacob Steiner (1796-1863,
a Swiss by birth), has been termed
the greatest geometrician of modern
times. The progress of analysis
had thrown into the background
purely geometrical researches, although a revival of these had commenced in France with Monge and
his followers, and had been further
promoted by Poncelet, as well
as simultaneously by Möbius and
Plücker in Germany. The labours
of the two latter remained for a
long time unknown and unrecognised. Steiner, who was self-
taught, who disliked the calculus,
and considered it a disgrace that
geometry could not solve her problems by purely geometrical methods,
undertook to find the common root
and leading principle which connected all the theorems and por-
isms bequeathed to us by ancient
and modern geometry ; he brings
order into the chaos, and shows
how nature with a few elements
and the greatest economy succeeds
in giving to figures in space their
numberless properties. He not
only completed that part of geometry which had been treated by the
ancients—the geometry of the line,
the conic sections or curves of the
second order, and the surfaces in
space corresponding to them—but
he also attacked problems which
before him had been solved only by
the calculus, and even succeeded in
carrying his methods beyond the
reach of the calculus of variations, specially invented to deal
with geometrical questions. Like
Fermat in the theory of numbers,

Poisson, Cauchy), that the great work of Gauss on the theory of numbers, which for twenty years had remained sealed with seven seals, was drawn into current mathematical literature, and became, as Newton's 'Principia' had become a century earlier, an inexhaustible mine of wealth for succeeding generations.

18. Chemical laboratories established in 1826 through Liebig.

About the same time the experimental side of exact research—the use of the chemical balance, through which Lavoisier and his followers had done so much to establish chemistry on a firm and independent basis—received a great impetus by the establishment of the *first chemical laboratories* within the pale of the universities.[1]   In this direction the greatest influence probably belongs to the small town of Giessen, where Liebig opened his celebrated laboratory in the year 1826.   It became the

Steiner in geometry left to his followers a large number of theorems and problems without proofs which he had solved by his methods ; and it was only in quite recent times that the Italian Cremona succeeded in definitely clearing up the whole of this original and valuable bequest. See Hankel, 'Die Elemente der projectivischen Geometrie, chapter i. ; Jacob Steiner, Werke, vol. ii. p. 495.

[1] On Liebig's laboratory see Hofmann's Faraday Lecture, p. 8. Chemical laboratories existed for teaching purposes before Liebig's at Giessen. Kopp ('Geschichte der Chemie,' vol. ii. p. 19) mentions one at Altorf, which was founded, 1683, by the council of the city of Nürnberg for academic teaching purposes. For the training of the modern school of chemists no man did more than Berzelius, in whose laboratory there were trained Chr. Gmelin, Mitscherlich, H. and G.

Rose, Wöhler, Magnus, Arfvedson, Nordenskiöld, Mosander, and others. Sir William Thomson (Lord Kelvin) in 'Nature,' vol. xxxi. p. 409, mentions the beginnings of laboratory-teaching at Glasgow by Prof. Thomas Thomson in 1828.   But what was probably peculiar to Liebig's laboratory was the systematic and methodical training, on a specially devised plan, in qualitative, quantitative, and organic analysis, by which young persons were introduced to a thorough knowledge of chemical properties and manipulations. The guides, text-books, and tables for analytic work of Will, Fresenius, and others were elaborated to meet the requirements of such methodical teaching. Almost simultaneously with Liebig at Giessen, Purkinje at Breslau laid the foundation for the first physiological laboratory. See Du Bois-Reymond, 'Reden,' vol. ii. p. 367.

training-school for the greater part of the eminent chemists outside of Paris, and the model for similar establishments, and extended its influence over the world—into England, Scotland, and America.   It also did more than any other institution of that kind for the development of ready and accurate methods of analysis, such as are now used in the remotest regions.   But it was significant for German chemistry, and for the cosmopolitan character of German science generally, that this brilliant development of experimental research was stimulated from two independent centres; that German chemists as little as German mathematicians attached themselves in a one-sided manner to the Paris school.

19. Cosmopolitan character of German science.

In mathematical science the classical style of Gauss, transmitted from the ancients through Newton, combined with the analytical or modern French style of Jacobi and Dirichlet to give to German research its character of universality.   In a similar manner, when chemistry again found a domicile in Germany and became an integral portion of the university programme, it had been trained in two different schools.   For there lived at that time in Sweden the eminent authority Berzelius,[1] who divides with Gay-Lussac the glory of being

---

[1] J. Jacob Berzelius (a Swede, 1779-1848), one of the most eminent and industrious of chemists, had a great influence on the development of modern chemistry by the number as well as by the accuracy of his experimental determinations, by his invention of methods and apparatus for analysis, and by his extensive proofs of several of the most important theories.   The latter directed the labours and governed the opinions of many—especially German—investigators. It was through him mainly that Richter's chemical equivalents and Dalton's atomic theory were extensively verified and applied to all parts of the science, to organic and mineralogical chemistry.   He also elaborated, in close connection with Davy's electrical discoveries, his celebrated electrochemical theory, which up to the year 1840 was very generally accepted by chemists; and he assisted through his repeated expositions

the master of the great German chemists of the middle
of the century. Mitscherlich at Berlin and Wöhler at
Göttingen belonged to the school of the former, whereas
Liebig had the good fortune to be introduced through
Humboldt into Gay-Lussac's laboratory at Paris as the
first pupil.[1]

and criticisms in breaking down the
older oxygen theory of acids in favour of Davy's more general views,
based upon his recognition of chlorine and iodine as elementary bodies.
His handbook of Chemistry, as well
as his 'Jahresbericht' (from 1820),
probably did more than any other
publications for the diffusion of accurate chemical information.

[1] Liebig has himself, in an autobiographical memoir published posthumously, so fully described the
merits of the two schools, and at
the same time given such a vivid
picture of the truly scientific spirit
which animated German universities at that time, that I am tempted to give here some extracts. Of
his studies in Paris he says : "What
influenced me most in the French
lectures was their inner truthfulness
and the careful omission of all mere
semblance of explanations: it was
a complete contrast to the German
lectures, in which, through a preponderance of the deductive process, the scientific doctrine had quite
lost its rigid coherence. . . . I returned to Germany (1824), where,
through the school of Berzelius,
. . . a great reform had already
begun in inorganic chemistry. . . .
I always remember with pleasure
the twenty-eight years which I
passed at Giessen : it was, as it were,
a higher providence which led me
to the small university. At a large
university, or in a larger town, my
powers would have been broken up
and frittered away, and the attainment of the aim which I had in

view would have been much more
difficult, if not impossible ; but at
Giessen all were concentrated in
the work, and this was a passionate enjoyment." "The necessity of
an institute where the pupil could
instruct himself in the chemical art,
by which I understand familiarity
with chemical operations of analysis
and adroitness in the use of apparatus, was then in the air, and so it
came about that on the opening of
my laboratory . . . pupils came
to me from all sides. . . . The
greatest difficulty presented itself,
as the numbers increased, in the
practical teaching itself. In order
to teach many at once, an ordered
plan was required and a progressive way of working, which had
to be thought out and tried. . . .
A very short time had sufficed for
the celebrated pupils of the Swedish
master to give to mineral analysis
. . . an admirable degree of perfection. . . . Physical chemistry
. . . had through the discoveries
of Gay-Lussac and Humboldt, . . .
and of Mitscherlich, . . . gained a
solid foundation, and in the chemical proportions the edifice appeared
to have received its coping-stone.
. . . No organic chemistry . . . then
existed ; Thénard and Gay-Lussac, Berzelius, Prout, Döbereiner,
had indeed laid the foundation of
organic analysis ; but even the
great investigations of Chevreul on
the fatty bodies received for many
years only scant attention. Inorganic chemistry still absorbed too
many, and indeed the best, forces.

Twenty years after Gauss's great mathematical achievements, two new discoveries announced to the scientific world that Germany had again taken a foremost position in chemistry. These were Mitscherlich's discovery of isomorphism in 1819,[1] and Wöhler's preparation of an organic compound from inorganic materials in 1828.[2]

In 1830 Liebig succeeded in finally establishing that simple and accurate method of organic analysis known by his name. Organic chemistry, in its modern sense,

20.
Liebig's organic analysis.

The direction I had received in Paris was a different one. . . . I saw very soon that all progress in organic chemistry depended on its simplification. . . . The first years of my residence at Giessen were almost exclusively devoted to the improvement of organic analysis, and with the first successes there began at the small university an activity such as the world had not yet seen. . . . A kindly fate had brought together in Giessen the most talented youths from all countries of Europe. . . . Every one was obliged to find his own way for himself. . . . We worked from dawn to the fall of night: there were no recreations and pleasures at Giessen. The only complaints were those of the attendant, who in the evenings, when he had to clean, could not get the workers to leave the laboratory." See 'Deutsche Rundschau,' vol. lxvi. pp. 30-39.

[1] Eilhard Mitscherlich (1794-1863), a pupil of Berzelius, discovered in 1819 that in compound bodies which crystallise in definite forms certain elements can be replaced by others in the proportion of their chemical equivalence without changing the form of crystallisation. Such elements are termed "isomorphous." Berzelius declared

this to be the most important discovery that had been made since the theory of chemical proportions had been established.

[2] This synthesis was the preparation of urea, a highly organic substance, out of the compounds of cyanogen, with the examination of which he and Liebig were then occupied. " It was the first example of the fact that an organic substance could, by chemical methods alone, be produced out of inorganic materials ; this discovery destroyed the difference which was then considered to exist between organic and inorganic bodies—*viz.*, that the former could only be formed under the influence of vegetable or animal vital forces, whereas the latter could be artificially produced" (Kopp, ' Geschichte der Chemie,' vol. i. p. 442). It must here be remarked that this statement is only correct if the substances, cyanic acid and ammonia, out of which Wöhler produced urea, are considered to be inorganic ; inasmuch as neither of them had then been produced otherwise than out of organic substances, the popular notion on Wöhler's important discovery requires this correction. See Kopp, ' Gesch. der Wissenschaften in Deutschland,' vol. x. p. 546

may be said to date from these and other simultaneous labours of Liebig and Wöhler.[1] But although the pure sciences, mathematics, physics, and chemistry, advanced on new lines in the hands of German students, and although theoretical investigations have always been favourite pursuits of theirs, as we shall have ample opportunity to note in the course of our further survey, the greatest contribution to the progress of science, and the most brilliant performances of the exact spirit of research which emanated from Germany during the first half of this century, lay in a different direction. And it is hard to believe that the conditions favourable to this peculiar growth could have been found anywhere else than in the German universities. The many elements of thought which meet on that ground, the equal dignity

[1] The joint labours of Liebig (1803-73) and Wöhler (1800-82), which have become of such importance to science, form one of the most interesting instances of scientific co-operation between two men pursuing different lines of thought and trained in different schools. See the preface to Hofmann's edition of Liebig and Wöhler's Correspondence. In Liebig's autobiographical sketch, quoted above, he thus enlarges on his relations to Wöhler: "It was my good fortune that, from the beginning of my career at Giessen, similar inclinations and endeavours secured me a friend, with whom, after so many years, I am still (between 1860 and 1870) connected by ties of the warmest affection. Whereas in me the tendency predominated to look for the likenesses of substances and their combinations, he possessed an incomparable talent for seeing their differences; acuteness of observation was joined in him to an artistic aptitude and to a genius for finding new ways and means of analysis such as few men possess. The perfection of our joint researches into uric acid and the oil of bitter almonds has been frequently praised; this is his work. I cannot sufficiently estimate the advantage which both my own and our joint aims derived from my union with Wöhler; for in them were combined the peculiarities of two schools, and the good which each had, attained its value through co-operation. Without grudge or jealousy we pursued our way hand in hand; if one required help, the other was ready. An idea can be formed of this mutual relation when I mention that many of the smaller productions which bear our names belong to one alone; they were charming little presents which one gave the other" (p. 39).

which there belongs to pure and to applied science, the continual contest which exists there between metaphysical and exact reasoning, and the general ebb and flow of rival currents of ideas, all seem to have been necessary to raise to the rank of an exact science those researches which deal with the phenomena of *life* and *consciousness* in their normal and abnormal forms of existence. In the hands of German students [1] chemistry and physics, botany and zoology, comparative anatomy and morphology, pathology, psychology, and metaphysics, have laboured from different and unconnected beginnings to produce that central science which attacks the great problem of organic life, of individuation, and which studies the immediate conditions of consciousness. *Physiology*, or to use its more comprehensive name, *Biology*,[2] may be

21.
Biology a
German
science.

[1] The two greatest discoveries in physiology belong to England. These are Harvey's discovery of the circulation of the blood in the seventeenth century, and Charles Bell's discovery of the difference of sensory and motor nerves in the early part of this century. The two men, however, who have done most to establish physiology as an independent science, whose systematic works have done most for the student of physiology, are probably Haller (see *supra*, p. 176), whose 'Elementa' cast into the shade all older handbooks, and Johannes Müller (1801-58), whose 'Handbuch' (1833-40) was translated into French and English. See Du Bois-Reymond, 'Reden,' &c., vol. ii. pp. 143, &c., 195, 360, who also points out how in other sciences, like mathematics, physics, chemistry, Germans made use almost exclusively of translations of French and English text-books and handbooks, whereas in physiology they furnished for a long period the systematic treatises for the whole world (vol. ii. p. 196). Physiology has therefore with some right been termed a German science (see Helmholtz, 'Vorträge,' &c., vol. i. pp. 339, 362; Du Bois-Reymond, 'Reden,' vol. ii. p. 265). Compare also what Huxley says, 'Critiques and Addresses,' pp. 221, 303. On the connection of physiology with all other sciences see likewise Helmholtz, *loc. cit.*; Du Bois-Reymond, vol. ii. p. 341; Huxley, 'Lay Sermons,' &c., p. 75; 'Science and Culture,' p. 52: "A thorough study of human physiology is, in itself, an education broader and more comprehensive than much that passes under that name. There is no side of the intellect which it does not call into play, no region of human knowledge into which either its roots or its branches do not extend," &c.

[2] The word "biology" seems to have been first used by G. R.

said to be a German science as chemistry has been named a French science. I have already referred to the great Haller in the last century, who may be called the father of physiology; to Blumenbach, the comparative anatomist; and to Liebig and Wöhler, who first among chemists succeeded in producing an organic compound by the processes of inorganic chemistry. I have now to add two names, which together mark a great revolution in our ideas of the structure of organisms, and link together the two sciences which had treated separately of the

22.
Cellular theory of Schleiden

animal and vegetable worlds. About the year 1838 Mathias Schleiden [1] propounded his cellular theory con-

Treviranus (1776-1837), a learned physician of Bremen, who began to write his 'Biologie oder Philosophie der lebenden Natur' in 1796 and to publish it in 1802 (6 vols., 1802-22). Lamarck used the word in his 'Hydrogéologie,' 1801. They, as well as Bichat about the same time, independently "conceived the notion of uniting the sciences which deal with living matter into one whole, and of dealing with them as one discipline" (Huxley, on the study of Biology, 1876, in 'American Addresses,' p. 136, &c.) The term, though of German origin, has not found favour in that country, and after having been used officially in France and England, makes its appearance in Germany only since the great works of the modern English school, headed by Darwin, have gained so much influence in Germany. In the meantime the biological sciences had been extensively represented at the German universities by chairs of physiology, zoology, botany, &c. According to Huxley, biology has been "substituted for the old confusing name of natural history," and "denotes the whole of the sciences which

deal with living things, whether they be animals or whether they be plants" (loc. cit., p. 138). It can be divided into three branches —(1) Morphology, which comprises the sciences of anatomy, development, and classification; (2) the science of the distribution of living beings, present and past; and (3) physiology, which deals with the functions and actions of living beings, and tries to "deduce the facts of morphology and of distribution from the laws of the molecular forces of matter" (Huxley, 'Lay Sermons,' &c., p. 83, 1864). To these three Huxley adds ('Ency. Brit.,' art. "Biology") the infant science of "ætiology," which "has for its object the ascertainment of the causes of the facts of biology and the explanation of biological phenomena, by showing that they constitute particular cases of general physical laws" (p. 688).

[1] Mathias Jacob Schleiden (1804-81), for some time Professor of Botany at Jena, was a man of peculiar ability and disposition, combining a philosophical mind with exact knowledge and a general literary taste, not frequently

cerning the structure and growth of plants. About the same time Theodor Schwann [1] extended this theory to animal organisms. A variety of circumstances combined to make the announcement of the *cellular theory*, which will always be associated with those two names, an epoch in the history of scientific, indeed of general, thought.

The historian of botany, Julius Sachs, describes the publication of Schleiden's great work as a burst of daylight,[2] and Du Bois-Reymond says: " In order to measure the magical progress which it marks, one must have witnessed the rise of the cellular theory, when it suddenly spread daylight in the darkness of the hidden structure

and Schwann.

to be found among men of pure science in Germany. Opposed to the idealistic philosophy as a follower of Fries, and on the other side to the dry systematisation of the Linnæan school, he was the man at once to broaden the scientific view and to create a popular interest in the " life of the plant "-world. The titles of his two best known works are characteristic, ' Die Botanik als inductive Wissenschaft' (1842-45), and his short-lived periodical (filled with the labours of his equally important co-editor, Nägeli), ' Zeitschrift für wissenschaftliche Botanik.'

[1] Through the friendship of Schleiden and Schwann (1810-82, a pupil of Johannes Müller and professor at Louvain), two independent courses of research and scientific thought were brought together. Schleiden placed the "cell" —a term used before him by Hooke, Malpighi, Grew, Wolff, Brown, and Mirbel—in the forefront of his description as the element of form and as the origin of life, or—as we now express it—as the morphological and embryological unit, in the plant. A similar series of great

names, beginning with Bichat and leading up to Johannes Müller, marks the studies of animal tissues. Schwann, struck with the analogy of Schleiden's nucleated cells and similar structures which he had observed in the notochord, conceived and verified on a large scale the idea "that a common principle of development exists for the most different elemental parts of the organism, and that the formation of cells is this principle." This is the beginning of the cellular theory, which produced at once a reconstruction of the whole of "general anatomy" by Jacob Henle (1809-85), and subsequently the "cellular pathology" of Rudolph Virchow. As the latter has himself said, he aims at the establishment of a general *biological* principle, and thus the discovery of Schleiden and Schwann is characterised as the transition from the "historical" to the "biological" study of animated nature.

[2] See Julius Sachs, ' Geschichte der Botanik vom 16 Jahrh. bis 1860,' p. 203, and in many other passages.

of animals and plants, where the rays of comparative anatomy and embryology could not reach."[1] This bold generalisation, which had been prepared by a long series of botanical and morphological researches in and out of Germany, met alternately with applause and criticism ; it gave rise to a long controversy, and was the starting-point of a whole line of important discoveries.[2] It secured for Germany a long period of supremacy in physiological science. This supremacy was more than maintained by a great volume of minute investigations, which emanated from the schools, and centred in the names, of E. H. Weber[3]

23.
Ernst Heinrich Weber

[1] Du Bois-Reymond, 'Reden,' vol. ii. p. 541, &c.

[2] "Whatever cavillers may say, it is certain that histology before 1838, and histology since then, are two different sciences—in scope, in purpose, and in dignity—and the eminent men to whom we allude may safely answer all detraction by a proud *Circumspice*."—Huxley in his valuable paper on "The Cell Theory" in the 'British and Foreign Medical Chirurgical Review,' 1853, vol. xii. p. 290.

[3] The three brothers Weber (Ernst Heinrich, 1795-1878 ; Wilhelm, 1804-91 ; and Eduard, 1806-71) may be looked upon as early representatives of the best form of German research on the lines now recognised as the true and fruitful ones in natural science. Born in an age when other great and more widely known reformers—such as Liebig, Schönlein, and Joh. Müller—freed themselves with difficulty from the prevailing metaphysical systems, they seem to have at once seized the true spirit of exact research without relinquishing the broader philosophical and encyclopædic view of the sciences which they cultivated. Living far into an age when the utilitarian spirit became equally seductive in an opposite direction, they preserved pure and undefiled within themselves the German ideal of *Wissenschaft* as a pursuit carried on for its own intrinsic value, not for any immediate practical object. Their position, especially that of the two elder brothers, is in this respect unique, and may be studied independently of the scientific ideas which they represented, and which will occupy us later on as a chapter in the history of thought characteristic of the German mind and the best type of the university studies. In three works of classical value— 'Die Wellenlehre auf Experimenten begründet' (E. H. and W. Weber), 1825 ; 'Die Mechanik der menschlichen Gehwerkzeuge' (W. and E. Weber), 1836 ; 'Elektrodynamische Maasbestimmungen' (W. Weber), 1846 onward—and in a great number of special investigations, the method of exact measurement was applied to physical, physiological, and even mental phenomena, and the foundation laid for a mechanical description and mathematical calculation. The later generalisations, known as Wilhelm Weber's law of electro-dynamics and E. H. Weber's law of psycho-physics, have given rise to

and Johannes Müller.   The school of the latter especially has the merit of having introduced over the whole field of physiological phenomena exact methods of inquiry, of having established physiological laboratories all over Germany similar to Liebig's chemical laboratory at Giessen, and of having effectually chased away the vague notions of the older metaphysical school, and diffused the true scientific spirit.   It boasts of having filled the chairs of medicine, physiology, and anatomy at the German universities with a long list of eminent teachers who have spread this true scientific spirit in every branch of the medical sciences,[1] which it has in consequence drawn into

long controversies and fruitful theories. Their joint labours cover fully half a century. See for a sympathetic picture of the position which the three brothers Weber held in the learned world the biography of Fechner by Kuntze, 1892, p. 243 : "They were among the first to raise the study of Nature among Germans to the eminence occupied by the philosophers and discoveries of the Latin races."

[1] The medical sciences, represented by the medical faculty, but also by those biological sciences which, like botany, zoology, anthropology, &c., belong to the philosophical faculty, now furnish the largest number of students to the German universities. In the beginning of the century the theological faculty, which then included the greater part of those who prepared themselves for higher teaching, stood at the head as regards numbers. Under the influence of the philo-logico-historical movement, which grew and culminated in the course of this century, and the rising tide of the exact sciences, the philosophical faculty for a time gained

and maintained the upper hand. Biological — including medical — studies now command the greatest attention. In his statistical report (contained in Lexis, ' Die deutschen Universitäten,' Berlin, 1893) Prof. Conrad gives an interesting table of the changing numerical proportion in the different faculties (vol. i. p. 125, &c.) Prof. Billroth in his admirable treatise, ' Ueber das Lehren und Lernen der medicinischen Wissenschaften,' Vienna, 1876, deals with this subject at all the German universities, including the Austrian. As Vienna is such an important centre of medical studies, the proportion of those students who cultivate biological studies would probably be still greater if we were to include the Austrian universities. I suppose the figure would be about 40 per cent of the whole. To Billroth's treatise I may also refer as confirming in relation to these more modern branches what I said above of the culture of *Wissenschaft*. See p. 279 and the whole section on the relation of the biological sciences to the university, pp. 411-446. It is

the circle of the exact or mechanical sciences. But not only in its far-reaching applications to medical knowledge and practice has the movement which centred in Weber and Müller shown its strength and importance; it has also, from the commencement, extended its influence in another direction. To it belongs pre-eminently the cultivation of that borderland which connects the natural and the mental sciences. Müller[1] himself began his career by a study of the mechanism of the perceptions of the senses. He affirmed the law of *specific energies,*

24.
Psycho-
physics.

interesting to note that Prof. Billroth does not employ the word biological, but uses the untranslatable compound *naturwissenschaftlich-medicinisch.*

[1] Johannes Müller (1801-58) has been termed the Haller of the nineteenth century, the Cuvier of Germany. A very good account of his work, which forms an important chapter in the history of German biology, is contained in Du Bois-Reymond's 'Gedächtnissrede auf Joh. Müller' (1858), reprinted with extensive notes in his 'Reden,' vol. ii. pp. 143-334. Müller is there considered as the last representative of a dynasty of philosophers who embraced the whole domain of "biology," which since has become divided into various sciences, notably the morphological and the physiological branches. He thus stands out as the master of some of the greatest modern representatives of natural and medical science, such as Schwann and Henle in anatomy, Brücke, Du Bois-Reymond, and Helmholtz in physiology, Virchow in pathological anatomy. He together with Lucas Schönlein (1793-1864) may be considered as the founder of the modern Berlin school of medicine, contemporaneous with which is the modern Austrian school, with the names of Purkinje, Skoda, Oppolzer, and Rokitansky. An excellent characterisation of the different positions and influences, of the cross-currents of thought, of the original homes and of the wanderings of the scientific spirit through the many German-speaking countries and the extensive network of German universities, will be found in Billroth, *loc. cit.,* pp. 307-366. If we imagine a similar life as existing all through the century in other domains of thought—in philosophy, theology, philology, mathematics, chemistry, law, and the science of history—we get a faint idea of the work of the German universities. In Lexis, 'Die deutschen Universitäten,' an attempt has been made to give such a picture. The picture, however, suffers by the exclusion of the Austrian universities, and these—notably in the medical world—hold such a very high position that the record of the united work is somewhat incomplete. The sciences are also in this record cut up into many branches, whereas in the earlier part of the century many of these were united and represented by one great name. Such a name was Johannes Müller in biology.

which declares that the differences of the sensations of light and colour, of sound, of touch, &c., do not depend upon the mode of irritation, nor even upon the different structure of the specific nerves, but upon the nature of the central sense organ. In the school of Müller the phenomena of voltaic electricity, which had been so seductive and misleading to an earlier school of physiologists not experienced in the methods of exact research, were again subjected to scientific investigation, and led to the brilliant researches with which the name of Du Bois-Reymond is so intimately connected. He is as ready as Helmholtz, who in his two great works on physiological optics and musical acoustics has founded new branches of science,[1] to acknowledge the leadership of Johannes

[1] Helmholtz (1821 - 95), equally celebrated as physiologist and mathematical philosopher, was educated under the influence of Johannes Müller on the one side, of Jacobi and the Königsberg school of mathematicians (Bessel and Neumann) on the other. If we add to this that he also made a profound study of those far-reaching speculations which originated in the philosophy of Kant, we realise how rare is the combination of ability and knowledge which he has brought to bear on the discussion of the most advanced problems in physics, biology, and psychology. In the sequel I shall have to refer so frequently to his writings that I confine myself here to giving the date of his principal, his epoch-making publications: 1847. 'Ueber die Erhaltung der Kraft'; 1858. 'Ueber die Integrale der hydrodynamischen Gleichungen, welche der Wirbelbewegung entsprechen' — both reprinted in 'Wissenschaftliche Abhandlungen,' Leipzig, 1882 and 1883, 2 vols. These two Memoirs may be considered as corner-stones of two of the most important modern theories in physical science, the "conservation of energy" and the "theory of vortex motion." In both, the name of Helmholtz is intimately allied with that of William Thomson (Lord Kelvin). Equally important and more comprehensive have been his researches in the physiology and psychology of sense-perceptions in his 'Physiologische Optik,' Leipzig, 1867; 'Lehre von den Tonempfindungen,' Braunschweig, 1863.

Helmholtz has also contributed largely to the discussion of two very important branches of modern speculation—first, the theoretical views on the nature of electrical phenomena expressed by the opposite conceptions of Wilhelm Weber in Germany and Faraday in England; second, the origin of geometrical axioms, especially the axiom referring to parallel lines. A great interest in this subject had been

Müller. And out of the circle of which E. H. Weber
was the centre, has emanated that work of Fechner,
'Elements of Psycho-physics,' which marks an epoch
in psychology : it is indeed mainly occupied with the exposition and application of what is termed Weber's law
of sensation.[1] In the course of the second quarter of the
century, the names of Gauss and Jacobi in mathematics,
of Liebig and Wöhler in chemistry, of Schleiden and
Schwann in the science of life, of Müller and Weber in
physiology, raised German science to the level previously reached by the French Academicians, by Laplace
and Lagrange, by Lavoisier and Berthollet, by Cuvier
and St-Hilaire, by Vicq-d'Azyr and Bichat. During

created by the posthumous publication of Riemann's celebrated Memoir, 'Ueber die Hypothesen welche
der Geometrie zu Grunde liegen,'
Göttingen, 1865. Helmholtz's invention of the ophthalmoscope in
1851 marks an epoch in ophthal-
mology.

[1] Gustav Theodor Fechner (1806-
87), professor at the University of
Leipsic, was an extraordinary man.
The wide range of his interests and
his great personal influence are well
described in his biography by Dr
Kuntze, ' G. T. Fechner, Ein
deutsches Gelehrtenleben,' Leipzig,
1892. Together with Lotze he may
be said to have brought about the
reform of German speculative philosophy, and in relation to this he
will occupy our attention largely
in a later portion of this book. He
belonged to the circle of which E.
H. Weber was the centre, and has
taken an important place in the
history of philosophy and science
by his now celebrated work, ' Elemente der Psychophysik,' 2 vols.,
Leipzig, 1860 ; 2nd ed., 1890. The

object of this work is to establish
" an exact doctrine of the relations
of body and mind," the principal
task being " to fix the measure of
psychical quantities." He says in
the preface : " The empirical law
which forms the principal foundation, was laid down long ago
by different students in different
branches, and was expressed with
comparative generality mainly by
E. H. Weber, whom I would
call the father of psycho-physics "
(Preface, p. v). In early life
Fechner did much, by his translations of Biot's ' Physics ' and Thénard's ' Chemistry,' as well as by his
own experimental works, to introduce the French scientific spirit into
German research. His psycho-physical labours have been continued
by Prof. Wundt ; his importance
as marking a turning-point in
German philosophy is brought out
in Paulsen's ' Einleitung in die
Philosophie,' Berlin, 1890. See
especially Preface, p. viii, and p.
318, where Fechner is placed before
Lotze.

the second half of the century, the influence of French
thought on German science has been less marked, partly
owing to the independent course which the latter, since
the age of Johannes Müller, has struck out for herself
in the biological sciences, partly through the more intimate intercourse which has set in between English and
German thought.   The three great scientific ideas which
the second half of the century has been establishing—the
law of the conservation of energy, Darwin's theory of
descent, and Faraday's novel conception of electrical
phenomena—have been elaborated mainly by the co-
operation of English and German research, though it
must be admitted that at least one of these developments
dates back to the beginnings laid by French science,[1]
whilst the views of Faraday are subversive of some of
the fundamental notions to which the works of the great
French mathematicians had given very general currency.
Before we can enter more fully on a review of these more
modern ideas, I must, however, give a picture of the state
of scientific thought in England during the first half of
the century.   This will be our subject in the last portion
of the present section.

[1] Darwin's theory of descent has
its forerunners in Lamarck and St-
Hilaire, whose merits in this respect are supposed to have been
overlooked owing to the overwhelming authority of Cuvier.   See Huxley, "Origin of Species" in 'Lay
Sermons,' 1891, p. 252; "Evolution in Biology" in 'Science and
Culture,' 1888, pp. 296, 313.   But
whilst it is true that Lamarck and
St-Hilaire entertained doubts as to
the fixity of species, the explanation of the particular manner in
which the change of species takes
place is entirely due to Darwin,
and without this further step
speculations as to the origin of
species would have remained for a
long time in the vague.   Lamarck's
speculations were of no real use to
Darwin, and had besides been anticipated by Erasmus Darwin.   On
the other hand, the researches of
Sadi Carnot were of great value in
the hands of Joule, Thomson, and
Helmholtz, who may be regarded
as the founders of the doctrine of
the conservation of energy.

25.
Spirit of ex-
act research
and *Wissen-*
schaft.

But it is my object at present not so much to dwell upon specific ideas or doctrines as on the growth, the diffusion, and the general character of scientific thought, as this has been established by the separate contributions of the three nations in the course of the first half of our century. I therefore cannot leave the subject of German science without still more precisely noting the peculiar character which scientific thought has assumed under the influence of the German university system. As we saw before, when the spirit of exact research, mainly through the influence of the great French mathematicians and physicists, became diffused in Germany, and entered the pale of the German universities, it was met there by that peculiar ideal of learning which the German language terms *Wissenschaft*. This encounter did not everywhere produce a favourable reception for the new school; but in the end it led, like every controversy, to a firmer establishment of the true principles of research. The life of the German universities had in the earlier centuries begun with classical studies; it had been reformed under the influence of the theological and juridical requirements of the Protestant Governments; and ultimately it had been entirely renewed under the influence of the classical and philosophical studies centred in the fourth or philosophical faculty. These classical and philosophical studies combined to create the ideal of *Wissenschaft*, or science, in the broadest sense of the word. This ideal formed the central conception in the new scheme of a higher and general education of the nation; it accompanied the great revival in art, poetry, and literature. In the

philosophy of Kant and Fichte, the republican notions
which led the political movements in America and
France had been reduced to a system and theoretically
proved; the discipline of a classical education was the
school in which leaders and youths were trained who
marched into the war against the great oppressor. This
ideal of *Wissenschaft* had thus acquired a practical meaning, an ethical—not to say a religious—significance; it
was allied to the religious revival preached by Schleiermacher and a section of the Romantic school. Of its
value as a principle for guiding research and learning it had given proof in that great circle of studies
which, since the time of F. A. Wolf and Wilhelm von
Humboldt, was comprised under the name of *Philology.*
Under its influence new universities were being founded
and academies remodelled.

Now, it is the peculiarity of all philosophical and
historical studies that they deal with one great subject,
which cannot easily be divided into a number of independent parts capable of separate treatment; since their
interest attaches mainly to the fact that they explore
the workings and manifestations of the human mind in
the past and in the present. These studies are therefore forced to keep always in the foreground the idea
of a great unity of action and purpose, to aim at completeness of view, and to refer all special researches to
general principles and standards. The encyclopædic view, 26. Encyclo-
in fact, is forced upon all philosophical and historical pædic view necessary in
sciences. Almost without exception the great masters philosophy and history.
and teachers who lived in the beginning of this century
adhered to this view, and however great in special and

detailed research, measured the importance of their results according to the light which they were able to throw upon the questions referring to the whole subject and its combined life and unity.

It was also natural, seeing that this comprehensive or philosophical treatment led to such great results in the historical sciences, that an attempt should have been made to deal with the phenomena of Nature by a similar conception. It was not a new or a far-fetched suggestion to regard Nature as the playground of a hidden intelligence, of an unconscious mind, just as history, language, and thought were viewed as the manifestations of the conscious human mind. After this the further conception was not remote that both the mind of Nature and the mind of Man are only two different sides of the universal or absolute Mind. The philosophy of Schelling was the first attempt to put this idea into an applicable form, the system of Hegel the first confident elaboration of it in its various ramifications and applications. At the time when the mathematical and physical sciences were leading the way in France, and gradually forcing their way into Germany, most of the universities in the latter country had one or more representatives of that new and apparently promising school which termed itself the "Philosophy of Nature." The trammels of this school had to be shaken off by those who, as they became gradually convinced of its barrenness in actual results, took up the cause of the exact or mathematical sciences now that they had been cultivated by many isolated labourers in Germany and in England, and had been

27.
Philosophy
of Nature.

for the first time connected into a great organisation by the French Academy of Sciences.

The opposition in which the new school of exact and detailed research stood to the representatives of the broad philosophical view gave rise to a great many currents of thought; for neither the former nor the latter presented a united front. Among those who advocated the exact methods of research there was a section which clung more exclusively to the empirical side, and cultivated the descriptive and experimental sciences; whereas others, whom we may call the French school of science, developed the mathematical methods, not without a certain ill-disguised contempt for pure empiricism.[1] On the side of classical and philosophical studies there was a section which cultivated the historical[2] in contradis-

28.
Conflict between the scientific and the philosophical views.

[1] On the relations of mathematical and experimental physics, and the different opinions which existed during the first half of the century, see Helmholtz's popular addresses in many places, but especially the discourse on Gustav Magnus (1802-70), who may be regarded as a representative of the experimental school in Germany. In the opinion of this school, which cultivated the borderland of physics and chemistry, of organic and inorganic phenomena, or investigated the less known phenomena of frictional electricity (Riess) or the complicated phenomena of meteorology (Dove), a danger existed that mathematical theories and elaborate calculations might lead to an estrangement from nature and observation, similar to that which speculative philosophy had created before. Helmholtz himself was met by this sentiment when he published his great memoir,

'Ueber die Erhaltung der Kraft,' in 1847; Poggendorf's physical periodical would not receive it, and Jacobi, the mathematician, was the only one who showed any interest in it. See Helmholtz, 'Wissenschaftliche Abhandlungen,' vol. i. p. 73; 'Reden,' vol. ii. p. 46.

[2] As the philosophy of Schelling promoted a study of nature, and in doing so prepared its own downfall, so the philosophy of Hegel led to a study of history, and thus to the proof of the insufficiency of its own generalisations. Many valuable beginnings of historical research emanated also from the Romantic school of literature. In all these instances philosophical interests led beyond the abstract logical and metaphysical treatment into the broad and fertile plains of actual life, be it that of nature or of art or of history. But the true methods of research in

tinction to the philosophical view, and another which elaborated what it termed exclusively the critical methods,[1] not without a certain suspicion regarding those who showed a desire to roam into outlying fields which did not permit of equally strict discipline and treatment. So far as this refers to the purely historical sciences, I shall revert to the subject when I come to treat of the principles which underlie and guide this line of studies. At present I am concerned with the growth and diffusion of the exact scientific spirit and its methods.

No one did more to spread the ideas and methods of French science in Germany than Alexander von Humboldt. He himself had done original scientific work[2] be-

29.
Alexander von Humboldt.

these extensive fields were afterwards found not so much in philosophical canons as in a love of detail and observation, and in the exercise of an unbiassed criticism of facts and records. For the relations of philosophy to history in respect of this, see Wegele, 'Geschichte der deutschen Historiographie,' München, 1885, 5th book, p. 975, &c. Equally important are—Gervinus, 'Grundzüge der Historik,' Leipzig, 1837 ; the 'Nekrolog auf Schlosser,' Leipzig, 1862, including the whole literature which it provoked ; and O. Lorenz, 'Die Geschichtswissenschaft,' Berlin, 1886, especially the first chapter.

[1] On the Critical school of philology, and the wider and narrower sense in which the aims and methods of the science of antiquity were defined, see Bursian, 'Geschichte der classischen Philologie in Deutschland,' München und Leipzig, 1883, p. 665, &c. ; also O. Ribbeck, 'Friedrich Ritschl,' Leipzig, 1879 and 1880. Further, the essays on Böckh, K. O. Müller, and Georg Curtius in the third volume of Ernst Curtius,

'Alterthum und Gegenwart,' Berlin, 1889 ; and, finally, the chapter on "Klassische Philologie" by Wilamowitz-Möllendorf in Lexis, 'Die deutschen Universitäten,' vol. i. p. 457, &c.

[2] Alexander von Humboldt (1769-1859) published in 1797, shortly after Galvani's great discovery, his 'Versuche über die gereizte Muskel- und Nervenfaser.' In the history of science his name will live as that of the man who organised that "scientific conspiracy of nations" which is peculiar to our century, and without which the study of geography, meteorology, astronomy, the phenomena of tides and magnetic disturbances—called by him magnetic storms — could not effectually be carried on. The fact also that on his return from his great travels he became next to Napoleon Bonaparte the most famous man in Europe, did more than anything else to raise the natural sciences in the popular mind to that eminence which earlier belonged to polite literature.

fore he left Germany for the extensive travels by which
he became celebrated, and through which he founded a
new science—the science that deals with the geographical
distribution of plant life.   Moreover, his absence from his
native country fell within that period during which the
philosophical school, headed by Schelling and Hegel, attained to its greatest power.   He was never drawn into its
vortex; on the contrary, he maintained a lifelong protest
against the spirit of its doctrine at a time when the circle
which surrounded him at Berlin came under its powerful
influence.[1]   He led a long line of ardent young workers
both to the right sources of scientific knowledge and
to an ultimate victory over the opposed school of
thought.   Though not a profound mathematician himself, he appreciated the part which mathematics were
destined to play in science.   Among other things, he
protected and encouraged younger mathematical talents,
and tried to draw Gauss from the solitary heights which
he inhabited into the midst of the scientific circles of
the day.[2]   Then there was the great influence which

---

[1] Cf. p. 178, note 1. It has latterly
become the fashion to say so much
against the mistaken methods of the
Naturphilosophie that it is well to
remember how many men of foremost rank in the natural sciences
belonged at one time to this school
or were influenced by it. Foremost
of all stands Oken (1779-1851), the
founder of the German Association
of Science, and editor of the periodical 'Isis.' Further, the comparative anatomist Carus (1789-1869);
Oersted (1777-1851), the discoverer
of electro-magnetism; Kielmeyer,
the friend of Cuvier (1765-1844);
Ignaz Döllinger (1770-1841), one of

the earliest evolutionists; D. G.
Kieser (1779-1862), a medical
teacher of great influence. More
or less influenced by the teachings
of this school were Goethe (1749-
1832); Karl Ernst von Baer (1792-
1876), whose impartial opinion on
the *Naturphilosophie* as early as
1821 is important. Further, Liebig (1803-73); Johannes Müller
(1801-58); Röschlaub (1768-1835);
Schönlein (1793-1864), the founder
of what is called the "natural-
history" school of medicine.

[2] See A. von Humboldt's Life by
Bruhns, translated by Lassell, 1873,
vol. ii. p. 145 *sqq.*

30.
Influence of
Berzelius
on German
science.
Berzelius exerted on German science through his teaching and his writings. From him emanated that great perfection of the purely experimental methods which in his own hands, as well as in those of Wöhler, Mitscherlich, Magnus, and others, led to an accumulation of detailed knowledge in chemistry of unforeseen importance and magnitude. His own annual reports, as well as Gmelin's celebrated handbook of chemistry, are monuments of this unparalleled industry.

Others, like Liebig, Johannes Müller, Lucas Schönlein, freed themselves under the influence of French science,[1] or by their own deeper insight, from the sway of the false and misleading philosophy to which they had at one time listened. A third section started from philosophical premises, but from premises opposed to the doctrines of Schelling and Hegel.

The school of Fries,[2] in which Schleiden was the most

[1] English science had an important but less marked influence on the development of naturalistic and medical studies in Germany. So far as the latter especially are concerned, see Billroth, 'Ueber das Lehren und Lernen der medicinischen Wissenschaften an den Universitäten der deutschen Nation,' Wien, 1876, p. 33. He roughly divides the medical schools of Germany into two groups, both descending from Boerhaave: the one, the modern Berlin school of Müller, Schönlein, Romberg, and Virchow, through Haller, Reil, Hufeland, and Röschlaub; the other, the modern Vienna school of Oppolzer, Rokitansky, and Billroth, through Gerhard von Swieten, De Haen, Stoll, Frank, Purkinje, and Skoda. Of French names which had great influence he gives Broussais, Corvisart, Bayle, Cruveilhier, and Laënnec; of English, John Hunter, Matthew Bailie, and Astley Cooper. He gives also the name of Immanuel Kant as an important influence in the development of the German schools of medicine.

[2] Jacob Fries (1773-1843) professor at Heidelberg and Jena, led the critical philosophy of Kant into the channels of psychology and anthropology. During the heyday of transcendental philosophy, the philosophy of Fries, like that of the Scotch school, was regarded with contempt by Hegel, and even by Herbart, the opponent of Hegel. It succeeded, however, in the end in influencing a considerable number of philosophical minds, who carried philosophical thought into the inductive sciences. Besides the psy-

illustrious name, carried on within the pale of the philosophical school of science itself a successful opposition to the philosophy of Nature.[1] But whilst much good and sound work was done by many who were content to remain outside of the favoured studies which set the tone of university culture during the classical and philosophical period of German thought, the great attack upon the mistaken canons of the philosophy of Nature came from that science which had probably suffered more than any other under the baneful influence of hollow theories and empty phraseology.

31. Philosophy of Nature and medical science.

Helmholtz describes the despair which had taken hold of thinking minds in the medical profession[2]: "My education fell within a period of the development of medicine when among thinking and conscientious minds there reigned perfect despair. It was not difficult to understand that the older and mostly theorising methods of treating medical subjects had become absolutely useless. But with the theories the facts which underlay them were so indissolubly entangled that these two were mostly cast overboard. How the science must be newly built up the example of the other natural sciences had made clear, but yet the new task stood of giant-height before us. A beginning was hardly made, and the first beginnings were

chologist Beneke and the theologian De Wette, these were principally members of the Jena school, Apelt, Schlömilch, and others, who edited 'Abhandlungen der Fries'schen Schule,' Jena, 1847; and foremost among them Schleiden, the reformer of botany in Germany. Schleiden's great work appeared with the title 'Botanik als inductive Wissenschaft.' It opened with a philosophical in-

troduction of 131 pages, in which inductive reasoning is recommended in opposition at once to the transcendental *Naturphilosophie*, and to dry empiricism. See Sachs, 'Geschichte der Botanik,' p. 203, &c.

[1] See Schleiden, 'Schelling's und Hegel's Verhältniss zur Naturwissenschaft,' Leipzig, 1844.

[2] See Helmholtz, 'Vorträge und Reden,' vol. i. p. 361.

often very crude. We cannot wonder if many honest, serious, thinking men then turned away in dissatisfaction from medicine, or if they from principle embraced an extreme empiricism."[1] "But the right kind of work brought forth its fruits much sooner than many had hoped. The introduction of mechanical notions into the theories of circulation and respiration, a better insight into the phenomena of heat, the more minutely elaborated physiology of the nerves, speedily produced practical results of the greatest importance; the microscopical examination of parasitic tissues, the stupendous development of pathological anatomy, led irresistibly from nebulous theories to real facts." And again[2]: "Whilst in the investigation of inorganic nature the different nations of Europe progressed pretty evenly, the recent development of physiology and medicine belongs pre-eminently to Germany. The questions regarding the principle of life

---

[1] Cf. Helmholtz, ibid., vol. ii. p. 178, in his discourse "Ueber das Denken in der Medicin": "At that time there were many among the younger doctors who, in despair about their science, gave up all therapeutics, and took to empiricism, such as was then taught by Rademacher. This on principle regarded as vain all hope of scientific insight." Not only the extreme empiricism of Rademacher (1772-1850), but still more the wild theories of Hahnemann (1755-1843) found during this age of general unsettlement many followers. See on the origin, the principles, and the spread of homœopathy, Häser, 'Geschichte der Medicin,' vol. ii. p. 793, &c. Häser gives the year 1816 as the date at which Hahnemann's doctrines began to be accepted in wider circles. "It must not be

forgotten that the heyday of homœopathy fell in that age when medicine, especially in Germany, was in a very deficient state, so that the accusations raised by Hahnemann and his adherents did not appear quite unfounded. It is even to be admitted that homœopathy has contributed to the reaction through which in our times the regeneration of the art of healing has been brought about, though this would have taken place without Hahnemann" (p. 803). Homœopathy has no scientific representative at any of the German universities, and yet it is admitted that it "still enjoys a great reputation in some influential circles among the general public" (Hirsch, 'Gesch. d. medicinischen Wissenschaften,' p. 570).

[2] Helmholtz, loc. cit., vol. i. p. 362.

are closely allied to psychological and ethical questions. To start with, here also that untiring industry is required which applies itself to pure science for purely ideal purposes, without immediate prospects of practical usefulness. And indeed we may glory in the fact that in this German scholars have always distinguished themselves by their enthusiastic and self-renouncing diligence, which labours for inner satisfaction and not for outer success."

This habit of self-renouncing labour, of singleness of purpose—in short, the ideal of pure science and its pursuit—had been elaborated in many a secluded workshop of a retired German university mainly under the influence of the classical and philosophical studies of the end of the last and the beginning of the present century. It was held up high and conspicuous by the priests of humanity, beginning with Lessing, Herder, and Kant, and ending in Schleiermacher, Hermann, and Böckh, at the head of a great army of devoted followers, travelling through the wilderness of national depression, barbarism, and despair into the promised land of freedom, culture, and hope. Such an ideal is of priceless worth, and it is this ideal which the philosophical and classical school of thought bequeathed during the first half of the century to that new school of thinkers which was destined to study, in an equally patient and unselfish spirit, the seemingly less elevated, but not less mysterious and fascinating, problems of Nature. Truly Gauss, Weber, and Johannes Müller worthily headed the new army of labourers.

32.
Science for
its own sake.

But though the elevated spirit in which scientific work is carried on may be the most valuable bequest of the classical and philosophical to the exact and empirical

33.
Bequest of
the classical
and philo-
sophical
school.

school, there were certain more tangible characteristics of German research, which were carried over from the older to the modern type of thought. It will be useful to define these more clearly.

In the course of the second half of the eighteenth century German literature and German philosophy had started from the beginnings laid by other nations, and after mastering and appropriating their achievements, had set out for a new course and a higher flight. Milton and Shakespeare [1] in epic and dramatic poetry; Ossian, the Percy Ballads, and Burns in song and lyric; Gibbon in history; Joseph Scaliger and Bentley in philology; Locke, Hume, and Spinoza in philosophy; Rousseau in prose,—all these great names of a later or earlier past had become familiar watchwords to German poets or students—to Lessing, Herder, and Goethe, to Schlegel, F. A. Wolf, and Wilhelm von Humboldt, to Böckh, Hermann, and Niebuhr, to Kant, Fichte, and Jacobi, before they came forward with their own creations. The same cosmopolitan spirit of looking elsewhere and everywhere for beginnings, and for co-operation in the united work of learning; the same historical taste, the same desire to glean from all quarters,—characterised the early decades of the revival of German science. Hence the many periodicals and annual reports; hence the fact that the

[1] These names are not given as they follow in time, but as they followed in their influence on German thought and literature. Thus the early representatives of the German revival were influenced by Milton and Pope more than by the greater Shakespeare: epic and didactic preceded dramatic poetry: Shakespeare was made familiar to German readers only through Goethe and Schlegel. Similarly the reaction against the school of Leibniz and Wolff in philosophy began with Kant's reply to Hume's sceptical philosophy, whereas the study of Spinoza influenced Kant's followers and opponents, Jacobi, Fichte, and Schelling.

nation which requires them least[1] possesses the most and the best translations of foreign authors. But the quality of greatest value for science which springs from the cosmopolitan and historical spirit is that of completeness and thoroughness of research.

Secondly, the German man of science was not only thorough, but was as little as the German philosopher or classicist had been, an isolated thinker. He was neither the member of an academy only, nor a solitary genius reduced to the resources of his own study. He lived mostly at a university, surrounded by others, whose labours came in contact with his own, or who treated the same subject from a different point of view. He had thus to define the limits of his science, and to see that no part of the common field was left uncultivated and unexplored. His object could not be to produce simply a work of individual greatness or of finished artistic merit; his work was an integral portion of the one great science; his

---

[1] This must not be misunderstood. A knowledge of the masterpieces of foreign literature was as necessary to the development of the German mind as it is to that of any other nation; it was and is more complete there than in any other country : what I mean is, that as a knowledge of French and English has been for a long time so common among the educated classes in Germany, translations are more easily dispensed with than in other countries. In spite of that, German literature abounds in excellent translations of the classics of France and England both in general literature and in science. It is also interesting to note that no modern language has succeeded so well in imitating foreign and classical metres as the German, hexameters having become domiciled in Germany through Voss and Goethe, the Alcaic and Sapphic metres through Klopstock and Herder, the more complicated stanzas through Platen, and above all through Donner's excellent renderings of the Greek dramatists. Rückert excelled in the imitation and reproduction of Persian, Indian, and Arabic poetry, and through him and Friedrich Bodenstedt German literature has been enriched by many lines of which it would be difficult to say whether their home was in Germany or in the far East, so perfectly is the spirit and diction reproduced. The well-known 'Weisheit des Brahmanen' of Rückert, and Bodenstedt's 'Mirza Schaffy' are examples.

labours had to fit in with the general plan, to find a place in the one great edifice.

35.
Combina-
tion of re-
search and
teaching.
Thirdly, the German man of science was a teacher ; he had to communicate his ideas to younger minds, to make the principles and methods of research clear, to guarantee, in his course of lectures, something like completeness, to give a comprehensive survey ; not to teach " une science faite," but to draw out original talent in others, to encourage co-operation in research, to portion out the common work to the talents which surrounded him, or it might be to direct the flight of the aspiring genius.[1]

[1] Here the two main objects of academic teaching are to impart a knowledge of the right method in the special science, and to give a survey of the whole domain of the science. The two principal institutions by which these objects are attained were first set going in the classical branches of study, and may be defined by two terms—the "seminary" and the lecture on "encyclopædia." Both terms are taken from earlier institutions. The seminary was originally a training-school for priests or teachers. Under such masters of methodical research as F. A. Wolf and Gottfried Hermann, the institution acquired a different character. "The seminaries are the real nurseries of scientific research. They were founded, indeed, with a different object; the first seminaries, the philological seminaries, which were started during the last century at Halle and Göttingen, were or should have been pedagogic seminaries for the future masters in the learned schools. In reality they were— especially that of F. A. Wolf— in the first place institutions in which the art of philological research was taught. This is even more the case in the philological seminaries and societies which during the nineteenth century have been conducted by G. Hermann, Fr. Thiersch, Fr. Ritschl, and others : they were nurseries of philologists, not of teachers. And the same may be said of the numerous seminaries which in modern times have grown up in the other sciences within the philosophical faculty, and also in the faculties of theology and law : they set up as their aim—with few exceptions —the training for scientific work and research, not the utilisation of knowledge for a practical purpose" (Paulsen in Lexis, 'Die deutschen Universitäten,' vol. i. p. 74, &c.) The same idea was in the mind of Liebig when he started the first chemical laboratory at Giessen (see supra, p. 188, note). The encyclopædic treatment of every large subject in a special course of lectures arranged for this purpose had the object of preventing the different studies from falling asunder or ultimately failing to unite in the realisation of one great aim. This great aim of all philological studies, for instance, was always held up by men like Wolf, Hermann, Böckh, and Ritschl, among

Lastly, the German man of science was a philosopher. Whatever his aversion might be to special philosophical doctrines, he had generally come under the influence of some philosophical school, the teaching of which he desired either to uphold or to combat. Sooner or later, consciously or unconsciously, he had to make clear to himself and to his disciples the underlying principles which he thought the right ones, to defend them against attacks from others, or to modify them, as progressing research made it necessary. If the historical sciences had benefited most by the philosophy of Schelling and Hegel, which attempted to give new and constructive views on the intellectual and ethical manifestations of the human or the general soul, the mathematical and phy-

whose favourite lectures were those on "encyclopædia" of philology. Something similar existed, and exists still, in theology, law, and what are called "*Staatswissenschaften*." All these terms are supposed to embrace a variety of studies which are organically combined in one whole, forming a cycle. In philosophy proper Hegel, and later Lotze, delivered well-known and largely attended lectures under the title of Encyclopædia. This is a remnant of the encyclopædic or organic treatment of knowledge sketched out by Bacon, and proposed as a basis for their celebrated work by Diderot and D'Alembert (see *ante*, p. 35 and note). The encyclopædia, as a learned dictionary, we have seen, has since become merely a synopsis. How different from this was the truly encyclopædic treatment given by men like Böckh can be seen from his correspondence with K. O. Müller, where he scolds his younger friend for undertaking to write the article "Topography of Athens" for "such a cursed publication as an encyclopædia," whereas he himself was regularly lecturing on "encyclopædia of philology," in which he took in earnest the idea of classical philology as "the historical science of the life of the ancient peoples" (see Curtius, 'Alterthum und Gegenwart,' vol. iii. p. 138, &c.) Now although the exact sciences when they became domiciled in the German universities did not in general copy this institution, yet the historical and philosophical survey, giving method and unity to a large circle of studies, has been upheld by many among the foremost men of science, especially in the medical faculty. Of these I only mention Joh. Müller (see Du Bois-Reymond, 'Reden,' vol. ii. pp. 195, 279) and his pupil and follower Jacob Henle, who in his lectures on anthropology took a philosophical survey of the whole subject of the medical studies (see 'Jacob. Henle' by Merkel, p. 271, &c.)

sical sciences have been most affected by the spirit of Kant's philosophy, which has ineradicably engrained in the German mind the necessity of a criticism of the principles of knowledge. Ever and anon some of the most brilliant intellects in mathematics and science have reverted to the same problems, and, on the whole, they have confirmed the position taken up by Kant a century ago.

It was thus under the influence of the exact methods of experiment and calculation taught by the great French school in the beginning of the century, and at the same time through the philosophical spirit peculiar to German science, that in the middle of the century the different sciences which deal with the phenomena of life and consciousness were remodelled. The great science of biology, based upon mechanical principles, was thus created, and the results gained in it brilliantly applied to the reorganisation of the medical profession. But this great reform does not belong exclusively to one great name; it is the work of a long line of thinkers : nor can I conceive that the exclusive employment of the methods of exact research would have so effectually brought it about, unaided by the philosophical, historical, and critical spirit which formed the peculiar characteristic of German thought before the exact methods had been generally introduced. And just because this reform required to be effected from so many different beginnings, and gradually elaborated and defended before it became firmly established, do the modern sciences of physiology and pathology deserve to be termed pre-eminently German sciences ; for no other

37.
Biology grown out of science and philosophy combined.

country possessed the necessary conditions and extensive organisations, the habits of combined study and patient co-operation, the large views and the high aims, which had been acquired at the German universities under the guidance of the German ideal of *Wissenschaft*, and under the sway of the philosophical and classical spirit.

A great authority,[1] who as much as any one represents the modern as distinguished from the earlier views in biological science, reviewing the different agencies which have brought about the great change, speaks thus.   He is referring to Johannes Müller, the father of modern physiology.   "The modern physiological school," he says, "with Schwann at its head, has drawn the conclusions for which Müller had furnished the premises.   It has herein been essentially aided by three achievements which Müller witnessed at an age when deeply-seated convictions are not easily abandoned.   I mean, first of all, Schleiden and Schwann's discovery, that bodies of both animals and plants are composed of structures which develop independently, though according to a common principle.   This conception dispelled from the region of plant-life the idea of a governing entelechy, as Müller conceived it, and pointed from afar to the possibility of an explanation of these processes by means of the general properties of matter.   I refer, secondly, to the more intimate knowledge of the action of nerves and muscles, which began with Schwann's researches, in which he showed how the force of the muscle changes with its contraction.   Investigations which were carried on with all the resources

38.
Du Bois-
Reymond
on Müller.

---

[1] See Du Bois-Reymond, 'Reden,' vol. ii. p. 219, &c.

of modern physics regarding the phenomena of animal movements, gradually substituted for the miracles of the 'vital forces' a molecular mechanism, complicated, indeed, and likely to baffle our efforts for a long time to come, but intelligible, nevertheless, as a mechanism. The third achievement to which I refer is the revival among us by Helmholtz and Mayer of the doctrine of the conservation of force. This cleared up the conception of force in general, and in particular supplied the key to a knowledge of the change of matter in plants and animals. By this an insight was gained into the truth that the power with which we move our own limbs (as George Stephenson did those of his locomotive) is nothing more than sunlight transformed in the organism of the plant: that the highly oxygenated excrements of the animal organism produce this force during their combustion, and along with it the animal warmth, the πνεῦμα of the ancients. In the daylight which through such knowledge penetrated into the chemical mechanism of plants and animals, the pale spectre of a vital force could no more be seen. Liebig, indeed, who himself stood up so firmly for the chemical origin of animal heat and motive power, still retains an accompanying vital force. But this contradiction is probably to be traced to the circumstance that the celebrated chemist came late, and as it were from outside, to the study of the phenomena of life. And even Wöhler still believes in a vital force, he who in his time did more than any one to disturb the vitalistic hypothesis through his artificial production of urea."

39.
"Vital force" abandoned.

It was a process of critical sifting similar to that which Kant[1] applied to our general metaphysical ideas, which in the middle of the century, through the writings of Berzelius and Liebig, of Schwann and Schleiden, of Henle, Lotze, and Du Bois - Reymond, gradually dispelled the older confused notions, and firmly established the mechanical view in the study of the phenomena of life.   But as we are forced to recognise the substance of much of Kant's philosophical criticism in the lucid expositions of Locke and Hume before him, so it has been pointed out that the words of the eminent French physiologist, Vicq-d'Azyr, contain the substance of the more modern ideas on life.[2]   It required the co-operation of the exact

40. Mechanical view in biology.

[1] The great influence which belongs to Kant in the development of modern German science has been frequently dwelt on. In more recent times some of the first representatives of the medical and biological sciences have dealt with the subject, and the opposition which fifty years ago originated in the extravagances of some of Kant's successors, has given way to a renewed recognition of the just claims of Kant. We may refer to Du Bois-Reymond, who, forgetting Lotze, calls Kant the last philosopher who took a part in the work of the naturalist ('Reden,' vol. i. p. 33); to Helmholtz, who in many passages of his popular addresses refers to the merits of Kant ('Vorträge und Reden,' 1884, vol. i. pp. 44, 368; ii. 58, 227, 234, 248, &c.); to Haeser ('Geschichte der Medizin,' vol. ii. p. 811). I will add to these the opinion of so great an authority as Prof. Billroth of Vienna, who, speaking of the two modern schools of medicine in Germany, says ('Lehren

und Lernen der medicinischen Wissenschaften,' &c., p. 334): "However great the degree of independence may be which the two parallel schools have attained, they would hardly have developed so rapidly without the powerful influence which came from France and in a lesser degree from England; nor yet without that of Immanuel Kant, who in his 'Autophysiology of Reason' enlightened German minds regarding their own selves, and who with his lively imagination fervently embraced natural science."

[2] The remarkable passage referred to is quoted by Du Bois-Reymond ('Reden,' vol. ii. p. 27): "Quelqu' étonnantes qu'elles nous paraissent, ces fonctions (viz., dans les corps organisés) ne sont-elles pas des effets physiques plus ou moins composés, dont nous devons examiner la nature par tous les moyens que nous fournissent l'observation et l'expérience, et non leur supposer des principes sur lesquels l'esprit se repose, et croit

spirit of research with the critical methods acquired in the school of philosophy, and the exhaustive survey of a large array of facts acquired through historical and classical studies, before the significance of this brilliant *aperçu* became evident; before the underlying ideas could become useful guides of research and progress. " Tantæ molis erat Romanam condere gentem."

Though the reform of the biological [1] sciences, and their application to pathological inquiries, are probably the greatest achievement which the methods of exact research, in conjunction with the philosophical spirit, can boast of in Germany in the century, the same habit

avoir tout fait lorsqu'il lui reste tout à faire." This was said at the end of the last century, and fifty years later Du Bois-Reymond (*loc. cit.*) could complain that the truth contained in these words was not yet generally admitted, in spite of the labours of Berzelius, Schwann, Schleiden, and Lotze. Compare also A. von Humboldt's own confessions on this point in his ' Ansichten der Natur,' vol. ii. p. 309, &c., edition of 1849.

[1] I must remind the reader here that though I use the word biological as denoting the more recent point of view from which all phenomena of the living world are being grouped and comprehended, and though the word seems to have been first used by a German, nevertheless the arrangement of studies at the German universities has hardly yet recognised the essential unity of all biological sciences. They are unfortunately still divided between the philosophical and the medical faculties. It is indeed an anomaly, hardly consistent with the philosophical and encyclopædic character of German research, that palæontology, botany, zoology, and anthropology should belong to the philosophical, whereas anatomy, physiology, and pathology are placed in the medical faculty. Eminent biologists and anthropologists, such as Schleiden, Lotze, Helmholtz, and Wundt, have accordingly belonged to both faculties. To place biological studies on the right footing would require a mind similar to that of F. A. Wolf, who evolved out of the vaguer idea of *humaniora* the clearer notion of a "science of antiquity," and who accordingly was able to convert the training-school of teachers, the seminary, into a nursery of students of antiquity. Whether a similar reform in the purely scientific interests of the "science of life," which is now mostly cultivated for the benefit of the medical practitioner, can be effected in this age, when practical aims are gradually taking the place of scientific ideas, is another question.

of thought has shown itself in other fields of research, and led to similar innovations. I will here only mention one other line of inquiry, where neither exact nor metaphysical reasoning alone suffices, but where a combination of both is essential. I mean the gradual change which, mainly through the writings of German mathematicians, has come over our fundamental conceptions in the region of geometry, algebra, and the theory of numbers. This subject belongs so essentially to the domain of pure thought that a history of thought seems specially called upon to take notice of it. Accordingly I intend to devote a special chapter to it. At present it interests us mainly because it is an outcome of that peculiar modification which the exact or scientific spirit of thought underwent when, introduced by French and English models, it came in contact with the philosophical and classical ideal of learning in Germany. I will repeat more clearly and concisely what I mean. The exact methods of thought, mainly elaborated in France, and there largely applied, give to science its accuracy and definiteness. In spite of this accuracy and definiteness, it is not immediately clear whether they will lead to completeness of knowledge, or whether they may not be misapplied. To guarantee completeness, to make sure that in the whole great field no portion has remained untouched and unexplored, that love of detail, that searching and exploring spirit, is required which is nursed pre-eminently by historical and classical studies. And to avoid the abuse of existing methods, there is further required that critical spirit which inquires into the value of principles

41.
Criticism of
principles
of mathe-
matics.

and the limit of their usefulness.　These three directions of thought mark three tolerably distinct attitudes of the human mind.　Skill in inventing and in applying new and precise methods—the exact habit or attitude of thought; love of detail, and the desire for complete and exhaustive knowledge—the historical habit or attitude of thought; lastly, the desire to become fully alive to the value of existing methods or principles, which implies a consciousness of the limited nature of one and every principle—the critical habit or attitude of thought.　The progress of mathematics and natural science depends primarily on the first; classical studies depend on the second; philosophical reasoning mainly on the last.　Each of the three nations which have led human progress and thought during the past centuries has probably been possessed of these three cardinal virtues in equal proportions.　For though Newton stands pre-eminent in the first, we have Laplace and Gauss and their numerous followers in other countries; though the great volume of classical learning and criticism has emanated from the schools of Wolf, Hermann, and Böckh, they themselves point back to Bentley and Joseph Scaliger; and even Kant's unrivalled enterprise was prepared by Hume, and dates back to Descartes.　There need, therefore, be no angry rivalry or carping jealousy.　We may point to the remarkably equal contributions of the three nations to the general progress of thought.　But a very different and truly legitimate interest prompts us to note how in the great performances of each nation, in the literature of each of the three languages, different factors have been at work—different

42.
The exact, the historical, and the critical habits of thought.

agencies have combined to produce the effect. In this regard the spectacles presented by French, German, and English thought differ. And there seems to me little doubt that during a considerable portion of this century the German universities, grown out of theological, legal, and medical studies, and widening gradually till they embraced and deepened all three by the philosophical, the classical, and the exact spirit of research, present that organisation in which the different elements of thought are most equally balanced, through which modern know-ledge and the scientific spirit have been most widely and successfully diffused, and that the German ideal of *Wissenschaft* embraces at once the highest aims of the exact, the historical, and the philosophical lines of thought.

43.
Combined in the German ideal of *Wissenschaft*.

Nor would it be right to pass from the consideration of this peculiar feature of nineteenth-century thought, which is an outcome of the German university system, without noticing the moral significance which this ideal of *Wissenschaft* acquired, and which marks it as a factor in progress and in culture of much more importance even than the lasting discoveries in science which it has made, or the monuments of learning which it has reared. It is not the political side of this movement which I refer to, not even pre-eminently the educational, though these are interesting and important enough to demand special his-torical treatment. What I should like to point to as the greatest in this movement is, that it belongs to the few and rare instances in the history of mankind when we see a large number of the most highly gifted members of

44.
Moral value of *Wissenschaft*.

a nation following a purely ideal cause, apart from the inducements which gain or glory may furnish. The pursuit of truth and the acquisition of knowledge for its own sake, as an ennobling and worthy occupation, has during a large portion of our century been the life-work of professors and students alike in the German universities. In the biographies of many of them we meet with that self-denial and elevation of spirit which is the true characteristic of every unselfish human effort. In perusing these records of high aspirations, arising frequently amid disheartening surroundings, these stories of privations cheerfully endured, of devotion to an ideal cause, glowing with all the fervour of a religious duty, we gain a similar impression to that which the contemplation of the Classical period of Greek art or the early Renaissance produces on our mind.

Once at least has science, the pursuit of pure truth and knowledge, been able to raise a large portion of mankind out of the lower region of earthly existence into an ideal atmosphere, and to furnish an additional proof of the belief that there, and not here below, lies our true home. We may perhaps have to admit with regret that this phase is passing away under the influence of the utilitarian demands of the present day; we may be forced to think that another—and, we trust, not a lower—ideal is held up before our eyes for this and the coming age. But no really unselfish effort can perish, and whatever the duty of the future may be, it will have to count among the greatest bequests of the immediate past that high and broad ideal of science which the life of the German universities has traced in clear and indestructible outlines.[1]

[1] The testimonies by illustrious foreigners to the great work of the German universities are frequent and well known, from the time when Mme. de Staël visited Germany, and her friend Villers wrote his 'Coup-d'œil sur les Universités d'Allemagne' in 1808, through the writings of Cousin, the verdict of Renan, of Cournot, of Dreyfus-Brisac, and of the American, J. M. Hart. To these often-repeated expressions I will add that of the great apostle of higher culture of our age, of Matthew Arnold, who sums up his interesting report on the German system of higher education in these characteristic words: "What I admire in Germany is, that while there, too, Industrialism, that great modern power, is making at Berlin and Leipzig and Elberfeld most successful and rapid progress, the idea of Culture, Culture of the only true sort, is in Germany a living power also. Petty towns have a university whose teaching is famous through Europe; and the King of Prussia and Count Bismarck resist the loss of a great savant from Prussia as they would resist a political check. If true culture ever becomes at last a civilising power in the world, and is not overlaid by fanaticism, by industrialism, or by frivolous pleasure-seeking, it will be to the faith and zeal of this homely and much-ridiculed German people that the great result will be mainly owing" ('Schools and Universities on the Continent,' 1868, p. 256).

CHAPTER III.

THE SCIENTIFIC SPIRIT IN ENGLAND.

1.
Scientific
organisation
abroad.

THE history of science in France and Germany during the first half of the present century is identical with the history of two great organisations, the Paris Institute and the German Universities. It is to them that we owe nearly all the great scientific work in the two countries: to the former we owe the foundation of the modern methods of scientific work during the last period of the eighteenth and the early years of the nineteenth century; to the latter we owe pre-eminently the diffusion and widespread application of those methods.[1] We now turn to the country which, in advance of France and Ger-

---

[1] In respect of this I cannot sufficiently recommend M. Maury's volume on 'L'ancienne Académie des Sciences,' which is as eloquent a testimonial to the scientific labours of eminent Frenchmen during the eighteenth century as the companion volume on 'L'ancienne Académie des Inscriptions et Belles Lettres' is a proof of the absence of philological studies during that period. The recent publication of Lexis' work, 'Die deutschen Universitäten,' is just as eloquent a testimonial to the labours of the German universities during this century. The first impression we get from the perusal of these two works is that for a long period France almost monopolised the exact sciences, just as later, for a similar period, Germany almost monopolised classical research, the science of antiquity. And yet the former was probably as much indebted to the Englishman Newton as the latter was to the Frenchman Joseph Scaliger for the character each acquired during the two periods I refer to.

many, had produced the greatest scientific model of modern times, a work which has probably done more than any other purely scientific work to revolutionise our scientific notions—the 'Principia' of Newton. In the subsequent history of the thought of this century, the next chapter will deal with the part that the Newtonian ideas have played throughout the whole period. We have now to turn our attention to the state of science in Great Britain during the period when Paris academicians and German professors combined to define and carry the spirit of modern scientific thought into the several mathematical, physical, and biological branches of research.

Considering that the great scientific institutions of the Continent—the Paris Institute, the scientific and medical schools in Paris, and the German universities—have done so much for the furtherance of science and the diffusion of the scientific spirit, it is natural that we should ask, What have similar institutions done in this country? These institutions are, indeed, mostly older than the academies and modern universities of the Continent. The Royal Society, if not older than the French Academy, is certainly older than the Paris Academy of Sciences.[1]

2. Similar institutions in Great Britain.

---

[1] The actual dates are as follows : The first Academy devoted to the pursuit of science seems to have been the "Academia Secretorum Naturæ," founded at Naples in 1560. Several societies devoted to the culture of literature and art existed in Italy, such as the Academy "della Crusca" (founded at Florence in 1582). The great French Academy, devoted exclusively to the study of the French language, dates from 1629, and received its charter in 1635. The Royal Society, though not the first scheme of its kind which was started in this country —for the establishment of a Royal Academy was discussed as far back as 1616—actually started (1645) in the private meetings described in 'Dr Wallis's Account of Some Passages of his own Life' (quoted by Weld, 'Hist. of the Royal Society,' vol. i. p. 30). These meetings, according to him, were suggested by a German, Theodore Hank, then resident in London. The members were "persons inquisitive into natural philos-

The universities of Oxford, Cambridge, Edinburgh, Dublin, and Glasgow [1] are older than most of the German universities which have done the great scientific work of this century. So far as wealth is concerned, no institution on the Continent could compare with the two older English universities, and the Royal Society had in the beginning of this century long emerged from the poverty which characterised her early history during the lifetime of Newton.[2] Let us look at the subject from a

ophy, . . . and particularly of what hath been called the New Philosophy or Experimental Philosophy." It formed a branch at Oxford in 1649, and received a royal charter in 1662, four years before the "Académie des Sciences" at Paris—which had also previously existed as a private gathering of savants at the houses of Mersenne, Montmort, and Thévenot—was formally installed in the Bibliothèque du Roi. The "Accademia del Cimento" at Florence was established in 1657 ; but it only lasted ten years. Very irregular were also the life and labours of the "Academia naturæ Curiosorum" (later called A. Cæsarea Leopoldina), founded at Vienna in 1652. The Accademia del Cimento printed an important volume of Transactions in 1666. The Royal Society published its first volume in 1665. The first volume of the 'Journal des Savants' is of the same year. Very complete information will be found on all foreign Academies in the 'Grande Encyclopédie,' art. "Académie."

[1] Although the dates of the foundation of Oxford and Cambridge are uncertain, they were certainly more than a century—probably two centuries—older than Prague, the first German university, founded by the Emperor Charles IV. in 1347. The older Scotch universities were founded in the course of the fifteenth century, about the same time that Leipsic appears to have had its origin through a secession from Prague. The German universities —Halle, Göttingen — which were the seat of modern erudition, have a much later date, as given in chap. ii. p. 159, above. Edinburgh was founded at the end of the sixteenth century, and Trinity College, Dublin, about the same time. Leyden, which exerted a great influence both on Scotch and German higher education during the seventeenth century, was somewhat older than Edinburgh.

[2] It appears from Weld ('History,' &c., vol. i. pp. 231, 241, 246, 316, 462, 473) that the financial position of the Royal Society was precarious, and frequently engaged the serious attention of the Council, during the whole first hundred years of its existence ; that as late as 1740 the whole revenue of the Society was only £232 per annum. An effort was then made to get in the large arrears of subscriptions and other contributions. In the following year the income seems to have exceeded the expenditure by £297. Weld adds, "It is a painful task to record these periodical visitations of poverty, which threatened the very existence of the Royal Society ;

different point of view. England has during the early part of the century, in all but the purely mathematical sciences, a greater array of scientific names of the first order than Germany, and nearly as great an array as France. Black, Herschel, Priestley, Cavendish, Davy, Young, Dalton, Faraday, Rowan Hamilton, Brewster, Lyell, Charles Bell, are all identified with one or more novel ideas or definite branches of research.[1] Great Britain had thus no lack

3. English science in the early part of the century.

there is, however, a proportionate amount of pleasure in witnessing the triumphant manner in which the small band of philosophers extricated their institution from serious difficulties, unassisted by Royal bounty and labouring alone on account of their love for science" (vol. i. p. 474).

[1] The following are the principal dates referring to the great discoveries made in this country during the half-century ending 1825 :—

1774. Priestley (1733-1804) discovers oxygen and a variety of other gases.
1775. Black (1728-99), Memoirs on latent heat.
1775. Maskelyne (1732-1811) measures the Attraction of Mount She-hallien.
1775. Landen (1719-90) expresses the arc of an hyperbola in terms of two elliptic arcs.
1778. Benjamin Thompson (Count Rumford, 1753-1814) first experiments on heat by friction.
1781, 13th March, Sir William Herschel (1738-1822) discovers Uranus.
1784. Cavendish (1731-1810) discovers the composition of water.
1786-97. Caroline Herschel (1750-1848) discovers her eight comets.
1798. Cavendish determines the density of the earth.
1799. Davy (1768-1829), essay on heat, light, &c.
1800. Nicholson and Carlisle decompose water with the voltaic pile.
1801. Dalton (1766-1844), theory of evaporation.
1801. Young (1773-1829), first essay on the theory of light and colour.
1802. Dalton, law of expansion of gaseous fluids.
1802. Playfair (1748-1819), 'Illustrations of the Huttonian Theory.'
1802. Wollaston (1766-1829), on Iceland spar, and undulatory theory.
1802-3. William Herschel, observations on nebulæ and double stars.
1802-3. Young expounds the principle of "Interference."
1803-4. Dalton proposes the atomic theory.
1804. Leslie (1766-1832), experiments on heat.
1804. Wollaston discovers palladium and other kindred metals.
1806. Davy isolates the alkaline metals.
1807. Young introduces the word Energy (lect. i. p. 75).
1809. Ivory (1765-1842), on the attraction of ellipsoids.
1810. Young (in 'Quarterly Review') explains the different refractions in crystals.
1810. Davy discovers chlorine to be a simple body.

either of great men of science or of great institutions,
and yet—in spite of these—we read in the course of
the first third of the century about the decline of
science in England.   That such could be seriously said
of a country which within fifty years had in astronomy
discovered a new planet (the first addition to the number
known to the ancients), had discovered oxygen, latent
heat, and the decomposition of water, applied the galvanic current for isolating the most refractory metals,
laid the groundwork for the undulatory theory of light,
established the atomic theory, put forth in statics and
dynamics two of the most important modern generalisations,[1] and introduced in the treatment of electric and

**4.
Alleged de-
cline of
science in
England.**

1810. Brown (1773-1858) publishes his 'Prodromus Floræ Novæ Hol-
    landiæ,' &c.
1811. Charles Bell (1774-1842) asserts the difference of sensory and
    motor nerves.
1813. Brewster (1781-1868) begins his experiments on refraction and
    dispersion.
1813. Davy discovers iodine.
1813. Wollaston publishes his synoptical scale of equivalents.
1814. Wells (1757-1817), essay on dew.
1815. William Smith (1769-1839) publishes his work on 'Strata.'
1815. Brewster gives his law for determining the polarising angle.
1815. Leslie (1766-1832) experiments on radiant heat and temperature
    of the earth.
1816. Prout (1785-1850), Memoir on the position of hydrogen.
1817. Young (in a letter to Arago) suggests transverse vibrations of
    light.
1819. Kater (1777-1835) measures the length of the seconds-pendulum.
1821. Faraday (1781-1867) discovers the rotation of a coil round a fixed
    magnet.
1821. Brown, monographs on botanical subjects.
1821. Sabine (1788-1883) experiments on the dip of the magnetic
    needle.
1823. Rowan Hamilton (1805-65) presents his paper on Caustics to
    the Irish Academy.
1823. Faraday condenses chlorine and other gases.
1824. Sir J. Herschel (1792-1871), observations of double stars.
1825. Sir J. Herschel, on the parallax of fixed stars.

[1] The two important generalisations I refer to are contained in :
  1. George Green, 'An Essay on
the Application of Mathematical
Analysis to the Theories of Electricity and Magnetism,' published

magnetic phenomena novel conceptions, the value of which other fifty years have hardly sufficed to realise —is, indeed, an extraordinary fact well worthy of careful examination. Certainly the language in which Cuvier with truth congratulates the French nation on the pre-eminence which it has attained in all branches of science contrasts strangely with the repeated attacks made in periodical literature, and in special pamphlets, on the state of science in England. And these not by persons ignorant of the great names and signal achievements just mentioned, but by men of note, occupying all but the very first places among the scientific men of this country.

It will suffice to give only two out of many examples of this criticism.

One of the earliest complaints regarding the culture of higher mathematics in this country will be found in an

5.
Criticisms
of Playfair.

at Nottingham by private subscription in 1828. The term "potential function," to denote the sum (V) obtained by adding together the masses of all the particles of a system, each divided by its distance from a given point, or in mathematical language $V = \int \frac{dm}{r}$, occurs there for the first time. See Green's mathematical papers, ed. Ferrers, 1871, p. 22. The function had before that time been used by Legendre and Laplace, but Green was the first to give a general mathematical theory of it. His essay remained unknown to the mathematical world, and the principal theorems were independently published by Gauss in his celebrated essay 'Allgemeine Lehrsätze über die im verkehrten Verhältnisse des Quadrats der Entfernung wirkenden Anziehungs- und Abstossungs-Kräfte,' 1839.

2. W. Rowan Hamilton's memoirs in the 'Philosophical Transactions' of 1834 and 1835, preceded by his theory of systems of rays in the 'Transactions of the Royal Irish Academy,' 1828. In these papers is contained his celebrated principle of varying action, which is a development of Maupertuis's principle of least—or stationary—action. A great deal has been written on this principle, which is now considered to be the most general principle of dynamics, as well for its mathematical usefulness in calculations (see Kirchhoff, 'Vorlesungen über mathematische Physik,' vol. i. pp. 28, 29), as from a physical point of view (Helmholtz, in 'Journal für Mathematik,' vol. 100). It has gained this importance since the conception of energy, or power to do work, has been placed at the base of the theory of all physical processes.

excellent review of Laplace's 'Mécanique céleste' by Playfair in the 'Edinburgh Review' of 1808.[1] "In the list of the mathematicians and philosophers to whom the science of astronomy for the last sixty or seventy years has been indebted for its improvements, hardly a name from Great Britain falls to be mentioned.[2] . . . Nothing prevented the mathematicians of England from engaging in the question of the lunar theory, in which the interests of navigation were deeply involved, but the consciousness that in the knowledge of the higher geometry they were not on a footing with their brethren on the Continent. This is the conclusion which unavoidably forces itself upon us. . . . We will venture to say that the number of those in this island who can read the 'Mécanique céleste' with any tolerable facility is small indeed. If we reckon two or three in London and the military

[1] 'Edinburgh Review,' vol. ii. p. 279, &c. John Playfair (1748-1819) was a native of Forfarshire, and Professor of Mathematics, and later of Natural Philosophy, at the University of Edinburgh. "Playfair was struck with the backwardness of the English mathematicians in adopting the results of the Continental analysts. While they boasted of Newton, they were unable to follow him, and the mantle of Newton had indeed passed over to France, where it rested ultimately on the shoulders of Laplace. Playfair accordingly set himself to diffuse among his countrymen a knowledge of the progress which science had been making abroad. This he did in a variety of ways,—by his articles in the 'Encyclopædia Britannica,' by his papers in the Transactions of learned societies, by his articles in the 'Edinburgh Review,' and by his class-teaching. As David

Gregory introduced the Newtonian philosophy, so Playfair introduced the Continental methods into the studies of the University of Edinburgh" (Sir A. Grant, 'The Story of the University of Edinburgh,' vol. ii. p. 302).

[2] Playfair here excepts his countryman, Colin Maclaurin (1698-1746), "in whose time the teaching of mathematics at Edinburgh reached a point which it cannot be said to have yet surpassed" (ibid., vol. ii. p. 299; cf. also vol. i. p. 271, where a programme published in 1741 is given of the mathematical and physical lectures at Edinburgh, which surpassed probably at that time the teaching of any other English or Continental university). Playfair might have excepted also Ivory and the Englishman Landen, both of whom were well known among Continental mathematicians.

schools in its vicinity, the same number at each of the two English universities, and perhaps four in Scotland, we shall hardly exceed a dozen, and yet we are fully persuaded that our reckoning is beyond the truth."

The other opinion I am going to quote dates from more than twenty years later, and is contained in a pamphlet by Charles Babbage,[1] who with Herschel and Peacock had done much to introduce at the University of Cambridge that knowledge of Continental mathematics which, according to the Edinburgh Reviewer, was so much needed. His 'Decline of the State of Science in England' (1830) was directed mainly against the Royal Society, as the review

6.
Babbage's
criticisms.

[1] Charles Babbage (1792-1871), a native of Devonshire, well known all over Europe through his calculating machine, was a very remarkable and original man. He lived during the age when the application of machinery to manufactures, trades, and arts produced the great reform in the industrial system of this country, and his talents, which might well have been employed in promoting pure science, were largely spent in solving problems of practical interest. An account of these several pursuits and schemes is given in his 'Passages from the life of a Philosopher,' London, 1864. Of his analytical machine we shall have occasion to speak hereafter (see p. 248). Of the beginnings of the new school of mathematics at Cambridge he gives the following account (p. 27). Having purchased for seven guineas a copy of Lacroix's 'Differential and Integral Calculus,' he went to his public tutor to ask the explanation of one of his difficulties. "He listened to my question, said it would not be asked in the Senate House, and was of no sort of consequence, and advised me to get up the earlier subjects of the university studies." Repeated experience of this kind had the effect that he acquired a distaste for the routine studies of the place, and devoured the "papers of Euler and other mathematicians scattered through innumerable volumes of the Academies of Petersburg, Berlin, and Paris." He then perceived "the superior power of the notation of Leibniz." It being an age for forming societies for printing and circulating the Bible at Cambridge, Babbage conceived the plan of a society for promoting mathematical analysis, and to parody one of the many advertisements he proposed to call it a society for promoting "the Principles of pure d'ism (d being Leibniz's symbol) in opposition to the dot-age (dots being Newton's notation) of the university." The most important result of this movement was the publication in 1816 of a translation of Lacroix's treatise, and of two volumes of examples in 1820.

of Playfair was against the English universities.[1] "That science has long been neglected and declining in England is not an opinion originating with me, but is shared by many, and has been expressed by higher authority than mine."[2] The author then proceeds to give extracts from the writings of Davy, Herschel, and others on this subject. "It cannot," he says, "have escaped the attention of those who have had opportunities of examining the state of science in other countries, that

[1] Some of the causes of the decline as given by Babbage are interesting, the more so if we remember that they were written at the period which marked the culmination of *Wissenschaft* in another country (p. 10): "The pursuit of science does not in England constitute a distinct profession, as it does in many other countries. . . . Even men of sound sense and discernment can scarcely find means to distinguish between the possessors of knowledge merely elementary and those whose acquirements are of the highest order. This remark applies with peculiar force to all the more difficult applications of mathematics; and the fact is calculated to check the energies of those who only look to reputation in England." In 1794 Professor Waring of Cambridge wrote: "I have myself written on most subjects in pure mathematics, and in these books inserted nearly all the inventions of the moderns with which I was acquainted; . . . but I never could hear of any reader in England, out of Cambridge, who took the pains to read and understand what I have written;" and "he then proceeds to console himself under this neglect in England by the honour conferred on him by d'Alembert, Euler, and Lagrange"

(see Todhunter, 'History of the Theory of Probability,' p. 453). Babbage remarks (p. 13) that "in England the profession of the law is that which seems to hold out the strongest attraction to talent," that science is pursued as a favourite pastime, and that mathematics "require such overwhelming attention that they can only be pursued by those whose leisure is undisturbed by other claims." "By a destructive misapplication of talent we exchange a profound philosopher for but a tolerable lawyer" (p. 37).

[2] One of the causes given by the Edinburgh Reviewer of 1822 (vol. xxxvii. p. 222) is the following: "In Cambridge there must always be a great number of men devoted to scientific pursuits; but from the want both of the facilities and the excitements furnished by such an association, apt to lose the spirit of original investigation,—a remark peculiarly applicable to those young men who yearly distinguish themselves in the favourite studies of the University, and who, after the laborious course of discipline by which they have attained the first object of their ambition, are prone, if left alone, to become the mere instruments for enabling others to pursue the same course."

in England, particularly with respect to the more difficult
and abstract sciences, we are much below other nations,
not merely of equal rank, but below several even of
inferior power."

" It is," says the Edinburgh Reviewer of 1816,[1] " certainly a curious problem with respect to national genius,
whence it arises that the country in Europe most generally acknowledged to abound in men of strong intellect
and sound judgment should for the last seventy or eighty
years have been inferior to so many of its neighbours in
the cultivation of that science which requires the most
steady and greatest exertions of understanding, and that
this relaxation should immediately follow the period when
the greatest of all mathematical discoveries had been made
in that same country."

It must be said that these opinions, expressed as they
were by men of the highest attainments, did not remain
unchallenged at home or unnoticed abroad.   It will be
interesting to see how they have been met.   Let us first
hear what Cuvier says in his Éloge of Sir Joseph Banks
in 1821[2] regarding the work of the Royal Society during
the period of forty-one years of his presidency : " During
this period, so memorable in the history of the human
mind, English philosophers have taken a part as glorious
as that of any other nation in those labours of the intellect which are common to all civilised peoples : they have
faced the icy regions of both poles ; they have left no
corner unvisited in the two oceans ; they have increased
tenfold the catalogue of the kingdoms of nature ; the

7.
Foreign
opinions on
English
science.

---

[1] 'Edinburgh Review,' 1816, vol.
xxvii. p. 98.

[2] See Cuvier, 'Éloges historiques,'
vol. iii. p. 79.

heavens have been peopled by them with planets, with satellites, with unheard-of phenomena; they have counted, so to speak, the stars of the Milky Way: if chemistry has assumed a new aspect, the facts which they have furnished have mainly contributed to this change: inflammable air, pure air, phlogisticated air, are due to them; they have discovered how to decompose water; new metals in great number are the outcome of their analysis; the nature of the fixed alkalis has been demonstrated by none but them; mechanics at their call have worked miracles, and have placed their country above others in nearly every line of manufacture." Another foreigner, Professor Moll of Utrecht, remarked in his reply to Mr Babbage's pamphlet[1]: "If Mr Herschel and some of his friends

[1] The pamphlet was entitled 'On the alleged Decline of Science in England.' By a Foreigner. London, 1831. It was by Dr Moll of Utrecht, and was introduced by a few lines from Faraday, who, without taking any side in the question, remarked that "all must allow that it is an extraordinary circumstance for English character to be attacked by natives and defended by foreigners." In the discussion on the subject by this writer, as also by Babbage, Herschel, Playfair, Whewell — pro and con. — a good many points of importance are brought out: some of them are still interesting, others refer to defects which have since been remedied. I will mention a few of them. Playfair, in the 'Edinburgh Review' (vol. xxxi. p. 393, 1819), thinks that the "very extensive dissemination of general knowledge, which is so much the case over the whole of this kingdom," is against the advancement of the higher branches of mathe-

matics. This refers probably to the absence of periodicals devoted to special sciences, such as the 'Annales de Chimie et de Physique,' published by Arago and Gay-Lussac in France. In the absence of these special organs, memoirs of original value, which marked an era in special researches, were scattered in general literary reviews, as Young's on Light and Hieroglyphics in the 'Quarterly,' Herschel's and Airy's in the 'Encyclopædia Metropolitana'; and much good mathematics was buried in the 'Ladies' Diary' among poetry of the "worst taste" and "childish scraps of literature and philosophy" ('Edin. Rev.,' vol. ii. p. 282, 1808). Another point is that "the researches of English men of science have been too much insulated from each other and from what is doing in other countries" (Whewell to Vernon Harcourt, 1831; see Life by Todhunter, vol. ii. p. 126). The British Association, which was founded very much as a result of this agitation,

have such a poor opinion of the English scientific journals, a different judgment is entertained abroad, as is well proved by the eagerness with which the German journalists seize upon every article issuing from the presses of their British colleagues. The value which is set in Germany upon the scientific pursuits of the English, the rapidity with which translations are made in Germany of whatever English philosophers of some reputation publish, shows abundantly that in that country at least, in *docta Germania*, a far greater value is set upon the productions of English science than is done by Mr Herschel and his friends." [1]

has remedied this defect; and special periodicals exist now in multitudes; but who could say that a third point has been sufficiently attended to—*viz.*, "the ignorance of foreign languages, which prevails both in England and in France: in England the number of those who acquire a smattering of French is very small, and still smaller is the number of those who know enough of German to read a book in that language without considerable trouble" (Dr Moll, *loc. cit.*, pp. 7, 8). A fourth defect existing at that time is worth mentioning, as we have long left the age of such drawbacks; it "is the high price in England of foreign books, in consequence of an importation duty." The paper duties were repealed in 1861.

[1] Moll, *loc. cit.*, p. 7. Another passage is of interest, as bearing upon the difference between the culture of science in England and in France: "At the time of the French Revolution it so happened, by the exertions of d'Alembert, Clairault, Condorcet, and others, that of all sciences mathematics were the most fashionable. . . . With this view the Ecole Normale was founded, which, though of short duration, was perhaps of more utility towards the extension of mathematical knowledge than all the universities of Europe together. It was there that Laplace, Lagrange, and Monge were lecturers, and men like Lacroix among the hearers. The study of classics having been in a great measure abolished by the French Revolution, mathematics were studied in its stead; and it thus happened that a number of mathematicians, unusually great, were scattered over the soil of France, and every one thought himself capable *de faire les x*, as they themselves called it, upon any given subject. But most of these investigations were all theoretical, and practical applications were foregone in almost every instance" (p. 11). "Mechanics in particular do not seem accessible, according to the tenets of the French school, to any man not well versed in sublime analysis. . . . Hence it arises that many have acquired a profound knowledge of the higher branches of mathematics, whilst the more elementary part of mathematics, which leads to the

8.
English re-
plies to
Babbage,&c.

The answers to the challenges of Babbage and the Edinburgh Reviewer given by English writers themselves cannot on the whole be said to be very reassuring. One of them counts the scientific periodicals in England and in France, but omits to weigh the merit of their respective contributions. Another points to the 'Ladies' Diary,' in which many curious mathematical problems, far beyond the mere elements of science, are often to be met with. A third, whilst in general admitting the correctness of Babbage's strictures, draws attention to the 'Penny Magazine' and the 'Cabinet Cyclopædia' as counterparts in England of the Reports of Cuvier and Berzelius abroad. The true position was probably recog-

9.
Foundation
of the Brit-
ish Associ-
ation.

nised by the founders of the British Association for the Advancement of Science about 1830,[1] who saw that, be-

most useful applications, is far less diffused in France than in England" (p. 12). "The principle of the division of labour [in science] is more acted upon in France than in England" (p. 14).

[1] The movement, which originated in the circle to which Babbage belonged, was — as stated above, p. 42 — to some extent copied from the German Association founded by Oken in 1822. The latter acquired a kind of European renown through the exertions of Humboldt in 1828, who succeeded in attracting a considerable number of celebrities—such as Gauss, Berzelius, Oerstedt, —who for themselves preferred a solitary to a "gregarious" mode of science. Babbage was a guest at this meeting at Berlin, and gave an account of it in an appendix to the 'Decline of Science.' A good account of the character and gradually declining influence of these German meetings will be found in Bruhns' 'Life of Hum-

boldt' (vol. ii. p. 127, &c., translation). They "degenerated after the usual German fashion into the unintellectual form of feasting." The British Association for the Advancement of Science, founded shortly afterwards on the 27th September 1831 at York, was the immediate outcome of a suggestion thrown out by Brewster at the end of a review in the 'Quarterly' of Babbage's 'Decline of Science.' He fully endorsed the latter's opinion, and was even more severe upon the universities, maintaining "that the great inventions and discoveries which have been made in England during the last century have been made without the precincts of our universities. In proof of this we have only to recall the labours of Bradley, Dollond, Priestley, Cavendish, Maskelyne, Rumford, Watt, Wollaston, Young, Davy, and Chevenix; and among the living to mention the names of Dalton, Ivory, Brown, Hatchett, Pond, Herschel,

sides a number of separate societies, " concentration was
needed in one association in order to give more systematic
direction to scientific inquiry, and that the first thing
needed would be to procure reports on the state and the
desiderata of the several branches of science." Babbage,
at the Oxford meeting in 1832, "expressed the general
feeling that meetings should be held in places likely to
bring science into contact with that practical knowledge
on which the wealth of the country depends." There is
also no doubt that in the course of half a century the
British Association has done a very extensive service
to science in the direction of supplying the wants which
its early founders clearly defined, and in bringing about
that concerted action and scientific co-operation which so
highly distinguishes the great academies and universities of
France and Germany.[1] It has done so without altogether
destroying that peculiar feature which characterises not
only the scientific but all the forms of the higher mental
work of this country. In no country has the voice of
public criticism been so free to unveil the shortcomings
which attach to all—even the highest—human effort. In
England there has existed for a long time the habit of
promoting advance in every department by the cultiva-

10.
Character-
istics of
higher men-
tal work in
England.

Babbage, Henry, Barlow, South, Faraday, Murdoch, and Christie; nor need we have any hesitation in adding that within the last fifteen years not a single discovery or invention of prominent interest has been made in our colleges, and that there is not one man in all the eight universities of Great Britain who is at present known to be engaged in any train of original research" ('Quarterly Review,' vol. xliii. p. 327, 1830). He then suggests "an

association of our nobility, clergy, gentry, and philosophers" (p. 342).

[1] The British Association has from the beginning had two features which did not exist in the German society — first, the Reports on the position of various branches of science, delivered by specialists of the highest ability; and, secondly, the Committees, which undertake to do special work requiring concerted action.

tion of party spirit, party criticism, and party shibbo-
leths, as the easiest method of enlisting popular favour [1]
and individual interest; for here there exists no central
authority which can create powerful organisations or dis-
burse public means without the distinctly and repeatedly
expressed support of a large section of the people. But
all this must not induce us, in our historical survey,
to dwell on the defects rather than on the excellence of
the British contributions to the growth and the diffusion
of science. Brilliant is undoubtedly the array of British
names which have during the first half of this century
become immortal by scientific labours, and it would be
narrow-minded simply to emphasise the fact that they have
not done so by the same means and through the same
organisations as the Continental nations have established
and perfected. For we must not forget that these even,
with all their rightly extolled universality and breadth
of spirit, have sometimes failed to recognise merit or to
encourage genius. In spite of the impartial dealings of
the Institute, on which Cuvier congratulates the French
people, there are several instances in which contributions of the first order lay unnoticed for many years.

11.
Academies
and univer-
sities not
always im-
partial.

[1] Referring to the British Association itself, Charles Lyell wrote
in 1838, after the Newcastle meeting, to Charles Darwin : "Do not
let any papers, whether of saints
or sinners, induce you to join in
running down the British Association. I do not mean to insinuate
that you ever did so, but I have
myself often seen its faults in a
strong light, and am aware of what
may be urged against philosophers
turning public orators, &c. But I
am convinced, although it is not
the way I love to spend my own
time, that in this country no importance is attached to any body
of men who do not make occasional
demonstrations of their strength in
public meetings. It is a country
where, as Tom Moore justly complained, a most exaggerated importance is attached to the faculty
of thinking on your legs, and where,
as Dan O'Connell well knows, nothing is to be got in the way of hom-
age or influence, or even a fair share
of power, without agitation " (' Life,
Letters, and Journals of Sir C. Lyell,'
London, 1881, vol. ii. p. 45, &c.)

Fourier's great work on the theory of heat, which for the first time propounded a universal method applicable to the mathematical treatment of almost every physical problem, inasmuch as it, so to speak, follows nature into the marvellous composition of the many movements out of which all her phenomena are compounded, lay buried for fourteen years in the archives of the Institute. That great authority had failed to recognise its paramount importance.[1] Fresnel's first memoir, which established on a firm mathematical basis the undulatory theory of light, was for years left unpublished, whilst the whole scientific world was anxiously expecting the results of his inquiries.[2] In Germany we have examples of similar

12.
Fourier.

13.
Fresnel.

[1] Jean Bapt. Jos. Fourier (1768-1830), of humble origin, in his celebrated 'Théorie analytique de la Chaleur' (Paris, 1822), and in previous memoirs, carried further the mathematical treatment of physical phenomena and introduced wider conceptions of mathematical quantities and their dependence— i.e., of a mathematical "function." His investigations have led to far-reaching applications in physical science (Ohm and Lord Kelvin), and to profound mathematical theories (Dirichlet, Riemann, &c.) The so-called "Fourier" series has thus a great applied as well as theoretical interest. Fourier's first memoir was presented to the Institute in 1807 ; an extract was published in 1808 ; a second memoir was presented in 1811 and crowned, but was not printed till 1824, two years after the great work itself had appeared. On the physical importance of Fourier's analysis see Helmholtz, 'Vorträge und Reden,' vol. i. p. 101, &c. ; Sir W. Thomson, Mathematical and Physical Papers, passim, but especially vol. ii. p. 41,

&c. On the purely mathematical interest that attaches to the Fourier series see especially Riemann, 'Mathematische Werke,' p. 218, &c. A very concise summary of the history of the series is also given by George A. Gibson in the 'Proceedings of the Edinburgh Mathematical Society,' vols. xi. and xii. We shall revert to this subject in a subsequent chapter.

[2] Augustin Fresnel (1788-1827) divides with Thomas Young the merit of having established the undulatory theory of light on a firm basis. His first memoir on Diffraction of Light was presented to the Academy in 1815, a more extensive paper in 1818 ; this was crowned in 1819, but not printed till 1826. Other papers of his were mislaid or lost. The delay in bringing before the world these important discoveries has been attributed to the opposition of Laplace and his party in the Institute, which even the influence of Arago could not overcome. See what Sir John Herschel says in 1827, referring to Fresnel's memoir of 1821 on

discouragement and neglect being thrown in the way of
the growth of new ideas.   Plücker of Bonn laboured for
many years on the union of the geometrical and analytical
methods in the treatment of geometry; but he found so
little appreciation that he abandoned his investigations,
and only resumed them when in after-years a similar line
of thought was independently developed in England.[1]

**14.
Plücker.**

Transverse Vibrations, which the
Academy had recommended to be
printed : " We are sorry to observe
that this recommendation has not
yet been acted upon, and that this
important memoir, to the regret
and disappointment of men of science throughout Europe, remains
yet unpublished " ('Ency. Metrop.,'
article " Light "). A full account
of the opposition and difficulties
which both Young and Fresnel
had to encounter will be found in
Whewell's 'History of the Inductive Sciences,' vol. ii. In earlier
times Réaumur seems to have exercised a similar tyranny in the
Academy of Sciences: see Maury,
' Les Académies d'autrefois,' vol. i.
pp. 280, 123; also Huxley, 'Critiques
and Addresses,' 1890, p. 112, &c.

[1] Julius Plücker (1801-68), professor at Bonn, equally known in
England by his scientific co-operation with Faraday and by that
with Cayley and Salmon, worked
both in physics and geometry on
independent lines.   In the latter
especially he brought about that
union of purely geometrical and
algebraic methods which has become so fruitful in the development
of modern geometry and modern
algebra.   He had two periods of
original geometrical work.   The
first began in 1826 (the year of
the revival of mathematics in Germany), and closed in 1846.   His
mathematical researches were little
noticed in his own country, whereas in France, and still more in

England, his name was well known.
After having published in 1846 a
'System of Geometry,' which contained his former results in a more
methodical form, he dropped his
mathematical researches for twenty
years, during which time he devoted
himself to physical investigations of
great originality.   By these, if he
had not been a personal friend, he
might almost have been called a
rival of Faraday (G. Chrystal in
'Ency. Brit.')   During a visit to
England in 1864 he was agree-
ably surprised to meet with appreciative interest from English
geometricians, who had independently worked on the same lines as
he had done twenty years earlier.
He was thus induced to resume his
favourite studies, and to develop an
idea which had already been expressed in his last-named work of 1846.
This led to a new fundamental conception of geometrical forms, in
which not the point but the line
is the element of space.   He was
not spared to complete this line-
geometry, but after his death his
pupils found sufficient material to
put his researches into a systematic
form under the title, 'Neue Geometrie des Raumes, gegründet auf
die Betrachtung der geraden Linie
als Raumelement' (Leipzig, 1868
and 1869).   See Clebsch on Julius
Plücker, Göttingen, 1872. A very
appreciative notice of Plücker, by
George Chrystal, will be found in
the 9th edition of the 'Encyclopædia Britannica.'

Grassmann, in his 'Ausdehnungslehre,' published in 1844, is now generally admitted to have originated quite a novel way of considering geometrical relations.[1] It took twenty years, however, before he succeeded in attracting any attention, and his great work, of which the first edition had been sold as waste-paper, was later on reprinted in its original form—mathematicians having now begun to study and recognise its intrinsic value.   Such cases of neglect have undoubtedly been much more frequent in England, where even at the present day no central organisation exists which annually collects and arranges the scattered labours of individual workmen, and where that historical and encyclopædic spirit is wanting which does its utmost to guarantee completeness and thoroughness of search and of research.   Men of the greatest eminence, pioneers

15. Grassmann.

16. Central organisation wanting in England.

[1] Hermann Grassmann (1809-77) was born, lived, and died at Stettin. He did not succeed till late in life, and fully thirty years after he had published his original investigations in geometry, in gaining for these the recognition and appreciation which they deserved. Neither he nor even Jacob Steiner at Berlin attained to positions worthy of their ability ; the latter, in spite of his connection with other great mathematicians, never filled the chair of an ordinary professorship, whilst the former never entered the sphere of university teaching at all.   The 'Ausdehnungslehre,' as a new branch of mathematics, appeared in 1844.   It is a science of pure extension, the application of which to empirical space is geometry. Similar investigations, in which space of three dimensions is considered to be merely a particular case of pure extension of any number of dimensions, which are not necessarily determined by the same pro-perties as our empirical space, have become familiar since the publication of Riemann's celebrated dissertation of 1854 (published in 1867), and since Helmholtz was led to similar investigations by considering the different dimensions or manifoldnesses of our sense perceptions (see his 'Vorträge und Reden,' in many passages).   Grassmann, who at the end of his life witnessed the growing appreciation of his ideas, had filled up the interval with entirely different studies, the translation of the 'Rig-Veda' (Leipzig, 1876-77), and the composition of a dictionary to the same (1872-75).   He seems to have been the only mathematician, besides Thomas Young, who combined the ability for exact mathematico-physical and for philological studies. Both can complain of having been very insufficiently appreciated by their contemporaries.   See Victor Schlegel, 'Hermann Grassmann,' Leipzig, 1878.

in their line of thought and discovery, have to the present
day remained popularly unknown to their countrymen,
who have not only neglected but reviled them, allowing
their great discoveries to be taken up as their own by
17.
Thomas
Young.
foreigners. Such was Dr Thomas Young, whom many
educated persons at the present day cannot distinguish
from the author of ' Night Thoughts.' [1]   The great founder

[1] Thomas Young (1773-1829), a
native of Somersetshire, attained
equal eminence by his discoveries
in connection with the undulatory
theory of light, in which he was
the first to assert the principle of
interference and that of transverse
vibrations, and by his discovery
of the key to the system of hieroglyphics. Of his discoveries and
suggestions some were published in
anonymous review articles (so especially his hieroglyphical papers);
some in his Lectures on Natural
Philosophy, delivered early in the
century at the Royal Institution,
and published 1807; some in the
'Transactions of the Royal Society'
(from 1800 onwards); and some in
various collective works, especially
the 'Encyclopædia Britannica.' The
remarkable fact that Young, of
whom Helmholtz says ('Vorträge
und Reden,' vol. i. p. 279) that he
came a generation too soon, remained scientifically unrecognised
and popularly almost unknown to
his countrymen, has been explained
by his unfortunate manner of expression and the peculiar channels
through which his labours were announced to the world. His frequently unintelligible style, his obscure and inelegant mathematics,
the habitual incognito which he preserved, his modesty in replying to
attacks, and his general want of
method in enunciating his ideas, contrast very markedly with the writings of some of his rivals, especially

in France, where the qualities of
style, method, and elegance were
highly developed, and where recognised organs existed for the publication of works of genius.   The
historian of thought, however, must
not omit to state that several great
names contributed, by the authority they commanded, to oppose
Young's claims to originality and
renown. Lord Brougham, shielded
by the powerful anonymity of
the 'Edinburgh Review,' and osten-
tatiously parading the authority of
Newton, submitted the views of
Young to a ruthless and unfair
criticism, the popular influence of
which Young probably never over-
came. The great authority on optics, Brewster, who has enriched
that science by such a number of
experiments and observations of
the first importance, never really
adopted the theories of Young and
Fresnel. In the other great branch
of research with which Young's
name is now indissolubly connected, in the science of hieroglyphics,
the authority of Bunsen decided
against Young and for the Frenchman Champollion. But this decision, which did so much to obscure the merits of Young, was
founded on an insufficient knowledge of the dates of Young's publications. Since these were collected by Leitch in the third volume
of the 'Miscellaneous Works' of Dr
Young (London, 1855), the chronology of his discoveries, which begin

of modern chemistry, who next to Lavoisier did more than any one else to introduce into this science mathematical ideas, John Dalton, grew old and infirm before his countrymen sufficiently recognised and honoured him. Deprived of all but the very meanest apparatus for the proofs of his theories, and yet able to do what he did, what might not such a genius have accomplished if he had possessed the means of a Gay-Lussac or a Regnault ?[1]

18. Dalton.

in 1814, has been well established. See Benfey, 'Geschichte der Sprachwissenschaft' (München, 1869, p. 729). Bunsen pronounced his verdict in his well-known work, 'Egypt's Place in Universal History,' published in 1845-57. On the whole, the words of Peacock, 'Life of Dr Young' (London, 1855), p. 472, are still correct: " His scientific works were rarely read and never appreciated by his contemporaries, and even now are neither sufficiently known nor adequately valued ; whilst if justice was awarded more promptly and in more liberal measure by his own countrymen to his hieroglyphical labours, these also were singularly unfortunate, as far as concerned the general diffusion of his fame, by coming into collision with adverse claims, which were most unfairly and unscrupulously urged in his own age, and not much less so by some distinguished writers in very recent times."

[1] John Dalton (1766-1844), a native of Cumberland, spent the greater part of his life in teaching elementary mathematics at Manchester, first at a college and then privately. In 1801 he propounded the law known under the joint name of Dalton and Gay-Lussac (who stated it six months later). In the years immediately following he elaborated his atomic theory, which was to account for the existence of those definite quantitative relations between the chemical constituents of bodies known already to Richter. It was published in 1805. But the man who did most to make known to chemists the ideas of Dalton was Thomas Thomson (1773-1852), Professor of Chemistry at Glasgow, who in 1807, in the 3rd edition of his 'System of Chemistry,' gave an account of the atomic theory based upon communications of Dalton. Two memoirs published in the 'Philosophical Transactions' of 1808—one by Thomson on "Oxalic Acid," and one by Wollaston on "Super-Acid and Sub-Acid Salts" —pointed to the great importance of the atomic theory, which (Wollaston prophetically added) would not stop short with the determination of the relative weights of elementary atoms, but would have to be completed by a geometrical conception of the arrangement of the elementary particles in all the three dimensions of solid extension. The real merit of having experimentally proved the theory of Dalton belongs to Berzelius, whereas Sir Humphry Davy opposed it for many years after it had been accepted abroad. Dalton himself by no means followed the development which his ideas underwent at the hands of others. For example, he opposed Gay-Lussac's law of volumes. He was on the whole more successful in working out his own

19.
Faraday.

Faraday, instead of being backed by a wealthy Academy and ample assistance, had during all the years when his great discoveries were being made, to keep alive, with an income scarcely exceeding a hundred pounds a-year, an institution which but for him the memory even of such names as Rumford, Young, and Davy would not have sufficed to preserve from utter ruin and collapse.[1] The author of one of the most suggestive treatises in the application of mathematics to physical phenomena,

20.
Green.

George Green, published it in 1828 at Nottingham by private subscription. Seventeen years later, William Thomson (Lord Kelvin) tried in vain to procure a copy

ideas than in comprehending those of others who, like Berzelius, Mitscherlich, Laplace, Liebig, and many later, contributed to the confirmation of the atomic theory. A good account of this is given in Henry's 'Life of Dalton' (1854) and in Kopp's 'Entwickelung der Chemie in der neueren Zeit' (München, 1873).

[1] Michael Faraday (1791-1867), though not a mathematician, introduced into the science of electricity those ideas which have since been developed into a mathematical theory approaching in completeness the mathematics of the undulatory theory of light. What the atomic theory has done for chemistry, Faraday's lines of force are now doing for electrical and magnetic phenomena. Dalton, though unacquainted with the higher mathematics of the French school, had essentially a mathematical or arithmetical mind. Faraday's peculiar ideas on the nature of electrical and magnetic action, though supported by an experimental knowledge many times surpassing in volume and accuracy that of Dalton, did not find much appreciation among his contemporaries. They were much more interested in his experimental researches than in his theories. In France and Italy Faraday's eminence was recognised early. Already in 1823 he was elected member of the Academies of Paris and Florence, almost before any society at home had received him. "The circumstances under which Faraday's work was done were those of penury. During a great part of the twenty-six years the Royal Institution was kept alive by the lectures which Faraday gave for it. 'We were living,' as he once said to the managers, 'on the parings of our own skin.' He noted even the expenditure of the farthings in research and apparatus. He had no grant from the Royal Society, and throughout almost the whole of his time the fixed income which the Institution could afford to give him was £100 a-year, to which the Fullerian professorship added nearly £100 more" (Bence Jones, 'Life and Letters of Faraday,' London, 1870, vol. ii. p. 344). See also Bence Jones, 'The Royal Institution,' p. 311.

of this document, of which he knew by a reference in another work. At last he got possession of a copy which had probably during all this time been buried in the library of a prominent mathematical tutor at Cambridge, with whom he had been in frequent intercourse. Thomson then took it with him to Paris, where Sturm and Liouville at once recognised its merits. He then published it in 'Crelle's Journal,' where it has ever since been referred to as a fundamental essay on the so-called potential theory.[1] One of the most original thinkers on mathematics, who introduced a novel principle into algebraical science, George Boole, never attained to a higher position than that of teacher at a remote Irish provincial College.[2] But perhaps the most signal example of the want of support which the

21.
Boole.

[1] See note 1 to p. 231; also Sir William Thomson, reprint of papers on "Electrostatics and Magnetism," 2nd ed., London, 1884, p. 2, note; p. 126, note.

[2] George Boole (1815-64), a native of Lincolnshire, was one of the few great and original mathematicians who, like Leibniz and Grassmann, and to some extent Gauss, looked at the logical as well as the purely arithmetical side of the language of symbols. Though his treatises on 'Differential Equations' (1859) and on 'Finite Differences' (1860) have become well-known text-books, and his 'Laws of Thought' (1854), in which he examined the foundations of the mathematical theories of logic and probabilities, remains a unique work, his principal services to science lie in the direction of the "calculus of operations." In this branch of mathematics, which is peculiar to England, the symbols indicating an arithmetical operation are separated from those denoting quantity and treated as distinct objects of calculation. In connection with these investigations, many of which have now penetrated into ordinary textbooks, Boole was led to examine the conditions under which and the forms in which algebraical expressions, whilst undergoing changes and transformations, remain, nevertheless, unaltered (invariant) (1841). By introducing this point of view he has, so to speak, created modern algebra; founding the extensive and fruitful science of "Invariants." Of this we shall treat later on. I now only refer to the further development of this subject in the hands of Cayley and Sylvester, and to the valuable sketch of the history of this branch of mathematics by Dr F. Mayer in the first volume of the 'Jahresbericht der deutschen Mathematiker-Vereinigung,' Berlin, 1892.

wealthiest of nations has shown to scientific genius is to be found in the history of Babbage's calculating engine. Yet this machine was approved by all experts —English and foreign—during the inventor's lifetime; and the Report of a Commission of the British Association appointed specially to examine into the matter, concluded by stating that the scheme was perfectly feasible, and might, if carried out, mark an invention as great probably as that of logarithms.[1] Who among us who has been interested in the promotion of institutions for higher education has not a story to tell of pecuniary troubles, continued through many a long year, whilst the wealth of the country seemed to exert its influence only in the direction of making the demands on a struggling establishment more formidable, the expenses more difficult to defray?[2]

[1] On Babbage see p. 233, note 1. The history of the "difference engines" and the "analytical engine" is given by Babbage himself in his 'Passages from the Life of a Philosopher.' See also Weld, 'History of the Royal Society,' vol. ii. p. 369, &c.

[2] Like the Royal Society, which for a century had to struggle with poverty, the Royal Institution has a story to tell of want of funds through a long period of its early existence. See Bence Jones, 'The Royal Institution,' London, 1871, pp. 202, 281. The Royal Institution was founded by Benjamin Thomson, Count Rumford (1753-1814), and had originally not a scientific, hardly even a higher educational object. The scheme arose in the mind of its founder after he had successfully exerted himself at Munich under the patronage of the Elector of Bavaria in founding industrial workhouses, improving the state of the army, and putting down beggary and immorality in the capital and country. His principle was to make "vicious and abandoned people first happy and then virtuous" (p. 31). After leaving Munich in 1793 and spending two years in Italy, similarly occupied, he visited London in 1795 in order to publish his Essays, which appeared separately between 1796 and 1802. The first essay contained "a proposal for forming in London by private subscription an establishment for feeding the poor and giving them useful employment, . . . connected with an institution for introducing and bringing forward into general use new inventions and improvements," &c., &c. (p. 44). The first outcome of this was the formation of a society for encouraging industry and promoting

But it is hardly the duty of the historian of thought to record that which belongs more to the impediments of mental progress than to its promotion, were it not that in and through these peculiar circumstances the genius of the nation has developed its main features, its strong character.   These are manifest as much in the department of science as they are in general literature and in the institutions of practical life.   British science through all the centuries, since the time of Roger Bacon, and in spite of the efforts of his illustrious namesake, has

23. Characteristics of English thought.

the welfare of the poor.   William Wilberforce was one of the original promoters ; Thomas Bernard, the founder of many other charitable institutions, one of its most active members.   To a committee of this Society Count Rumford submitted, in 1799, his proposals for forming the Royal Institution, and it was accordingly founded in February of that year on private subscriptions of fifty guineas each.   It was described as a "public Institution for diffusing the knowledge and facilitating the general introduction of useful mechanical inventions and improvements, and for teaching by courses of philosophical lectures and experiments the application of science to the common purposes of life."   In the course of a very few years the original character of the Institution entirely changed, the aim of influencing directly the condition of the poor was lost sight of, and little remained besides the result of "bringing science into some degree of fashion" and "affording a new employment and amusement to the higher classes of life."   The interest of the Institution for the history of thought is the fact that in its laboratory Davy and Faraday conducted their researches, and that they, as well as Young, Coleridge, and Sydney Smith, there delivered their lectures.   And the history of the Royal Institution is also typical of the history of other establishments for higher culture in this country : it has been in its main features repeated on a larger or smaller scale in many provincial societies, and notably in the colleges of Manchester, Birmingham, Liverpool, Newcastle, Leeds, Bristol, Nottingham, &c.   Started by persons with large but nevertheless insufficient means, or by subscriptions and endowments of moderate extent, obliged to gain popularity and fashionable support in order to meet their growing expenses, these institutions have depended mostly on individual energy for their first successes, and have all had to pass through periods of great difficulty, till in course of years they have acquired a special character of usefulness and defined their peculiar sphere of action.   The absence of a definite programme and a great waste of energy and funds over special departures are not uncommon features of these developments.

refused to congregate in distinct schools and institutions
or to be localised in definite centres.   The Royal Society,
the Royal Institution, the British Association, and many
other smaller societies, have all more or less started with
the programme of Lord Bacon, and have failed to realise
it : everywhere the schemes of co-operation or organised
scientific research have encountered the opposition of
individual pursuits or of local interests.

Newton could not secure the use of Flamsteed's observations, which on their part remained uncompleted and
unpublished through the want of appreciation of others.
Great schemes in practical life have been carried out
by the unaided efforts of eminent persons, and great
ideas have been put forward with all the power and
all the resources of individual genius,[1] but no great

**24.
Absence of
schools of
scientific
thought.**

master in scientific research in this country can point
to a compact following of pupils—to a school which
undertakes to finish what the master has begun, to carry
his ideas into far regions and outlying fields of research,
or to draw their remoter consequences.   Newtonianism
was a creation of Voltaire ; the school of Locke is to be
found in France ; the best realisation of Bacon's schemes
are the Encyclopédie, the French Institute, and the
foreign Academies.[2]   Dr Young's discoveries in optics

[1] See Huxley, 'Lay Sermons,
&c.,' edition of 1891, p. 43 : "England can show now, as she has been
able to show in every generation
since civilisation spread over the
West, individual men who hold
their own against the world, and
keep alive the old tradition of her
intellectual eminence.   But in the
majority of cases these men are
what they are in virtue of their
native intellectual force, and of a
strength of character which will
not recognise impediments.   They
are not trained in the courts of
the Temple of Science, but storm
the walls of that edifice in all sorts
of irregular ways, and with much
loss of time and power, in order to
obtain their legitimate positions."

[2] See above, pp. 34, 95.

and hieroglyphics were made known to the learned world through his French contemporaries.   Dalton,[1] Charles Bell,[2] Faraday, Darwin, and Maxwell, no less than Bentley and Gibbon,[3] have furnished the text for lecture-courses in German universities, and created a whole literature of pamphlets and scientific memoirs.[4]   English societies may sometimes honour and admire, but they do not support, their great representatives, and these themselves often refuse to be tied by exclusive academic duties, still more by official restrictions.   Two characteristics have marked most of them : they have, at all expense and sacrifice, guarded their individual freedom of thought, and they have almost always shown a great desire to combine some application with their abstract researches, to take part in the great practical work of the nation.   Continental thinkers, whose lives are devoted to the realisation of some great ideal, complain of the want of method, of the erratic absence of discipline, which is peculiar to English genius.   The fascination which practical interests exert in this country appears to them an absence of full devotedness to purely ideal pursuits.[5]

25.
Individual character and practical tendency of English science.

[1] See above, p. 245, note.
[2] See above, p. 193, note.
[3] See above, p. 169, note.
[4] Germany may be said to have produced *Darwinismus* in this century as France created *Newtonianisme* in the last.   Huxley writes ('Life of Darwin,' vol. ii. p. 186) : "None of us dreamed (in 1860) that in the course of a few years the strength (and perhaps I may add the weakness) of *Darwinismus* would have its most extensive and most brilliant illustrations in the land of learning."   Quite recently Prof. Boltzmann at Munich, and M. Poincaré, have published courses

of lectures on Maxwell's electric theories.

[5] What appears irksome to an English genius—the red tape of academic restrictions, the barriers of officialism, and the duties of the teacher—melted away in the glow of enthusiasm and love of truth which animated the great leaders and founders of university culture abroad ; as Goethe has told us that the rigid form of the sonnet melts in the fervour of the love-song :

" Das Allerstarrste freudig aufzuschmelzen
Muss Liebesfeuer allgewaltig glühen."
—Sonette No. 14.

The English man of science would reply that it is unsafe to trust exclusively to the guidance of a pure idea, that the ideality of German research has frequently been identical with unreality, and that in no country has so much time and power been frittered away in following phantoms, and in systematising empty notions, as in the Land of the Idea; but he would as readily admit that his own country is greatly deficient in such organisations for combined scientific labour as exist abroad, and that England possesses no well-trained army of intellectual workers.

26.
English pe-
culiarities
more pro-
nounced
during early
part of the
century.¶

These differences between English and Continental science were most pronounced in the first half of the present century, when Germany developed her university system, when France clearly defined the exact scientific methods, and when the encyclopædic view—peculiar to the historical and philosophical pursuits of the earlier years—gradually became dominant in the exact sciences also. Since then the intercourse of the different nations has done much to destroy these national peculiarities. The reform of the universities, in which Germany was engaged in the early years of the century, did not touch the English universities before the middle of the century. In the meantime quite different demands had sprung up all through the civilised world; and as nothing repeats itself in history, it will be impossible to reach in this country the same broad organisation for purely intellectual work as Germany can rightly boast of during the period we are dealing with. Some persons doubt whether it will be maintained in Germany. It appears still more doubtful whether such an organisation could now be created in the face of the industrial spirit of our age. Ever since the latter half of the eighteenth century schemes for a general education of the masses have attracted the thought and the attention of philanthropists and statesmen in many countries of Europe. But the directions taken by these educational efforts have been characteristically different in the different countries, and their success, so far as the great masses of the people are concerned, has been very partial indeed. It is true that during the first thirty years no country possessed such distinguished schools of science as did France in the great scientific and medical institutions of her capital. It is also true that no country equalled Germany in her system of universities and higher schools, which had come under the influence of classical learning and philosophical ideals. England, which at that time took no part in the educational movements of the Continent,[1] possessed, neverthe-

---

[1] This statement requires two qualifications. Firstly, both Milton and Locke have had great influence in spreading enlightened views regarding the principles and the object of education in general—especially in the direction of enlarging the idea of education, so as to make it comprise something more than merely instruction and pedantic teaching. I cannot find, however, that in England, either in the direction of higher university education or of a general system of popular education, their influence has been very marked. Locke's influence abroad, through his psychological analysis of the mind, has been very considerable. Secondly, in the direction of practical education, of the endeavour to reach large numbers of the people by educational institutions, we must look with admiration to the early work done in Scotland, which in this respect somewhat resembles Switzerland. The Scotch system of parochial schools, and their influence on the education of the people, has been too little studied abroad, though rightly extolled at home. It is true that, with the exception of Calvin, none of the great Continental educationalists—such as Fénelon, Rousseau, Pestalozzi, or W. von Humboldt—have had any direct influence on Scotland ; nor has the educational work of Scotland produced any great educational literature like that which Switzerland can boast of, and which has brought the theory of education so prominently before the world. But nevertheless there it stands, this creation of John Knox and the early Reformers. " Civilised

27.
Unique
character of
English uni-
versities.
less, something peculiar in her two great universities. It was neither the scientific, nor the classical, nor the philosophical spirit exclusively which reigned there; if any or all of them had ruled, we should not meet with those repeated complaints that higher mathematics were absent in Cambridge, that no philological studies were cultivated in either of the universities, and that philosophy was represented merely by Aristotle, Butler, Locke, and Paley.[1] According to the representatives of the university

Europe has never witnessed a nobler spectacle than the first Protestants of Scotland in the assembly of the nation demanding that from the funds before abused by a licentious superstition one-third should be devoted, not to increase the revenue of the Reformed Church, but to the education, the universal education, of the youth in all departments of instruction, from the highest to the lowest" ('North Brit. Rev.,' 12, p. 483).

[1] As to the deficient mathematical teaching at Cambridge, see p. 233, note, &c. The complaints regarding the teaching of other subjects are frequent, but belong to a later date, the middle of the century, when the Royal Commission of Inquiry, which was appointed under the Government of Lord John Russell on the 31st August 1850 and expired with the presentation of its report on the 30th August 1852, attracted the attention of the public to university reform, and gave rise to a very full discussion of the whole subject in the various literary papers and reviews. The two older universities are called "citadels of political prejudice and sectarian exclusiveness, instead of being the temples of liberal arts and the repositories of science" ('Brit. Quart. Review,' 1860, July, p. 205). Theology is stated to be "the last

thing taught at Cambridge" (ibid., p. 221); there was no professor of Latin, none of English literature, of logic and metaphysics, of modern languages (p. 225). In 1849 Cambridge had no laboratory; the universities took no part in the legal training of lawyers ('Edin. Rev.,' April 1849, p. 511); Oxford afforded no training in natural science (ibid.) Cambridge "sacrificed to the monopoly of a severe geometry every other exercise and attainment of the human mind. There was no theological study, no study of history, none of moral science, none of chemistry, none even of experimental philosophy" (ibid., p. 514). These criticisms were fully justified by the Reports of the Commissions published in 1852. See on the teaching of Theology at Cambridge, Report, pp. 89, 102; Evidence, pp. 88, 168, 190, 216: on the teaching of Latin, Rep., pp. 98, 102; Evid., pp. 165, 176, 289: on the teaching of English, Evid., pp. 124, 136: of modern Languages, Rep., pp. 26, 101; Evid., pp. 165, 216, 300: of Law, Rep., pp. 35, 182; Evid., pp. 123, 190: of Natural Sciences, Evid., p. 115, &c. In 1874 the 'Edinburgh Review' could point out that during twenty years, whilst the examination for the Indian Civil Service had been thrown open, the English universities had practically contributed no

system, what England did possess was the ideal of a *liberal education*. But none of these three forms of intellectual training—neither the scientific in Paris, nor the classical in Germany, still less the liberal in England—touched the great masses of the people. They all did good work in their respective lines; but they left, or would by themselves have left, the country in darkness. The beginnings of general popular education are to be traced independently in Switzerland, in Scotland, and in many of the small States of Germany.[1] The great scientific

28.
Ideal of
Liberal Edu-
cation.

candidates to the competition (April 1874, p. 342). "Nothing about university life was more striking" to the Edinburgh Reviewer "than the contrast between the efforts and the high aims of the few, the culture and solid result achieved by them—and the utter uselessness of it to the many" (p. 354). The 'Quarterly Review' of June 1826 notes "a growing taste for the cultivation of physical science as characteristic of the state of the public mind in England" (p. 159), and refers to the "measures which have been carried into effect throughout the country with great harmony of design, although chiefly by the unassisted exertions of private individuals, . . . the recent establishment of numerous literary and philosophical institutions in our metropolis and many of our provinces" (ibid., p. 154).

[1] The great Reformers—Luther, Melanchthon, Zwingli, and Calvin— alike took a great interest in education, which they intended to be universal and popular. But their success, so far as the education of the people was concerned, remained everywhere very partial. A real organisation of primary schools was not attained. They prepared for it by introducing the vernacular languages, the reading of the Bible, the popular hymns. Their main efforts lay in the training of good teachers for church and schools in the reorganisation of what were called the Latin schools. In the course of the sixteenth and seventeenth centuries the smaller Protestant States of Germany—especially Saxony, Würtemberg, Brunswick, the northern cities Hamburg and Lübeck—received under various forms what was called "Eine Kirchen- und Schulordnung." Luther's tract of the year 1524, addressed to the "burgomasters and councillors of all towns of the German land, that they should found and maintain Christian schools," was the beginning of this movement. In Scotland burgh schools, also grammar (or Latin) schools and lecture schools, "in which the children were instructed to read the vernacular language," existed long before the Reformation. But to John Knox is due the scheme for popular education contained in the 'First Book of Discipline.' The parochial schools were started in many instances by voluntary or ecclesiastical assessment through the efforts of the Reformed clergy. The foundation of the subsequent system of parochial schools was laid

schools of France trained the civil and military engineers in that country, and produced text-books for the

in the statute of 1696. It must not be forgotten, however, that the "Order of Jesus" (founded 1540), whose higher educational work has found so much appreciation from men like Sturm—the Protestant educationalist — Lord Bacon, and Descartes (see the quotations in Schmidt's 'Geschichte der Pädagogik,' 4th ed., vol. ii. p. 248), was also active in the direction of popular and primary education. In emulation of the Protestant movement, it had introduced "school regulations" in many Catholic countries, and even founded a special order —the "Patres piarum scholarum" (1600)—for the education of the poorer classes (ibid., p. 253). Whether the statute of 1696 is the earliest official document referring to popular education and providing the means of maintaining an adequate number of schools (one in 1000 of population) to teach the lower classes, I cannot say. It appears that Duke Ernest of Gotha, in the course of the seventeenth century, established a general system of primary education in his territory which was "quite unique, at first an object of ridicule, but then very soon of emulation" (ibid., p. 333). The regulations were certainly most wise and liberal, and attendance was made compulsory. The question of popular education was taken up on a much larger scale by Frederick the Great in the middle of the eighteenth century. The year 1763, which marks the end of the Seven Years' War, is also the year of an edict which forms the basis of the regulation of popular education for the whole monarchy : it establishes village schools with compulsory attendance. It met with much opposition, and its ends were only slowly

realised, and only as training-schools, where a sufficient number of teachers were educated, sprang up, and as popular school and story-books were provided. Campe, with his edition of 'Robinson Crusoe,' marks an epoch in this direction. In fact, the cause of universal popular education remained in the hands of private persons, frequently of men of great insight and organising ability—such as A. H. Francke (1663-1727), the indefatigable friend of the poor and of orphans ; Basedow (1723-90), the founder of the Philanthropin and populariser of Rousseau's ideas ; Von Rochow (1734-1805), the friend of the country - folk and founder of village schools ; Von Felbiger (1724-88), the adviser of Maria Theresa and Joseph II., the organiser of the popular educational system in Austria (1770-80) : or else it was dependent on the casual favour of enlightened princes and sovereigns. At length, in the middle of the eighteenth century, training-schools for teachers, so-called "seminaries," were founded all over Germany. A beginning had been made by Duke Ernest of Gotha (1601 - 75), but had been neglected like many other beginnings. But in the second half of the eighteenth century no less than thirty-three seminaries were founded all over Germany, including Austria. For details on this important and interesting subject, see the third volume of Schmidt's 'Geschichte der Pädagogik.' Freytag's 'Bilder aus der deutschen Vergangenheit' also contains many interesting details ; but above all I would recommend for the countries of the west and south of Germany the valuable researches of C. T. Perthes contained in his 'Politische Zustände und Personen

higher scientific training of the whole of Europe;[1] but no serious effort was made, during the brilliant days of the First Empire, to secure for the nation the blessing of a popular education. This state of things continued under the Restoration; the real beginnings of an organised primary system are to be found in Guizot's celebrated law of 1833. In Germany the influence of Pestalozzi and Zschokke in the south; of Basedow, Francke, and the school of Kant and Herder, and, later, of Herbart in the north,—stimulated many Governments to establish a system of popular schools for the education of the masses, and a system of seminaries for the training of a popular teaching staff. This movement was chiefly carried on independently of the reform of the universities and higher schools, over which the ideal of *Wissenschaft* exercised a powerful spell. Under the latter were trained the leaders and higher teachers of the nation, as well as the members of the learned professions. The educational influence of this ideal on the more gifted among the student class was the very highest and best; but it hardly

in Deutschland zur Zeit der französischen Herrschaft,' 2 vols., Gotha, 1862 and 1869. As unfortunately this work, with its collection of interesting and not easily accessible facts referring to the inner history of the German people, has no index, I give the following references : Compulsory education in Kur Trier in 1712, vol. i. p. 225 ; in Kurmainz, 1750, vol. i. p. 19 ; popular education in Baden, vol. i. p. 411 ; in Bavaria, vol. i. pp. 436, 467 ; in Würtemberg, vol. i. p. 537 ; and the chapter on Joseph II.'s school reform, vol. i. pp. 153-170. The seminary or training-school being thus the centre and beginning of national education in Germany, as it has also, with a different constitution, become the centre of scientific work (see p. 214, note), it is interesting to note that Scotland, so far advanced in educational work, had no real training-school for teachers before Stow started his Normal School in Glasgow (see 'Chambers's Encyclopædia,' art. "Education"), and that the "seminary" for higher scientific work has to this day not yet been introduced into this country.

[1] See above, p. 44, note.

reached the multitude of less gifted minds, who always gave themselves to bread-studies ; and it must necessarily fail yet more when not only the future teachers and leaders, but the masses of the nation, flock into the halls of the universities. Imperceptibly a differentiation has taken place in Germany between the educational work which was meant to reach the people at large and the intellectual

29. Union of education and instruction. instruction of a select few. But it is exactly this differentiation of education and higher instruction which the champions of a *liberal education* in England have desired to avoid.[1]   In France, very soon after Rousseau's time, dis-

---

[1] The two developments in Germany start from different centres. The purely educational movement began in Switzerland with Pestalozzi (1746-1827). His forerunner was Martin Planta (1727-1772), his successors were legion, all over Europe, including sovereigns, statesmen, and philosophers. He created an enthusiasm for education, which was to begin at home, not in the school ; to depend on the influence of the mother ; to be founded on a religious spirit ; to direct itself to the development of the body as much as of the mind ; to rest primarily on observation and experience, not mainly on memory and learning ; and then to absorb the whole mind and the entire man, not exclusively the intellect. It was to begin from below, not from above, with the people, the poor, the unfortunate and deserted ; on the part of the teacher it was to be a sacrifice, an end in itself, not a profession. The greatest followers of Pestalozzi were Von Fellenberg (1771-1844), the founder of Hofwyl and other industrial schools for poor and deserted children among the peasant population of Switzerland ; Johannes Falk (1760-1826), the founder of a great number of houses for the poor and the fallen, of the "Society of Friends in Need" ; J. H. Wichern (1808-1881), the founder of the "Rauhe Haus" near Hamburg ; lastly, the celebrated Fröbel (1782-1852, a native of Thüringen), the founder of the Kindergarten. The other—not to say opposite— development was centred in F. A. Wolf, in whose school the ideal of *Wissenschaft* with its enormous influence on universities and high schools was elaborated.   In the history of this development, with which our second chapter dealt, the name of Pestalozzi does not occur.   The term "popular" was for a time banished as identical with the βαναυσία of the ancient Greeks.   The two movements find a connecting-link in the extra-academical, the classical literature of Germany, notably of Herder and Goethe, to whom we must add Fichte and Schleiermacher.   The present age is working towards a fusion of both interests, of the educational and higher scientific, the bridging over of the gap which had been left ; it is trying to remove the estrangement which existed in the middle of the century.

cussions on educational matters confine themselves to the
ends and means of general or higher instruction; [1] in

We may say that no educational
scheme can be permanently satisfactory that does not regard with
equal favour, and does not find equal
room for, the two ideals of Pestalozzi and Wolf. It is interesting,
however, to note that neither in
Switzerland nor in Scotland, the
two countries in which popular
education has been longest at
home, do we find a really great
development of the higher institutions and centres of learning; the
universities in these two countries
have always stood somewhat in the
relation of higher schools to the
rest of the educational establishments; but both countries have
produced and reared some of the
greatest geniuses of all time—geniuses who have given to German
and English literature and science a
fame over the whole world and for
all ages ; they would have sufficed,
had they stayed at home, to form
academies and universities of the
first order.

[1] Compare chapter i. pp. 112, 142,
&c. We are indebted to France
for three great educational influences which have left indelible traces
over the whole domain of European
thought. These proceed from the
Paris University, the model of higher
education ; the great school of Port
Royal, that model of secondary
education ; and the 'Émile' of
Rousseau, which gave to the educational aspirations of Basedow, of
Kant, and of Pestalozzi a definite
direction. It has, however, frequently been stated that the valuable side of Rousseau's ideas
was developed outside of France.
"C'est une chose remarquable,"
says M. Compayré, "que l'influence
du philosophe de Genève se soit
surtout exercée à l'étranger, en
Allemagne et en Suisse" ('His-

toire critique des Doctrines de
l'Éducation en France,' 5me ed.,
1885, vol. ii. p. 101). "Il y avait,
chez Rousseau," says M. Bréal,
"un côté généreux et vivifiant :
l'amour de l'humanité et particu-
lièrement de l'enfant, la confiance
dans ses facultés et le respect de son
activité intellectuelle. Cette partie
là, qui était le germe de vie déposé
dans les œuvres de Rousseau, nous
l'avons laissée aux étrangers." In
French writers a great deal of discussion is to be found on the difference between education and instruction. Duclos (1704-72) in his
celebrated 'Considérations sur les
mœurs de ce siècle' (1751), in
the second chapter, which treats of
Education and Prejudice, says : "On
trouve parmi nous beaucoup d'instruction et peu d'éducation. On
y forme des savants, des artistes
de toute espèce ; chaque partie des
lettres, des sciences et des arts y
est cultivée avec succès, par des
méthodes plus ou moins conven-
ables. Mais on ne s'est pas encore
avisé de former des hommes, c'est
à dire, de les élever respectivement
les uns pour les autres, de faire
porter sur une base d'éducation
générale toutes les instructions particulières," &c. When the successive
Governments of the Revolution took
up the question of a national education, the formula of Condorcet
quite inevitably became more and
more the leading principle. Condorcet distinguished "instruction"
—i.e., knowledge positive and certain, truths of fact and calculation
—from "education"—i.e., "political and religious beliefs." He gives
the State the power to extend the
former, whilst he denies it the right
to direct and dispense the latter (see
Hippeau, 'L'Instruction publique
en France pendant la Révolution,'

Germany, education and higher instruction present independent developments; in England alone the genius and language of the nation have refused to admit of any curtailment of the original sense of the word. This continued to imply a discipline of the character as well as of the mind, practical as well as intellectual training. So much has been said in this country and abroad regarding the shortcomings of the English universities and higher schools, that I feel it a duty to point to the positive gain which this ideal of a liberal education [1] has

1881, vol. i. p. xvii; also Compayré, *loc. cit.*, vol. ii. p. 280, &c.) Every Government which has attempted to systematise, to centralise education, has been forced also to secularise it, to reduce it to instruction, leaving out what many consider the central problem of education, the training of the character and the discipline of the feelings and the heart. Considering the large organisations which have been developed in England by the unaided efforts of working men, such as the trade-unions and the co-operative societies, and looking at the amount of self-government, self-control, and self-denial which they demand from their members, one might be tempted to say that England is the best educated, though it may be the worst taught and the least informed, of the three nations now under review.

[1] The term "liberal education" has acquired a peculiar significance in the history of English culture and thought. It cannot be translated into French or German with any certainty that the real significance of the term or the subject which it denotes is conveyed. It is interesting to note how each of the three nations has given to special words of the once common Latin language a peculiar pregnancy, denoting a peculiar form of thought or culture which they have especially elaborated. Thus "science" in the modern sense is a product of French thought, *Wissenschaft* a product of German thought. England has reserved to itself the elaboration of a "liberal education." I am at a loss how to translate it into French, unless I am permitted to use simply the word education in its contrast to instruction and *enseignement*, not as this was defined by Condorcet, but as it is understood in the writings of modern French educationalists, such as Gréard, Bréal, Compayré, and others. To convey the meaning of "liberal education" to a German, I would revert to the Greek phrase, the ἐλευθέριος παιδεία of the post-classical age. The fact is that down to the middle of the century the Germans in discussions on the work of universities and high schools always talk of *Wissenschaft*, English writers always talk of "liberal education." To a German scholar's heart *Wissenschaft* is dear beyond anything; to an English university man it is "liberal education." The former will sacrifice everything to *Wissenschaft;* the latter will not part with "liberal

been. For it is the principal object of this work to attempt to portray the actual progress of thought, the valuable contributions of each of the three nations to the

education." In Germany, the real home of the educationalist or *Erzieher* has not been the university ; the home of the man of science has not been and is not the university in England. The German educationalist can point to a special creation of his own, the *Volksschule.* The English man of science has no organisation to point to except it be the select society of a dozen great names of world-wide fame, corresponding to the solitary and unconnected heights of Homer, Sophocles, Dante, Shakespeare, and Goethe in literature. To descend, however, from generalities to the real thing, I give here some extracts referring to English university life, chosen from among hundreds, all variations on the same theme. Dr Thomas Young, who knew both German and English universities, having studied at Göttingen and taken his degree at Cambridge, was not indebted to any university for his position or his knowledge ; yet he significantly defends the English universities against the criticism of the Edinburgh Reviewer : "We do not intend to imply a censure of the system adopted by our universities ; . . . for it must be remembered that the *advancement* of learning is by no means the principal object of an academical institution : the *diffusion* of a respectable share of instruction in literature and in the sciences among those classes which hold the highest situations and have the most extensive influence in the State is an object of more importance to the public than the discovery of new truths. . . . We think that we have observed numerous instances, both in public life

and in the pursuit of natural knowledge, in which great scholars and great mathematicians have reasoned less soundly, although more ingeniously, than others, who, being somewhat more completely in the possession of common-sense, . . . were still far inferior to them in the refinements of learning or of science" ('Quarterly Review,' May 1810, reprinted in Miscellaneous Works, vol. i. p. 235, &c.) I shall now give a quotation from an entirely different source, from one who in his department was equally well acquainted with German and English thought and life. In 1830 E. B. Pusey attempted to give his friend, Prof. Tholuck of Halle, a sketch of what had been "recently done in English theology." He begins by referring to the "practical character of the nation" and "the different condition of the universities," and then continues as follows : "Few, if any, of our writings have originated in an abstract love of investigation : our greatest and some immortal works have arisen in some exigencies of the times. . . . A German writes because he has something to say ; an Englishman only because it is, or he thinks it is, needed " ('Life of Pusey,' vol. i. p. 238). The man who did most for the widening of the circle of university studies in England during the first half of the century was William Whewell (1794-1866), whose influence at Cambridge extended over more than a generation. In the beginning he assisted the movement begun by Babbage, Herschel, and Peacock, and published several text-books on mechanics and dynamics, in which the influence of Continental, especially

general stock of ideal possessions, not merely to criticise the shortcomings and failures of separate schools of thought, or separate sources of mental development. Only in the aggregate of these different ideals is to be found the inventory of the intellectual possessions, the outcome of the higher work of the century.

30.
Educational organisations in England.

When the modern scientific methods and their impelling force, the mathematical spirit, made their way from France to Germany during the first quarter of the century,

French models, can be clearly traced. Between 1830 and 1850 his influence exerted itself in two directions, firstly by the publication of his 'History of the Inductive Sciences' (3 vols. 1837; a second edition appeared in 1847, a third in 1857), and, secondly, by a series of papers and pamphlets referring to university education. As the ideal and definition of this Whewell adopts the term "liberal education." The first of these papers appeared in the 'British Critic' (No. 17, 1831, "Science of the English Universities"). Then followed in 1836 "Thoughts on the study of Mathematics"; "Additional Thoughts," 1836; "On the Principles of English University Education," 1837; "Of a Liberal Education in General" (Part 1, 1845; Part 2, 1850; Part 3, 1852). The second part of the little work on Liberal Education gives a history of the various changes previous to 1850 through which the University of Cambridge tried to meet the growing demands of the times for a wider and more liberal programme of higher scientific work. In these various writings the work of education and "original research" (a term introduced by Whewell—see Todhunter, 'Life of Dr Whewell,' vol. i. p. 50), the nature of "permanent" and "progressive" studies at the university, of "university" and

"college" education, of "tutorial" and "professorial" teaching, are fully discussed. In the course of thirty years the university of Cambridge added to the examinations for mathematical honours the "Classical" Tripos (1822), the "Moral Sciences" Tripos and the "Natural Sciences" Tripos (1848); also a "Board of Mathematical Studies" (1848). Dr Whewell's great influence declined when in 1850 Royal Commissions were appointed to "inquire into the state, discipline, studies, and revenues of the universities of Oxford and Cambridge." He "regarded the Commission as an unwarranted and undesirable intrusion into the affairs of the university." The results of this inquiry belong to the second half of the century. Although this movement, which was brought about by many influences, has somewhat changed the issues, the central idea which in England tries to assimilate the higher work and thought of the nation is that of education. The term liberal education, which for twenty years, from 1830 to 1850, formed the banner of university reform, has since somewhat yielded to "scientific," and more recently to "technical," education; the influence of the universities has gone out in the work of university extension in the provincial towns; still

they there met with a powerful intellectual organisation, the German university system, in which classical and philosophical studies had elaborated the ideal of *Wissenschaft* —of science in the larger sense of the word. Gradually, and not without opposition, the exact or mathematical spirit was received into this system, and has since become an integral portion of it. In England the older traditions which clung to the two great universities, and the higher

the whole movement can be defined as an educational movement. Whereas in Germany about a generation earlier the term *Wissenschaft* gained the upper hand and governed the intellectual life of the nation, purely educational movements being separated from it, in England the purely scientific interest has never gained the upper hand, and can still complain of having nowhere a full and complete representation. Around the writings of Whewell as a centre may be grouped those of A. Sedgwick ('A Discourse on the Studies of the University of Cambridge,' 1833, 5th ed., 1850); Sir Wm. Hamilton (articles in the 'Edinburgh Review,' reprinted in 'Discussions on Philosophy, &c.,' 1853); Sir John Herschel ('A Preliminary Discourse on the Study of Natural Philosophy,' 1831); the criticisms of Lyell ('Travels in North America,' 1845), and of the 'Edinburgh,' 'British Quarterly,' and 'Westminster' Reviews ('Edin. Rev.,' Ap. 1849, Jan. 1874, 'Brit. Quart.,' Nov. 1850, 'West. Rev.,' Jan. 1855). Whoever desires to gain an insight into the different, frequently diametrically opposite, considerations which moulded and governed the reconstruction of the German university system on the one side, and on the other side widened in England the older ideas of university education, should compare the documents relating to the foundation of the University at Berlin in the beginning of this century (collected by Rudolf Köpke, 'Die Gründung der Königlichen Friedrich-Wilhelms-Universität zu Berlin,' Berlin, 1860) with the writings referred to in this note, and centering in Whewell's pamphlets and essays. The personification of the German scheme was Wilhelm von Humboldt, of whom Böckh said in his 'Logos epitaphios': "He was a veritable statesman, penetrated and led by ideas—a statesman of a Periclean greatness of spirit. Philosophy and poetry, eloquence, historical, philological, linguistic erudition, were fused in him into undisturbed harmony and wonderful symmetry." The reforming and revolutionary ideas of Fichte, the classical ideals of Wolf, the historical interests of J. Müller the historian, the literary interests of Schlegel, the philosophical interests of Schleiermacher, were combined by Humboldt into a realisable scheme. Stein said of him in 1810 : "Prussia has intrusted the management of her educational and scientific institutions to a man possessed of a remarkable intellect and of great firmness of character, and who utilises these qualities in his sphere of action with glorious loyalty" (ibid., pp. 61, 62).

practical interests of a select class which upheld those traditions, prevented any of the Continental ideals, be it the philological of F. A. Wolf, or the philosophical of Fichte, or the scientific of Laplace and Cuvier, from establishing themselves in the older seats of learning. And they were, after all, the only organisations for higher culture which possessed a historical character and continuity. Around these centres, partly in a friendly, more frequently in a hostile spirit, other institutions, other centres of culture and learning, had grown up. Let us rapidly survey these more recent institutions. It is hardly necessary again to mention the Royal Society, which was an early offspring of the older universities, a kind of overflow of the scientific interests from them into the capital. More recent was the Royal Institution, the creation of that extraordinary man, Benjamin Thompson, Count Rumford. Like the Royal Society, it was dependent upon private subscriptions and on the popular interest created by its lectures. These were very promiscuous, exhibiting no plan or unity. In the early years Dr Young and Davy lectured there, as well as Coleridge and Sydney Smith. Later it became the home of Faraday, and through him, and many other illustrious lecturers, has done much to spread a taste for natural, especially experimental, science, in the higher and cultivated classes. It has been a means of diffusing the scientific taste, more perhaps than the exact scientific spirit, in the stricter sense of the word. Whilst its lectures may have kindled in many a young listener the love of scientific work, the Institution did not fulfil the early intention of its founder, nor did its laboratory play the part of some of the great laboratories of Paris or of Germany, in turning out a large number of well-trained experimentalists.   Davy may be said to have educated Faraday, though he was suspected of having become jealous of him, and Faraday declared he received only one valuable suggestion from any member of his audience during the whole course of his lecturing.   It is the strongly marked individuality of all these great men, expressed in their persons, their lives, and their works, rather than the character of the institution itself, which has given celebrity and historical importance to the Royal Institution.   John Dalton's [1] position in the Literary and Philosophical Society of Manchester was similar to that of Davy and Faraday in the Royal Institution ; and as Faraday can in some sense be called a pupil of Davy, so can Prescott Joule [2] be termed a pupil of Dalton, whom

32.
Manchester
Literary and
Philosophi-
cal Society.

---

[1] See note, p. 245.

[2] James Prescott Joule (1818-89), a native of Salford, "received from Dalton his first inducement to undertake the work of an original scientific investigator." He was one of the first who tried to measure electrical action in terms of the units of well-known mechanical or chemical changes. His publications began in 1840. Weber's 'Elec-trodynamische Maasbestimmungen,' that great monument of exact measurement, was published in 1846. Mayer's first publication, containing a calculation of the mechanical equivalent of heat, bears the date 1842. But the great publication of Gauss, in which he measures magnetic action in ordinary mechanical (or absolute) units, dates from 1832: 'Intensitas vis magneticæ terrestris ad mensuram absolutam revocata' (Comm. Societ., Götting., 1832, &c.)

Joule in 1843 published the first of his accurate determinations of what is termed in physical science "J" or "Joule's equivalent of heat." He read successively papers on this subject before the meetings of the British Association, first at Cork (1843), giving the constant "J" as 838, then as 770, then as 890 in 1845 (Brit. Assoc. at Cambridge), lastly at Oxford (1847) as 781·5. From this meeting dates the acquaintance and scientific co-operation of Joule and Thomson (Lord Kelvin) and the gradual recognition of the importance of the subject by other men of science (see Thomson's address on Joule, 1893, in 'Popular Lectures and Addresses,' vol. ii. p. 558 *sqq.*) Helmholtz's memoir, "Ueber die Erhaltung der Kraft," which was theoretical—as Joule's were experimental—dates also from 1847.

he succeeded as president of the Society.   These names are identified with some of the greatest work in experimental science.   Some of them may be said to be identified with quite original theoretical ideas which have governed the development of great departments of research ever since.   Dalton's atomic theory in chemistry, however, received a tardy recognition in England, and was firmly established only by foreign research, while Faraday's " lines of force " remained a mystery to electricians,[1] till William Thomson and Clerk Maxwell made them the groundwork of our most recent conceptions. It is well to note that neither Young, nor Davy, nor Faraday, nor Dalton, nor Joule belonged to the circle of Cambridge men, and that probably none of them received any inspiration from that official school of English mathematics.[2]   In the early years of the century that

[1] See Helmholtz on Faraday's ideas in ' Vorträge und Reden,' vol. ii. p. 277.   " Since the mathematical interpretation of Faraday's theorems has been given by Clerk Maxwell in methodically elaborated scientific formulæ, we see, indeed, how much definiteness of conception and accurate thought were contained in Faraday's words, which seemed to his contemporaries so indefinite and obscure.   And it is indeed remarkable in the highest degree to observe how, by a kind of intuition, without using a single formula, he found out a number of comprehensive theorems, which can only be strictly proved by the highest powers of mathematical analysis.   I would not depreciate Faraday's contemporaries because they did not recognise this;   I know how often I found myself despairingly staring at his descriptions of lines of force, their number and tension, or looking for the meaning of sentences in which the galvanic current is defined as an axis of force, and similar things. A single remarkable discovery can indeed be brought about by a happy chance, . . . but it would be against all rules of probability that a numerous series of the most important discoveries, such as Faraday produced, could have had their origin in conceptions which did not really contain a correct, though perhaps deeply hidden, ground of truth."

[2] Young resided at Cambridge to take his medical degree on his return from Göttingen ; but though his biographer has inserted a chapter on Cambridge in the ' Life of Young,' and though Young's first great discovery, that of the interferences of waves of sound and light, fell within that period, there is no evidence that his scientific studies were promoted by Cambridge influ-

centre had, indeed, to receive aid from a still more secluded and unacademic quarter. Undergraduates of Cambridge used to migrate from the seat of teaching which has been immortalised by Newton to the remote Yorkshire village of Sedbergh, where John Dawson,[1] one of the few British analysts who held their own against the great foreign authorities, taught the higher mathematics for five shillings a-week.

33. John Dawson of Sedbergh.

During the latter part of the eighteenth century a formidable rival to the learning of Oxford and Cambridge had sprung up in the Scotch universities. These were teaching centres, more after the manner of the foreign universities. They had been started on the model of the University of Paris or of the older Italian universities; some had their origin in the educational movement which, especially in those countries where the doctrines of Calvin prevailed, accompanied the Reformation.[2] All through the

34. The Scotch Universities.

---

ences; in fact he makes a disparaging remark regarding British as compared with Continental mathematics. See Peacock's 'Life of Dr Young,' p. 127.

[1] John Dawson (1734-1820), the son of a poor "statesman" of Garsdale, tended his father's sheep till he was twenty. He studied mathematics with innate love and ability, inventing a system of conic sections out of his own brain. By teaching he gained a little money. In 1756 he instructed three young men—of whom Adam Sedgwick's father was one—before they went up for their Cambridge studies. He then became assistant to a surgeon at Lancaster. Having saved £100 he walked to Edinburgh and studied medicine there. His funds spent, he returned to Sedbergh, where he practised as a surgeon. When he had saved a larger sum he proceeded

with this to London. After taking his degree in 1767, he settled in his native county to practise his profession and teach the higher mathematics to Cambridge undergraduates. They flocked to him in the summer, and between 1781 and 1794 he numbered eight senior wranglers among his pupils. In 1797 and subsequent years he counted four more. In 1812 he ceased teaching. He wrote papers on the "precession" and the lunar theory, and followed the development of higher mathematics on the Continent. See 'Life and letters of Adam Sedgwick,' by J. W. Clark and T. M'K. Hughes, 1890, vol. i. p. 61, &c.

[2] Details referring to the foundation of the Scotch universities are given by Sir A. Grant in the first volume of his 'Story of the Univer-

seventeenth and eighteenth centuries they stood in intimate relations with such Continental centres of study as
Paris, Geneva, and the Dutch universities. Adam Smith
and David Hume were in direct and very intimate intercourse with French thought, the former having obtained in
France a knowledge of the novel views of the great political economists of the pre-revolutionary period. Edinburgh
became in the first half of the last century, under the
influence of John Monro and his son Alexander (1697-
1767), who was a pupil of Boerhaave, a medical school
of great importance, rivalling London in its foreign rep-

sity of Edinburgh,' 2 vols., 1884.
Three of them—St Andrews, Glasgow, and Aberdeen—were founded
in the century preceding the Reformation ; St Andrews about
1411 by Bishop Wardlaw, because
Scotch students had been un-
popular and "molested" at Oxford.   The University of Glasgow
was founded in 1450, reference
being made to the University of
Bologna in the Bull of Pope Nicholas
V. ; but it has also been observed
that "the customs and technical
phraseology showed an imitation of
the institutes of Louvain, then
and for all the following century
the model university of Northern
Europe, of which a Scotchman,
John Lichton, had been Rector"
(p. 21).   Aberdeen was started by
Bishop Elphinstone, who had studied
in Glasgow and Paris, and been professor, both there and at Orleans, of
canon and civil law.   In the pre-
amble to the Bull of Pope Alexander
VI. the Universities of Paris and
Bologna are referred to (p. 29).
But the universities seem not to
have flourished previous to the Reformation, when they were "purged"
and a new spirit and order infused
into them. St Andrews was to have
four faculties, named as in foreign

universities—Philosophy, Medicine,
Law, and Divinity (p. 63). Glasgow and Aberdeen were to have
two faculties, of which the first
was to be Philosophy (or Arts),
the second to comprise Law and
Divinity. The 'Book of Discipline'
contained a very complete scheme
of higher graded education ; but
this was only gradually and partially realised ; secondary schools
being wanting, the "colleges" had
to descend to elementary teaching
(p. 67). A jealousy also existed on
the part of those in power regarding the older universities, these
being—as the King of France declared when refusing to grant to
the Academy of Geneva the rights
of a university—hotbeds of heresy
(p. 125).   Accordingly the latest
academic creation in Scotland was
the foundation by the "Town
Council and ministers of the city"
of the College of Edinburgh (pp.
99, 121, 127) between the years
1561 and 1578, King James's charter dating from 14th April 1582.
"But it did not, like the older universities, commence with a blaze
of success and then collapse.   It
started from a humble beginning
and steadily expanded into greater
things" (p. 158).

utation.[1] Edinburgh had also one of the earliest chairs
of chemistry. It grew into an independent centre of
original scientific work when in 1783 the Royal Society
of Edinburgh was incorporated. Ever since the foundation of the Scotch universities, mathematics had been
studied independently in Scotland, where John Napier
of Merchiston had at the end of the sixteenth century
invented logarithms. " Whether we consider the great
originality of the idea, the difficulty of carrying it into
effect in the state in which algebraical analysis then was,
or the immense practical and theoretical value of the invention, we shall have little difficulty in claiming for Napier
the honour of a discovery unsurpassed in brilliancy in
the whole history of mathematics."[2] From that time the

35.
The Royal
Society of
Edinburgh.

[1] " In 1738 the foundation-stone
of that building which was till recently the Royal Infirmary of Edinburgh was laid, and a great public
enthusiasm on the subject was manifested. Drummond, the greatest
Ædile that has ever governed the
city of Edinburgh, and Monro, were
appointed the Building Committee,
and they paid the workmen with
their own hands. All classes contributed : landowners gave stone ;
merchants gave timber ; farmers
lent their carts for carriage of
materials ; even the masons and
other labourers gave one day's work
out of the month gratis, as it was a
building for the benefit of the poor "
(Sir A. Grant, *loc. cit.*, vol. i. p.
306).

[2] Quoted by Sir A. Grant (*loc.
cit.*, vol. ii. p. 293) from Chrystal's
unpublished Inaugural Address,
' John Napier, Baron of Merchiston '
(1550-1617). The ' Mirifici Logar-
ithmorum Canonis Descriptio ' appeared in 1614. The ' Logarithmo-
rum Chilias prima ' of Henry Briggs

(1556-1630), professor at Oxford,
contains the first table of common or decimal logarithms.
Kepler (1571-1630) received the
invention with great enthusiasm as
of immense importance to astronomy. "The more one considers
the condition of science at the time,
and the state of the country in
which the discovery took place,
the more wonderful does the invention of logarithms appear. . . .
It is one of the surprises in the
history of science that logarithms
were invented as an arithmetical
improvement years before their
connection with exponents was
known. It is to be noticed also
that the invention was not the result of any happy accident. Everything tends to show that it was
the result of many years of labour
and thought undertaken with this
special object ; Napier succeeded in
devising, by the help of arithmetic
and geometry alone, the one great
simplification of which they were
susceptible — a simplification to

science was cultivated at the different Scotch universities, which supplied Oxford with a Professor of Astronomy (preferred to Halley), in the person of David Gregory. "David Gregory not only introduced the 'Principia' to Edinburgh students, but he also brought them to the notice of Englishmen."[1] The Philosophical (afterwards called the Royal) Society of Edinburgh was much indebted to Colin Maclaurin,[2] who almost alone with Landen and Ivory maintained the reputation of British mathematicians during seventy years, whilst the Continental school was revolutionising that science. A successor to Maclaurin in the mathematical chair at Edinburgh, John Playfair,[3] introduced the Continental methods into the studies of the Scotch universities about the end of the last century. He was one of the early contributors to the 'Edinburgh Review,' which in politics, literature, and science inaugurated a new kind of criticism, and led a powerful attack upon all those traditional forms of government, taste, and learning which prevented the free expansion of ideas and the progress of science and practical interests. Though not always judiciously used, the

36.
The 'Edinburgh Review.'

which the following two hundred and eighty years have added nothing" (Glaisher in 'Ency. Brit.,' 9th ed., article "Napier").

[1] David Gregory (1661-1708) has "the honour of having been the first to give public lectures on the Newtonian philosophy. This he did in Edinburgh five-and-thirty years before these doctrines were accepted as part of the public instruction in the university of their inventor" (Sir A. Grant and Chrystal, loc. cit., vol. ii. p. 296). Cambridge writers, headed by Whewell, are loath to admit any reluctance on the part of their university in accepting the Newtonian philosophy, in spite of Whiston's testimony to the contrary. See on this Whewell's 'History of the Inductive Sciences,' 3rd ed., vol. ii. p. 149, &c.

[2] Colin Maclaurin (1698 - 1746) published, 1742, a 'Treatise on Fluxions,' 2 vols. 4to. In 1740 he shared with Daniel Bernoulli and Euler the prize of the French Academy for his 'Essay on the Tides.'

[3] John Playfair (1748-1819) was Professor of Mathematics and then (from 1805) of Natural Philosophy.

influence of that review must have been very powerful in rousing the older English universities out of a state of stagnation, and especially in stimulating younger minds in the direction of the long-delayed reform of studies. An important step in this direction was taken by three undergraduates of Cambridge—Herschel, Babbage, and Peacock—who in 1812 formed the Analytical Society, with the distinct object of introducing the more modern and powerful analytical methods developed mainly by Euler and Lagrange, and deposited in their numerous Memoirs in the publications of the foreign academies.[1] In harmony with them worked Whewell, Airy, and Sedgwick, who did much to enlarge the programme of mathematical and scientific studies, though they very staunchly upheld that the real object of university education could not be identified with any special method or school of thought, but was expressed in the specific ideal peculiar to England, that of a liberal education.[2]

37. The Analytical Society of Cambridge.

The universities of Scotland, unlike those of England, instead of nursing an exclusive spirit, and encouraging only scanty intercourse between teachers and students of different centres, lived in constant exchange of professors and ideas—much in the same way as has always been the custom on a larger scale among German and other Continental universities. Though this is destructive of that individual character of the university or the college which

38. University life in Scotland.

---

[1] See note 1 to p. 233; also for many details Rouse Ball's 'History of the Study of Mathematics at Cambridge,' 1889, p. 120, &c.

[2] On Whewell and his writings on university education see note to p. 261. Sir George Biddell Airy (1801-1891) published in 1826 'Mathematical Tracts' (2nd ed., 1831) on the lunar and planetary theories, &c., for the use of students in the university.

is so highly prized by many English fellows, it is certainly more conducive to the progress of studies and of research, and it is the cause why in the early history of recent science the universities of Scotland have played so much more important a part than those of England. Whilst in England modern science was cultivated outside the pale of the universities by Priestley, Davy, Wollaston, Young, Dalton, Faraday, and Joule, to whom we may even add Green and Boole, all eminent Scotch men of science, such as Gregory, Simson, Maclaurin, Playfair, Black, Thomson, Leslie, Brewster, and Forbes, were university professors, many of whom did not confine their labours to one centre, but spread the light of their ideas and researches all over the country.[1] Whilst England has been great in single names, Scotland has certainly in proportion done more

[1] Napier of Merchiston remained outside the pale of the universities. At that time the College of Edinburgh had no mathematical professor; but Glasgow had, and so had Aberdeen. James Gregory was educated at Aberdeen, was then professor at St Andrews, and subsequently at Edinburgh. Colin Maclaurin was educated at Glasgow, then professor at Aberdeen and at Edinburgh. Playfair was educated at St Andrews, and lectured there before coming to Edinburgh. Leslie was trained at St Andrews, and was then professor first of mathematics and afterwards of natural philosophy at Edinburgh. Black was educated at Glasgow and Edinburgh, and was professor at both universities. Brewster studied at Edinburgh, and was subsequently principal of St Andrews and then of Edinburgh. Forbes, as student and professor, belongs exclusively to Edinburgh, and so did in earlier times Robert Simson, the great mathematical professor. Adam Smith belongs exclusively to Glasgow, though he had lectured in Edinburgh before he was appointed professor at Glasgow. But the contrast between England and Scotland becomes still more prominent if we look at the medical sciences and note the great array of celebrated professors at Edinburgh, Cullen, Brown, Gregory, Alison, Hamilton, Syme, Simpson, Christison, and Charles Bell, whereas the equally great names of John and William Hunter, of Jenner, of Astley Cooper and Bright, have no connection with the English universities; Sydenham was only slightly connected with Oxford and Cambridge, and even Harvey never occupied a prominent position at Oxford. Through situation or constitution the English universities were unable to open a field of activity for these celebrated men.

to diffuse modern scientific knowledge. The great publishing firms of Edinburgh have also for more than a
century done much through Cyclopædias, Reviews, and
Magazines to spread general information of all kinds; [1]
whilst Hume, Adam Smith, and the subsequent Scotch
school of metaphysicians have exerted their influence
during the whole of this century, not only in Great
Britain, but over the whole of Europe. [2] In the more
circumscribed domain of scientific thought a powerful
influence has again been exerted from Scotland as a
centre, and through the larger instrumentality of the
University of Cambridge, on the study of mathematical
and experimental physics, and what we may term the
spirit and method of these sciences. This influence be-

---

[1] The most popular Cyclopædia,
that of Chambers, had its origin in
Edinburgh in 1860. It was founded
on the tenth edition of Brockhaus's
'Conversations-Lexicon.' The more
important 'Encyclopædia Britannica' was published there also in
1771, 3 vols.; 2nd ed., 1777. The
'Edinburgh Review' was established in 1802 by Jeffrey, Scott,
Horner, Brougham, and Sydney
Smith; it was the first successful
"Quarterly," carried on independently of the booksellers, after
several unsuccessful attempts had
been made in a similar direction by
Adam Smith and Hugh Blair in
1755, and after Gilbert Stuart and
William Smellie had issued from
1773 to 1775 the 'Edinburgh Magazine and Review.' No such periodical ever attained to the circulation of the 'Edinburgh Review,' of
which at one time 20,000 copies
were sold. The first high-class
monthly Magazine was also printed
in Edinburgh by Blackwood in
1817, with Scott, Lockhart, Hogg,

Maginn, Syme, and John Wilson as
contributors. 'Tait's Edinburgh
Magazine' was the first shilling
magazine. The brothers William
and Robert Chambers, in 1832,
started the Journal named after
them. They also brought out many
popular works of sterling merit,
mostly written by Robert Chambers, than whom none did more to
introduce a knowledge of nature
into popular reading, and to give a
healthy tone and moral influence
to the cheap literature which has
become such an important factor
in modern culture.

[2] Whilst Locke exercised the
greatest influence on French philosophy, Kant starts more directly
from Hume. The literature of the
Restoration in France again attaches itself to the Scotch metaphysicians, notably Reid. It is
interesting that both Kant and
the greatest representative of the
French "Ideology," De Tracy, were
of Scotch descent.

longs to the second half of the century, and is centred in
the two names of William Thomson (Lord Kelvin) and
James Clerk Maxwell, who may be said to have jointly
revolutionised natural philosophy. It began with the appearance of George Stokes's and William Thomson's important contributions to mathematical physics, and with
the publication of that suggestive and stimulating—but
unfortunately unfinished—work by Thomson and Tait on
Natural Philosophy. It was represented to the fullest
extent in Clerk Maxwell's activity in the Cavendish
Laboratory at Cambridge. But the consideration of this
subject belongs to a later chapter of the present work,
and is only mentioned here in connection with the intellectual intercourse and exchange which has existed all
through this century between the invigorating spirit of the
north and the more conservative spirit of the southern
portion of the island. Besides Scotland another centre
—the Dublin School—has gained European renown
through a series of mathematical labours of the highest
importance, some of them of an originality hardly yet
sufficiently recognised. This school is represented by
the names of Rowan Hamilton,[1] MacCullagh, Sal-

39.
The Dublin
Mathemati-
cal School.

[1] Of Rowan Hamilton's dynamical "principle of varying action"
I have spoken in a note to p. 231.
William Rowan Hamilton (1805-65)
cannot with the same certainty as
Kant and De Tracy be claimed as
of Scotch descent. Indeed he
seems to belong distinctly to Ireland. See Tait's article in the
'North British Review,' September
1866, and Perceval Graves's reply in
'Life of W. R. Hamilton' (3 vols.,
1882-89, vol. i. p. 5). He was one
of the few quite original mathe-

maticians who, like Gauss, led the
way into new channels of thought
and succeeded in breaking through
the traditional forms of this science,
which more than any other is hampered in its development by transmitted customs and habits of representation. Thus, after ten years of
research and thought in connection
with the representation of extended algebraical forms by means of
the different directions in space, he
succeeded in establishing the fundamental principle of his theory of

mon ;[1] nor should we forget the suggestive writings of George Boole.[2] The influence of these men originated outside of Cambridge, and a history of mathematics at that university does not contain their names,[3] though the ideas of which they have been the bearers have largely entered into the text-books and the teaching of the Cambridge school.

So far I have mainly dealt with one side only on which the progress of science depends, namely, the methodical use of experiment, measurement, and calculation : this

quaternions — complex quantities which are compounded of a purely algebraical or quantitative element and three distinct elements corresponding to the three directions or dimensions of space. He was the first to work out this calculus, and the labour occupied twenty years of his life. In Hamilton's calculus of quaternions, distance (or length) and direction are introduced as they naturally present themselves when we deal with geometrical or physical problems, instead of all quantities being reduced to lengths, as was the case in the Cartesian geometry. Hamilton thus broke through the conventionalism of the latter and showed how the consideration of directions in space forces us to extend the original operations of arithmetic. It is interesting to note how simultaneously Grassmann (see p. 243, note 1) in his ' Ausdehnungslehre ' (1844) and Von Staudt in his ' Geometrie der Lage' (1847), quite independently worked at similar extensions of our arithmetical and geometrical conceptions, and how subsequently quaternions, in which Hamilton had seen a powerful method for solving geometrical and physical problems, present themselves as a special form of the extended algebra and geometry elaborated from these different beginnings. Whilst the practical usefulness of the calculus has been demonstrated by some extensive applications, as, for example, to spherical trigonometry, the ideas contained in it— frequently without Hamilton's notation—are gradually finding their way into text-books, and the strangeness which for half a century prevented the labours of Hamilton, Grassmann, and Von Staudt from being generally appreciated, is disappearing. A popular exposition of the relation of quaternions to general arithmetic is given in O. Stolz, ' Grössen und Zahlen,' Leipzig, Teubner, 1891.

[1] The excellent treatises of Salmon on ' Higher Algebra,' ' Higher Plane Curves,' ' Geometry of Three Dimensions,' and ' Conic Sections ' have in their German translations by Fiedler done a great work in systematising and popularising modern conceptions in algebra and geometry. See Gino Loria's treatise on the " Principle Theories of Geometry " in the German translation by Schütte, Leipzig, 1888, p. 25, &c.

[2] See p. 247, note 2.

[3] See Rouse Ball, ' A History of the Study of Mathematics at Cambridge,' 1889.

side had been very largely developed by the great French naturalists and mathematicians in the beginning of our period. The change in the higher branches of science which took place during the first half of the century is greatly owing to them, and to the later German school, which was much influenced by them. If we compare the contributions of British science in these branches, they are indeed inferior in bulk, and still more so in methodical arrangement; but among them is a small number of works of the first order which are embodiments of scientific ideas of the very highest importance. Introduced into the great edifice of scientific research which was being planned and erected on the Continent, they mark the very corner-stones of the building, standing out in bold and conspicuous prominence. But it is a fact that no Academy existed in this country which was zealous in collecting and arranging all the best labours of scattered philosophers, no university which was anxious to attract and train promising intellects, no comprehensive text-books and hand-books, ensuring right guidance, correctness of knowledge, and completeness of study, no historical and philosophical traditions guaranteeing that novel contributions should make their appearance under favourable conditions, or supplying the most appropriate *mise en scène* for new ideas.

40.
Importance of British contributions to science.

It is the French Institute, in the earlier years of the century, and the German university system, with its many local ramifications and literary organs, during the whole of the century, which have done the great work of systematising and diffusing scientific knowledge, and of introducing the exact spirit of research. There is

41.
Diffusion of scientific knowledge on the Continent.

something casual and accidental about the great ideas which British men of science contributed during the first half of the century.   Each of them chooses an isolated position, a special form of delivery, frequently a language and style of his own.   They attach little or no importance to the labours of others, with which they are frequently unacquainted.[1]   Important papers are lost or buried, as in the case of Cavendish and Green. Novel ideas are communicated in unintelligible language and symbols, and accordingly neglected.   This was the case with Dr Young's writings, and to a certain extent with Faraday's.   The greatest discoveries were unduly postponed through the absence of assistance, as seems to have been the case with Adams's discovery of Neptune,[2] perhaps with Stokes's anticipation of spectrum analysis.[3]

42.
Isolation of English men of science.

[1] This is correct of most of the great men referred to in the course of this chapter. Among them, however, Rowan Hamilton forms an exception. Though working on quite original lines, he took a great interest in the labours and suggestions contained in the writings of his forerunners and contemporaries, as the historical notices in the preface to his 'Lectures on Quaternions' (1853) prove ; likewise his correspondence with De Morgan (see 'Life of Sir W. R. H.,' vol. iii.)

[2] The story of the discovery of Neptune has been frequently told. The first publication of the elements of the suspected planet, which enabled a search to be made, came from Leverrier to the Paris Academy of Sciences on the 1st July and the 31st August 1846. In consequence of this publication, Galle at Berlin, requested by Leverrier to search in the neighbourhood of δ Capricorni, and comparing his observations made on the same night on which he received the request, 23rd September 1846, with Bremiker's map, actually found the planet.   Subsequently it became known that Adams of Cambridge had already communicated his elements in September and October 1845 to Challis and Airy, and that the former had actually seen the planet on the 4th and 12th of August 1846, but — for want of equally detailed maps — had not compared the observation and established the discovery. See Whewell's 'History of the Inductive Sciences,' third ed., 1857, vol. ii. p. 460, &c. ; also Wolf, 'Geschichte der Astronomie,' p. 537, &c.

[3] It appears from a communication of Sir William Thomson (Lord Kelvin) to Kirchhoff immediately after the latter had published in 1859 his explanation of the identity of the dark lines in the solar spectrum with the bright lines in the spectra of coloured flames, that Stokes, soon after the publication

What might not these great minds have accomplished had
they attached the same importance to style and form as
most of the great French men of science, or had they been
called upon to teach a number of eager pupils, anxious,
not to take honours and degrees, but to understand and
further elaborate the suggestions of their masters, as has
been the custom and tradition in Germany ?　The history
of English science during the first half of the century
consists of a series of biographies, or of monographs on
single ideas and points of view.　We are struck by the
individual greatness of the minds which produced them,
their originality or the suddenness of their appearance.
An *éloge* by the permanent secretary of the Academy has
usually been considered sufficient to satisfy the historian
of science in France ; the life of every great philosopher
in Germany is identical with the history of a phase of
thought or with a school of research ; in England alone
the person of the thinker has nearly always claimed the

by Miller in 1845 and by Foucault
in 1849 of observations relating to
this subject, had suggested in the
course of conversation that there is
a correspondence between emission
and absorption of the same kind of
light by the vibrating molecules of
the same body, according as it is
used as a source or a screen for
light.　Had this idea of Stokes's,
which suggested the presence of
sodium in the atmosphere of the
sun, been followed out at the time,
the discovery of spectrum analysis
would have taken place ten years
earlier.　Actually, the various publications, beginning with Fraunhofer's description of the dark lines
in the solar spectrum in 1814 and
proceeding through the observations of Herschel, Talbot, Drummond, Miller, Angström, Plücker,
Swan, and Balfour Stewart on
the absorption and radiation of
heat, found their consummation
when Bunsen and Kirchhoff settled
the main point in question—*viz.*,
"that the bright lines of an in-
candescent gaseous body depend on
the chemical constituents of the
same."　Then at length spectrum
analysis became possible.　See on
this matter Kirchhoff's own historical *résumé* of the year 1862, reprinted in 'Gesammelte Abhandlungen' (Leipzig, 1882), p. 625,
&c. ; also Sir William Thomson's
'Baltimore Lectures,' shorthand
notes, 1884, p. 100, and Stokes's
translation of Kirchhoff's first paper
in 1860 ('Philos. Magazine,' March
1860).

greater share of popular attention.[1]   His mental labours have preserved an individual character, shutting them out during his life from common contact, and limiting their fertilising power, like that of an oasis in the desert, to a narrow circle of casual visitors.   Minds like Newton and Faraday, full of new life, but modestly content with deepening and strengthening their secluded vigour, refrained from boastful publicity or ostentatious parade, working for all ages rather than for a special school or a passing generation.   It is the individualism of the English character, the self-reliant strength of natural genius, which comes out most strongly in its great examples of scientific work.   In characters of smaller breadth, in intellects of lesser power, these tendencies show themselves in ways which we cannot always admire or commend : in the emulation for place and position, in the competing for

43.
Individualism of the English character.

[1] This explains the remarkable richness of English literature in biographies, containing copious collections of correspondence, and the almost total absence of such literature in France, which, on the other side, is rich in memoirs, written by statesmen and authors themselves. As the students of nature have usually little time for autobiography, we possess of the long list of great names in modern French science hardly any personal records such as are so plentiful in English literature.   What we miss in many of these elaborate and frequently gossiping narratives is a just appreciation of the position of the subject of the biography in the history of science, literature, and thought, a definition of the exact place and importance which belongs to him and his work.   This is what is given in such a masterly and condensed form in the better *éloges* of Fontenelle, of Cuvier, of Arago, and other secretaries of the French Academies.   In Germany biographical literature is less developed than in this country, and memoirs are almost absent—those of Varnhagen von Ense and of Perthes, among literary men, being remarkable and rare exceptions.   Similarly the great correspondence carried on by Goethe through nearly sixty years is a unique monument of his genius and his influence, comparable only to that of Voltaire during the last century.   R. Haym in his biographies of Hegel, Wm. von Humboldt, and Herder, which combine the biographical with the historical and critical elements, has done a great work, and these books are invaluable contributions to the history of thought.   Justi's 'Winckelmann' is of equal importance ; but Dilthey's 'Schleiermacher' is unfortunately unfinished.

honours and championships—in all the noble and ignoble
forms of racing, where much energy, which might more
usefully have been merged in co-operative action, is
sacrificed for the sake of individual distinction.   But
where the height of genius forbids emulation, where the
towering intellect has distanced all records, this individualism has produced single specimens of the greatest
work, examples of the highest moral worth.   It is not in
the courses of scientific work alone that we shall have
occasion to mark the peculiarity of British, especially of
English, thought; but it is interesting to note how even
in this sphere, which more than any other seems to bear
an international and cosmopolitan character, the genius
of the nation strongly asserts itself, baffling every effort
to control it or to lead it into more conventional channels.   The last fifty years have done much to destroy
the peculiarly national customs, the idiosyncrasies of the
different peoples.   English institutions have been copied
in France, and German customs introduced into England;
it has recently been stated that the older type of scientific
amateur which existed in this country is dying out, being
rendered impossible by the more complicated machinery
of science, the manifold conditions on which progress depends.   It seems to me doubtful whether this view is
correct.   Surely the advance of the highest kind of
thought will always depend upon the unfettered development of the individual mind, regardless of established
habits, of existing forms of expression, or of adopted
systems; just as the diffusion and wholesale application of
single discoveries will depend on a ready and efficient machinery and organisation; whilst their influence on gen-

44.
Changes
during the
last fifty
years.

eral thought and literature will depend on the cultivation of a perfect form, of an expressive and elegant style. The French alone in the beginning of the century could boast of the last; the Germans have most successfully developed the second; whilst England, the country of greatest individual freedom, has been the land most favourable to the growth of genius as well as eccentricity, and has thus produced a disproportionate number of new ideas and departures. Nor is it to be desired that the reliance of genius on itself should be in any way curtailed, as it is impossible to foretell whence the new light will come which is to illuminate future ages. This individualism of the English mind presents other accompanying features, and these are of great interest to the historian of thought. They manifest themselves in the province of science as much as in other provinces. We will now study them more closely; in the sequel we shall meet with them in other departments also.

Hitherto our observations on English science have nearly all referred to only one side of modern scientific work,—the side on which lie the experimental, measuring, and calculating sciences; those sciences which abroad are termed " exact "; in which mathematical notions and methods, be it of measurement or of calculation, obtain. But these sciences cover only one side of reality. We noticed how in France, during the great scientific epoch, the other side of nature, that which exhibited and was filled by the phenomena of life, was simultaneously explored with equal originality and equal success. As Laplace was the great representative of the one, so Cuvier was the great representative of the other. We have also seen how in

Germany this latter department of research was specially cultivated, how all the mathematical, experimental, and philosophical sciences combined to organise the one great science of physiology or biology, with its central and crowning problem—the problem of consciousness. We also noted how this science worked a great reform in the whole domain of medical theory and practice. Let us now return to the question, What has Great Britain done during the first half of this century in this great department of scientific thought? Single great names, like those of Harvey,[1] marked in former centuries discoveries in the natural sciences equal to those of Newton in the mathematical; the name of Ray[2] is still preserved in the

45.
British contributions to biology.

---

[1] William Harvey (1578-1657), a native of Kent, received his medical education in Italy, especially in Padua, under Fabricius of Acquapendente. The discovery of the circulation of the blood belongs to the year 1616, and is almost contemporary with Napier's invention of logarithms. This discovery is contained in the manuscript of Harvey's lectures preserved in the British Museum, but the publication did not take place till 1628 ('Exercitatio anatomica de motu corporis et sanguinis in animalibus,' published at Frankfort). Although Harvey was drawn into long controversies by his publication of this work, he had the satisfaction of seeing his discovery generally recognised. Descartes abroad took Harvey's part in his letter to Beverwijck in 1637, and in his 'Discours de la Méthode,' published in the same year ; and it is noteworthy that—as has been the case with many subsequent English discoveries—the first great acknowledgment came from the Continent, notably Holland. The acceptance in France by the faculties of Paris and

Montpellier was less rapid, and in England it is well known that Lord Bacon took no notice either of Harvey's discovery or of Napier's invention. See James Spedding's preface to the "De interpretatione Naturæ Prœmium" in works of Lord Bacon, vol. iii. p. 507, &c.; also Harvey's own opinion on Bacon, ibid., p. 515. Hobbes, on the other hand, "was eager to accept Harvey's revolutionary discovery" (Croom Robertson, 'Hobbes,' p. 123), and refers to Harvey in the dedication of the 'De Corpore' (1655) as "the only man I know that, conquering envy, hath established a new doctrine in his lifetime" (ibid., p. 187 n.) On Harvey's other works, notably on the work 'De Generatione,' see, *inter alia*, Huxley, 'Science and Culture,' 1888, p. 333, &c.

[2] John Ray, or Rajus, as he is called abroad (1628-1705), a native of Essex, was a Cambridge man ; he, however, gave up his fellowship in 1662, feeling himself unable to subscribe to the Act of Uniformity of 1661. He was one of the first great classifiers of plants ; he col-

Society called after him: in more recent times Hutton formed a school in geology which was opposed to that of Werner, emanating from Germany.[1]   Hunter, the anato-

lected a vast amount of information, beginning with the neighbourhood of Cambridge and extending it in travels over Great Britain and the Continent with Willoughby. The 'Historia Plantarum'—describing 18,625 species of plants—appeared from 1685 to 1704 in 3 vols. The first volume contains a chapter on the anatomy and physiology of plants, which was much extolled by Cuvier and recommended for republication. The "Ray Society," started in 1844 "for the publication of works on Natural History," brought out among many other excellent and celebrated works (such as Darwin's 'Monograph of the Family Cirripedia'), Memorials (1844) and Correspondence (1848) of John Ray: it also translated that eccentric specimen of the "Naturphilosophie" Oken's 'Elements of Physio - philosophy,' 1847. A contemporary of John Ray was Nehemiah Grew (1628-1711), one of the first to make extensive use of the microscope (invented in Holland between 1590 and 1600) for the examination of the anatomy and physiology of plants. After Oldenburg he was Secretary of the Royal Society together with Hooke. The Society printed his 'Anatomy of Plants.' About the same time it seems to have exhausted its funds in printing Willoughby's 'Historia Piscium,' so that it was unable to carry out its design of defraying the cost of printing the 'Principia.' This was generously done by Halley. See Weld, 'History of the Royal Society,' vol. i. p. 309, &c.

[1] Beneath the strife of the Wernerians and Huttonians, or the Neptunists and Plutonists as they

were termed, the real merits of Robert Jameson (1774-1854) and James Hutton (1726 - 97) have sometimes been overlooked. Both were ardent naturalists who spent their lives in observation and study of nature. They made Edinburgh for some time the centre of geology in this country. Jameson was fifty years Professor of Natural History, founded the first school of Natural History in this country (see Cossar Ewart's address, quoted by Sir A. Grant, 'Story of the University of Edinburgh,' vol. ii. p. 444), trained a number of eminent naturalists, among whom are Edward Forbes and Grant (N.B.—The name of Darwin must be added with caution, see his 'Autobiography,' vol. i. p. 44, &c.), founded the Edinburgh Museum of Natural History, which includes the Huttonian collections, and founded the Wernerian and Plinian Societies of Natural History. James Hutton, though not a teacher like Jameson, exerted a great influence through John Playfair, who popularised his views in his 'Illustrations of the Huttonian Theory of the Earth' (1802). It is termed by Geikie a "classical contribution to geological literature." Though the opposition of Hutton's theoretical views to those of Werner gave him a great reputation as a theorist, it is claimed for him that he first among geologists disclaimed the intention of investigating the origin of things, and thus put an end to the cosmogonies of the eighteenth century. Such had been promulgated in all the three countries by the most illustrious philosophers and naturalists, by Burnet, Buffon, and Leibniz. On Hutton's great merits see especially Huxley, "Essay on Geolo-

mist, acquired a world-wide reputation in the latter part
of the eighteenth century.

Many other students of nature could be added to this
list.   Perhaps none has acquired greater popular celebrity

46.
Jenner.

than Jenner.[1] This he acquired through his extraordinary
discovery, by which he grappled successfully with one of
the most prevalent and distressing epidemics from which

47.
English love
of nature.

former generations had to suffer.   The study of animated
nature, the observation of the sky and the heavens, have
always been favourite occupations of Englishmen.   The
love of travels abroad and of the country at home has
favoured a close intercourse with nature.   A fickle and
humid climate invited the superior skill of the agriculturist
and the gardener, and rewarded them with heavier crops
and more luxuriant verdure.[2]   The chill of the long winter

gical Reform" (1869.   Reprinted
in 'Lay Sermons and Addresses,'
No. 11).   He is there considered
as the first representative of "Uni-
formitarianism" against the older
"Catastrophism."   Uniformitarian-
ism has been followed by "Evolu-
tionism."

[1] Edward Jenner (1749 - 1823),
one of the greatest benefactors of
mankind, spent twenty years on
the farms of Gloucestershire, following the advice of his friend and
master John Hunter, "Don't think,
but try," before he undertook the
first inoculation of cowpox on the
14th of May 1796.   About the end
of the century the process of vaccination, which dispelled the older
process of inoculation—introduced
into England by Lady Mary W.
Montagu in 1721 — had become
generally known in Europe.   The
governments of the Revolution in
France and the Academy of Sciences had at the end of the century
occupied themselves a good deal

with the cure of smallpox, both Voltaire and d'Alembert having taken
great interest in the subject.

[2] The yield of an acre in wheat
is in England about 30 bushels or
one ton of grain ; next comes Belgium, then Germany, then France ;
the average yield in the United
States of America is barely one-half
of that in England.   The yield of
an acre in Scotland exceeds slightly
that in England.   In Scotland farming is carried on with much skill
and enterprise, and, in spite of the
severe climate, gardening is probably further developed there than
in any other country.   It appears
that the first voluntary organisation for the improvement of agriculture was the "Society of Im-
provers in the Knowledge of Agriculture in Scotland" formed in
1723, of which the Earl of Stair
was one of the leaders.   Though it
counted 300 members, it was short-
lived : its 'Select Transactions'
were published by Maxwell in 1743.

stimulated active exercise and outdoor sport; the abundant rains, which fed the many rivulets with a constant supply of fresh water, suggested the cultivation of that pastime of which Izaak Walton had left a classical description, long before Rousseau in France made the love of nature a fashionable sentiment.   Lord Bacon pointed to the study of natural phenomena as the only source of knowledge.   Evelyn wrote a treatise on forest-trees, and the old-fashioned English flower-garden is immortalised in Bacon's 'Essays,' in the "Winter's Tale," in Cowper's "Task," and in the works of many other poets. Through the literature of the eighteenth century there runs a vein of increasing love and knowledge of natural objects and natural scenery, beginning in Thomson and Gray, widening and deepening in Erasmus Darwin and Cowper, and attaining full vigour and originality in Burns and Wordsworth, as also in the school of English landscape-painting.   William and Caroline Herschel com-

Next came the Bath and West of England Society, 1777; the Highland Society, 1784; and the National Board of Agriculture, 1793. The 'Farmer's Magazine' was started in 1800. About the same time that Lawes and Gilbert in England and Liebig in Germany gave such an impetus to scientific farming through their experiments and publications, "Mr John Finnie at Swanston, near Edinburgh, having suggested (1842) to some of his neighbours the desirableness of obtaining the aid of chemistry to guide farmers in many departments of their business, the hint was promptly acted upon, and these Mid-Lothian tenant-farmers had the merit of originating an Agricultural Chemistry Association (the first of its kind), by which funds were raised, and an eminent chemist engaged" ('Ency. Brit.,' article "Agriculture," vol. i. p. 305).   There is probably no country where farming is such a favourite pursuit of gentlemen of leisure and wealth as Great Britain, or where the intelligence of higher society and of the universities is so liberally transferred to the benefit of the country, of its population, its crops, and its livestock.   Among many examples of the past and present I mention as an outcome of this spirit the little volume by Sir Thomas Dyke Acland, 'On the Chemistry of Farming' (London : Simpkin & Co., 1891), and his liberal patronage of agriculture in the west of England.

menced the long line of amateur star-gazers of this country; Luke Howard's study of clouds drew from the kindred spirit which lived in the great Goethe a loving memorial;[1] and John Dalton was induced by the mists and fogs of his native lake country to join in the foundation of the modern science of meteorology.

48.
Union of individualism and naturalism in England.

We now discover the reason why the strong individualism of the English character, which prompted new departures and inspired new ideas in science, as it produced adventures and novel enterprise in life and arts, has not more frequently led to discouraging failures in the latter, or to eccentricity and dreaminess in the former; why it has, on the whole, alike in practical work and in scientific study, been rewarded by signal success. The rare genius, gifted with the power of original thought, who found no academy ready to call him, no schools where he could be trained, no university eager to nurse and develop his

---

[1] Luke Howard (1772-1864), a member of the Society of Friends, was one of the many lovers of nature and amateur naturalists of this country in whom new sciences—like that of meteorology — are nursed during their unpretentious infancy. He himself gave a simple narrative of his life and doings to the great Goethe, who, attracted by his attempted classification of clouds (about 1802, published in his 'Climate of London'), had addressed some lines to him, accompanying them by a statement in verse of Howard's description of the stratus, cumulus, cirrus, and nimbus :—

"Er aber, Howard, giebt mit reinem
      Sinn
Uns neuer Lehre herrlichsten Gewinn :
Was sich nicht halten, nicht erreichen
      lässt,
Er fasst es an, er hält zuerst es fest ;

Bestimmt das Unbestimmte, schränkt es
      ein,
Benennt es treffend !—Sey die Ehre Dein !
Wie Streife steigt, sich ballt, zerflattert,
      fällt,
Erinnre dankbar Deiner sich die Welt."

Goethe subsequently tried to get some information about Howard's way of life, "so that I might see how such a mind is formed, what opportunities, what circumstances, have led him into ways of looking at Nature naturally, have taught him how to devote himself to her, so as to find her laws and to prescribe these again to her in a natural human manner." In his autobiographical narrative (reprinted in the last volume of Goethe's Works) Howard refers to the meteoric phenomena of 1783, mentioned also in Cowper's Letters (13th June 1788), and White's 'History of Selborne.'

talent, did not retire into the depths of his own consciousness, or surround himself with the artificial atmosphere of erudition.   The result of such a process
can be abundantly traced in other countries and other
literatures.   In England the isolation from society and
the solitariness of genius threw him into the arms of
Nature, and she has in many instances, in science, in
poetry, and in art, rewarded and refreshed him by a
novel inspiration—she has lifted her veil to his loving
eye and revealed to him one of her secrets.   The individualism of English science has been tempered by
its naturalism.   A type of this peculiar form of the
naturalist was Gilbert White, the natural historian of
Selborne.[1]

---

[1] A long list might be given of
these retired nature-loving souls,
among whom Charles Darwin will
always rank as the greatest and
most conspicuous.   I give here a
few names in addition to those
mentioned in the text.

John Gough of Kendal (1757-
1825) might, according to John
Dalton (see his Life by Henry, pp.
9 and 10), "be deemed a prodigy
in scientific attainments. . . . Deprived of sight in infancy by the
smallpox, . . . possessing great
powers of mind, he bent them
chiefly to the study of the physical
and mechanical sciences.   It was he
who first set the example of keeping
a meteorological journal at Kendal;
. . . he knew by the touch, taste,
and smell almost every plant within
twenty miles ; he could reason with
astonishing perspicuity on the construction of the eye, the nature of
light and colours, and of optic
glasses," &c., &c.   For about eight
years Dalton and he were intimately
acquainted.

George Edwards (1694-1773) of
Stratford, Essex, was the author of
the 'History of Birds,' which he
published between 1743 and 1764
in six volumes.   He had journeyed
through France and other countries,
and gave engravings of six hundred
subjects not before delineated by
naturalists.

Still more remarkable was Thomas
Edward (1814-86), the shoemaker
of Banff, who, having been turned
out of three schools for his zoological propensities, without friends,
without a single book on natural
history, not knowing the names of
the creatures he found, gained a
knowledge unique in its freshness
and accuracy.   At the University
of Aberdeen, where he exhibited
his collections, he was told by the
professors that he came "several
centuries too soon," as they had
then no chair of Natural History.
His life has been written by Smiles,
1876.

Edward Forbes (1815-54) of
Douglas, Isle of Man, a born lover

Not long after Ray and Linnæus had attempted the artificial and logical classification of living beings, and about the same time that Buffon in France infused into the literature of his country a somewhat pretentious love of nature, Gilbert White, in a simpler and more healthy style, betook himself to describe the aspect that nature presented when viewed from the quiet home of an English country parson. He may be said to have represented that other

49.
White of
Selborne.

of nature, "led an unusually full life, occupied in promoting science and arousing enthusiasm and awakening intelligence in others. To almost every department of biology he rendered much service, especially by connecting various branches together and illustrating one by the other. Though his published works have been few, his ideas have been as the grain of mustard-seed in the parable" ('Dictionary of National Biography'). After holding various badly paid offices in London and elsewhere, he succeeded Robert Jameson as Professor of Natural History at Edinburgh (see 'Memoir of E. Forbes,' by G. Wilson and A. Geikie, 1861).

Hugh Miller (1802-56), the self-taught stonemason of Cromarty, combined the soul of an artist with that of a naturalist. His writings occupy a place by themselves in English Literature. "The principal scene of his own investigations was the Cromarty district, where he ransacked every wrinkle of the hillside, and traced every stratum sawn through by the watercourse, and where on the beach at ebb, in indurated clay of bluish tint and great tenacity, belonging to the old Red Sandstone formation, he discovered and dug out nodules which, when laid open by a skilful blow of the hammer, displayed organisms that had never been seen by the human eye." In September 1840

there appeared in the 'Witness' a series of articles entitled "The Old Red Sandstone." They formed the nucleus of a book of this title which established the reputation of Miller as an original geologist, as a practical thinker and fascinating writer. 'My Schools and Schoolmasters' is a masterpiece of the English language. "In an age prodigal of genius, yet abounding also in extravagance, glare, and bombast, the self-educated stonemason wrote with the calmness and moderation of Addison." "The fossil remains seem in his glowing pages to live and flourish, to fly, swim, or gambol, or to shoot up in vegetative profusion and splendour, as in the primal dawn of creation" (Carruthers, quoted by Peter Bayne in 'The Life and Letters of Hugh Miller,' 2 vols., 1871).

David Robertson, the naturalist of Cumbrae in the Firth of Clyde (born in 1806), was a farm-labourer till he was twenty-four, then took to the study of medicine, and had afterwards for many years a china and hardware shop in Jail Square, Glasgow. He gained a sufficient independence to be able to retire in 1860 to Great Cumbrae, where he devoted the rest of his life to a study of nature. Especially in "the marine section, by his own unaided efforts, he opened up in a remarkable degree the zoology of the Firth of Clyde.

side of natural science, which does not try to comprehend nature through the artificial arrangement or classification of a museum, but in those connections, among her own animate and inanimate objects, which constitute reality, and are the characteristics of life and development. It was the real, not the artificial, Jardin des Plantes, where he and his successors tried to study natural objects and the habits of living beings.[1] Another re-

Many animals, till then accounted rare, are now known to exist as common objects, while the annals of science have received many important additions of animals altogether new to natural history records — discoveries which have caused the Firth of Clyde, and more particularly the Cumbrae Islands, to become one of the best explored and most widely known districts of Britain" (Gray, Secretary of the Glasgow Natural History Society, quoted by Thomas R. R. Stebbing in his 'Naturalist of Cumbrae,' London, 1891).

William Pearson (1767-1847) of Borderside, Crosthwaite, near Kendal, was a self-educated yeoman, who after many years spent in a bank at Manchester retired to a small patrimonial estate on the southern border of Westmorland. He possessed a choice collection of books, representing fully the English poets of all ages, and in translation the best German authors. "Of the habits of birds and other native creatures around him he was a watchful observer, and he described them in purest English with a charm that suggested no disadvantageous comparison with White of Selborne" (see Groves, 'Life of Hamilton,' vol. iii. p. 15). He was a friend of Wordsworth.

To this list, which could be indefinitely extended, I might add another, beginning with Thomas

Bewick (1753-1828), the reviver of wood-engraving in England, who lent his art and life to the delineation of nature. 'British Birds' (1797-1804) is a standard work on the borderland of art and science, in which many other British artists have, in humbler or more extensive fields, laboured with so much faithfulness and success.

[1] The 'Complete Angler' and the 'Natural History of Selborne,' are types of a class of literature peculiar to this country. In these classical productions we are introduced into the nursery of English thought, poetry—nay, of science itself. These, as the nation draws ultimately its wealth from the produce and culture of the land, on their part receive valuable ideas from a study of nature. The purity and originality of English art and poetry have their home in the same region. Gilbert White (1720-93) was born and lived in the little Hampshire village of Selborne. He was one of five brothers, all of whom, in various positions and vocations of life, followed the study of nature in its minute and local aspects, combining with it an antiquarian taste. He may not only be classed with the naturalists, but belongs also to that class of writers, peculiar also to England, who devote their time to the compilation of local records, of county histories, and to the preservation of the relics and memorials

action against the theorising methods which had come
over from the Continent led to the formation of the
Geological Society in the year 1807. At that time
the war of the Wernerians and Huttonians, or, as they
were also called, the Neptunists and Plutonists, was rag-
ing in the northern metropolis. The Geological Society
of London was established with a view to " multiply and
record observations, and patiently to await the result at
some future period—that is, its founders resolved to apply
themselves to descriptive geology, thinking the time not
come for that theoretical geology which had then long
fired the controversial ardour of Neptunists and Plutonists." [1] Fifty years after the formation of this society

of country life in bygone centuries.
The series of letters written between the years 1765 and 1787
containing "the observations of
forty years," and published, 1789,
with the title ' The Natural History
and Antiquities of Selborne,' had
the object "of laying before the
public his idea of parochial history,
which, he thinks, ought to consist
of natural productions and occur-
rences as well as antiquities." To
him "nature is so full that that district produces the greatest variety
which is the most examined." He
early insists on the necessity of
monographs in natural history ;
suggests the usefulness of a "full
history of noxious insects"; gives
in a series of letters a faithful and
minute description of the swallow
tribe as they are found in his
country ; traverses the Downs of
Surrey with a loving eye a hundred
years before they became celebrated
through the greater Darwin ; makes
valuable observations about "earth-
worms," suggesting a monograph
on them ; suggests, in an age which
was governed by the systematising

mania, that "the botanist should
study plants philosophically, should
investigate the laws of vegetation,
should promote their cultivation,
and graft the gardener, the planter,
and the husbandman on the phy-
tologist," as "system should be
subservient to, not the main object
of, pursuit."

[1] "The one point the catastro-
phists and the uniformitarians
agreed upon when this society was
founded was to ignore it [*viz.*, geological speculation]. And you will
find, if you look back into our records, that our revered fathers in
geology plumed themselves a good
deal upon the practical sense and
wisdom of this proceeding. As a
temporary measure I do not pre-
sume to challenge its wisdom ; but
in all organised bodies temporary
changes are apt to produce permanent effects; and as time has
slipped by, altering all the conditions which may have made such
mortification of the scientific flesh
desirable, I think the effect of the
stream of cold water which has
steadily flowed over geological specu-

the author from whom I quote, Dr Whewell, in the third
edition of his 'History of the Inductive Sciences,' could
still say that "their task was not yet finished, their mission not yet accomplished—that they had still much to
do in the way of collecting facts; and in entering upon
the exact estimation of causes, they have only just thrown
open the door of a vast labyrinth which it may employ
many generations to traverse, but which they must needs
explore before they can penetrate to the Oracular Chamber
of Truth."[1]   One of the many individuals in this country
who "had long pursued his own thoughts without aid and
without sympathy"[2] was William Smith.   "No literary

51.
William
Smith.

lation within these walls has been
of doubtful beneficence" (Huxley
on "Geological Reform," Address
to the Geological Society, 1869;
reprinted in 'Lay Sermons,' &c.,
1891, p. 207).

[1] See Whewell, 'History of the
Inductive Sciences,' 3rd ed., vol. iii.
pp. 428, 518. Lyell, 'Principles of
Geology,' 3rd ed., vol. i. p. 102, &c.

[2] Whewell, loc. cit., vol. iii. p.
427. William Smith (1769-1839),
a native of Oxfordshire, has been
called the Father of English Geology. He was—like so many other
naturalists of this country — an
amateur in his scientific studies,
which were conducted on the occasions of his elaborate surveys of
Oxfordshire, Warwickshire, and
Somersetshire in connection with
the engineering of several canals.
He initiated in England the science
called on the Continent "Strati-
graphy," observed the successive
layers in the geological structure
of the country, and in 1799 prepared a tabular view of the order
of the strata and their organic
remains in the neighbourhood of
Bath. For many years after this

he was occupied in preparing his
Geological Map of England and
Wales, which appeared on the five
miles to the inch scale in 1815 in
fifteen sheets. He was popularly
known as "Stratum Smith," but
remained almost unknown abroad,
as he himself also seems to have
taken little notice of Continental
geology or prevailing theories.
Though he began earlier than Cuvier and Brongniart, they anticipated him by publishing in 1811
their mineralogical description of
the Paris Basin, thus becoming the
founders of the science of palæontology (see Peschel, 'Geschichte
der Erdkunde,' München, 1877, p.
714, &c.) Of the Geological Map
Lyell says ('Principles of Geology,'
vol. i. p. 101) that it "remains a
lasting monument of original talent
and extraordinary perseverance; for
he had explored the whole country
on foot without the guidance of
previous observers or the aid of
fellow-labourers, and had succeeded
in throwing into natural divisions
the whole complicated series of
British rocks."

cultivation of his youth awoke in him the speculative love of symmetry and system; but a singular clearness and precision of the classifying power, which he possessed as a native talent, was exercised and developed by exactly those geological facts among which his philosophical task lay. Some of the advances which he made had been entered upon by others who preceded him; but of all this he was ignorant, and perhaps went on more steadily and eagerly to work out his own ideas from the persuasion that they were entirely his own." In what he did and published, beginning with the year 1790, " we see great vividness of thought and activity of mind unfolding itself exactly in proportion to the facts with which it had to deal." [1]

About the same time that geological studies received a great impetus in this country from two distinct centres— the philosophical teaching in the Scotch metropolis, and the more empirical labours of the Geological Society—a signal discovery in another line marked a great step in anatomy and physiology. This was Charles Bell's discovery, in the year 1807, of the difference between sensory and motor nerves, "doubtless the most important accession to physiological knowledge since the time of Harvey." [2]

52.
Charles Bell.

[1] Whewell, *loc. cit.*, p. 423.

[2] This statement, taken from Dr Henry's 'Report of the British Association,' vol. vi., and repeated by Whewell (*loc. cit.*, vol. iii. p. 352), probably requires a correction, since Du Bois-Reymond and others have placed in their true historical position the great merits of Descartes, who by the discovery of the principle of "reflex action" "did for the physiology of motion and sensation that which Harvey had done for the circulation of the blood, and opened up that road to the mechanical theory of these processes which has been followed by all his successors" (Huxley in his address to the British Association at Belfast, 1874; reprinted in 'Science and Culture, &c.,' p. 200, &c.) The first enunciation of the principle of reflex action had been variously ascribed to Joh. Müller, Prochaska, Willis, till Du Bois-Reymond in his most interesting 'Gedächtnissrede

Bell's career was a unique one.   He had early severed his connection with the great medical schools of Edinburgh, where his brother taught.   He lectured and practised privately in London, where he gained a considerable reputation; but in his case also it was on the Continent that his greatness was more generally recognised.   As in Dalton's case, his countrymen were slow to do him justice.[1]   In France he had so great a name that a celebrated

auf Joh. Müller' (Berlin Acad., 1859) showed how the merit of enunciating it is due to Descartes, whose tract on 'Les Passions de l'Âme' was published in 1649. Both Du Bois-Reymond and Huxley give full extracts from the writings of Descartes. There seems, however, to be some doubt to what extent Descartes substantiated his mechanical view of the action of the nervous system by actual experiments. Richet in his 'Physiologie des Muscles et des Nerfs' (Paris, 1882, p. 505, &c.) refers to this, and while giving Descartes his due, also says that practically from the time of Galen to Charles Bell no marked progress had been made in the knowledge of the nervous system, and that this belongs almost entirely to the nineteenth century (pp. 502, 507, 514). Huxley, who takes a much higher view of the merits of Descartes, says he was not only a speculator, but also an observer and dissector (loc. cit., p. 201), and actually places him at the head of modern physiology (p. 334, &c.)

[1] Charles Bell (1774-1842) was born at Edinburgh. His elder brother, John Bell (1763-1820), who was a lecturer of great repute in the extra-mural School of Surgery at Edinburgh, first drew his attention to the medical profession. It was only late in life, and after he

had gained his European renown, that he was appointed to the Chair of Surgery at the University of Edinburgh, which had been created in 1831, and it does not appear that he was at all sufficiently appreciated in this position : he used to say, "I seem to walk in a city of tombs," being unknown in the city of his birth (see Sir A. Grant, 'University of Edinburgh,' vol. ii. p. 453). Whilst Charles Bell established the difference of sensory and motor nerves, and dispelled "the confusion which prevailed up to that time in the minds of anatomists and physiologists regarding the functions of the various nerves," the merit of proving by strict experiment the correctness of Bell's theorem belongs to Johannes Müller (1831), who showed it in the frog, and to Magendie and Longet, who succeeded in exhibiting it in warm-blooded animals. Up to the date of Müller's experimental proof nobody regarded "Bell's doctrine as more than an ingenious and indeed plausible, but nevertheless not sufficiently demonstrated, idea" (see Du Bois-Reymond, 'Reden,' vol. ii. p. 176, &c. ; also Henle's description of the demonstration given by Müller in Paris on the 13th September 1831 to Humboldt, Dutrochet, Valenciennes, and Laurillart, in 'Jacob Henle,' by Merkel, 1891, p. 83).

anatomical professor, when Bell visited his lecture-room, dismissed his class with the words, " C'est assez, messieurs, vous avez vu Charles Bell."

In Germany one of the great achievements of Johannes Müller, through which he acquired European celebrity, was his actual experimental proof of Bell's thesis, with which he had occupied himself for many years.

Instances might be indefinitely multiplied, showing the individual greatness, but also the isolation, of English men of science and their discoveries ; how the latter emanated so frequently from the depths of original genius in intimate communion with nature ; how they as frequently lacked those social advantages, that organisation for development, which the great schools and establishments of the Continent all through the century have possessed in so eminent a degree.   Not only in the study of nature has this individual character of British research

53.
Historical
geography.

shown itself, though it is here most conspicuous.   In the exploration of foreign lands and the monuments of bygone civilisations—in the historical branches of research, we meet with similar pioneer work.   Who does not recall the names of Dr Young and of Layard ?   I will mention only one instance of this kind, where individual ability joined to fortuitous circumstances laid the foundation of a new branch of research on the borderland of natural and political history, the geography of ancient and modern Greece—the exploration of the land which produced the most remarkable, and perhaps the most intense, culture which the world has yet seen.   Note what Ernst Curtius [1]

[1] See his essay in the 'Preussische Jahrbücher,' vol. 38, on M. W. Leake, and his discourse, "Der Wetteifer der Nationen in der Wiederentdeckung der Länder des Alterthums" (1880), both reprint-

says,—the man to whom we are most indebted for the systematic historical and artistic study of this remarkable country; whose mind has better than any other succeeded in representing to itself the natural and ideal features of that country and that bygone race, and who has drawn in his writings a series of pictures, reproducing that past glory in unequalled perfection. In tracing the beginnings of the modern science of archæology or historical geography, he assigns to England and Englishmen a foremost place as pioneers. " In England there was no mediæval tradition which suggested expeditions to the East, nor did there exist any external occasion or public interest, but it was a free and purely human attraction which led Britons to the classical soil, and private means have made all the sacrifices that were required in order to satisfy a craving of the soul.[1] . . . England became the

ed in that valuable collection, 'Alterthum und Gegenwart,' 3 vols., Berlin, 1882 and 1889. In the rediscovery of the countries of ancient civilisation, Italians made the beginning with Cyriacus of Ancona (from 1412 to 1442). Then follow the French—Jacob Spon of Lyons, a German by birth, being among the earliest (1675). The generation that succeeded the age of Scaliger produced the first maps of Greece (Paulmier). Then follows England, where the name of Arundel has acquired a doubtful celebrity through that wholesale acquisition of ancient relics which Mr (afterwards Sir William) Petty and John Evelyn carried on in his name in Greece and Asia Minor. It is interesting to note here the position that Germany holds in the growing science of archæology, of which Winckelmann may be considered the founder. "The Germans possessed no advantages and resources by which they could take part in the contest of nations over the rediscovery of the countries of ancient history. . . . Whilst in Italy it was national feeling, in France political relations with the East, in England the love of collecting and travelling common among the aristocracy, which established the connection of the Old World with the New, in Germany it was the workroom of the professor" (Curtius, *loc. cit.*, vol. ii. p. 229).

[1] E. Curtius, *loc. cit.*, vol. ii. p. 226. "In the year 1742 Stuart and Revett wandered among the ruins of Rome, and recognised that in its relics they beheld only later and degenerate forms of ancient art. Six years later they set sail for Greece. It was, after Cyriacus of Ancona and Jacob Spon of Lyons, the third journey of exploration; but it was the first in scientific importance" (p. 227).

treasury of the wonders of the East, and whilst the Continent was closed to her, her travellers flocked to Hellas,
registering with marvellous patience, watch in hand, on
the back of the slowly marching mule, piece by piece, the
remains of antiquity. . . . The political mission, headed

54.
Martin
William
Leake.

by Martin William Leake, was as such quite unsuccessful;
for science, it was of priceless value: from the moment
that Leake trod on classic soil the reminiscences of Homer
and Herodotus were kindled, and he saw clearly his life-
work before him.   Under the powerful impressions produced by the great table-land of Asia Minor with the
solitary snow-peak Argaios, deeply moved by the deserted
places, marching over Grecian inscriptions, over sarcophagi
and temple ruins, he felt the irresistible charm of the
attempt to explore and to understand these homes of
ancient culture.[1] . . . The scientific result was a lasting
gain for the civilised world, and the travels which he
made from 1805 to 1807 mark an epoch in our knowledge of Grecian antiquity." [2]

But the labours of the pioneer in science, life, or art,
which form so conspicuous an element of this country's
mental work during the first two-thirds of the century,
must be supplemented and carried further by a great
army of patient and trained explorers.   Original ideas
must be cast into an appropriate and elegant form; new
discoveries must be extended and criticised by strict
methods of research; erudition and philosophy are required to guarantee completeness and depth.   In the
large domain of the historical sciences these labours of

[1] E. Curtius, *loc. cit.*, p. 307.
[2] Ibid., p. 312.

the school and the study are even more important than in the exploration of nature, and thus it is not surprising that in these especially the bulk of the work, though frequently begun by Englishmen, has been carried on by the great schools and academies of the Continent. In the regions of exact science, with which we are at present more immediately concerned, there will always be a much greater inducement for original minds to forsake the beaten track, the recognised method or system.

The genius gifted with a larger field of vision and a keener glance will always feel the longing to return to Nature herself, and the practical man will be allured by the prospects of application of science in the arts and industries. Both will find their reward; nor is it likely that the works of Faraday and Darwin should be the last illustrious examples of great and far-reaching ideas sprung from the living intercourse of original genius and nature without the support of any school; or that the practical success of the Atlantic cable will be the last fruit of the rare combination of highest mathematical genius with industrial and commercial enterprise. The historian of thought is forced to admit that such rare combinations are most likely to spring up amongst a people who have always opposed the rule of systems and methods, of schools and academies; who have nursed and cherished an intimate communion with nature; and for whom practical interests and adventures have always preserved an irresistible attraction.

Living in an age when the foundation in England and in Germany of institutions similar to the Académie Française has been seriously discussed,[1] when the British Association has been copied abroad,[2] and when scientific men of eminence are joined in conference as to the advisability of founding a professorial university in London, in imitation of the great University of Berlin, it seems appropriate to recall the various ways and means by which, mainly in this century, the exact spirit of research, the mathematical method of investigating nature and reality, has been established and diffused.

55.
Work of
the three
nations
compared.

France was the country in which the modern scientific methods of measurement, calculation, and classification were first practised on a large scale, reduced to a system, and employed for the investigation of the whole of nature. The Academy of Sciences, together with the High Schools of Science, the Natural History collections, and Medical Institutions, all in close connection, furnished an organisation of the highest intelligences of the nation, by which

---

[1] See Matthew Arnold's essay on 'The Literary Influence of Academies,' and Du Bois - Reymond, 'Uebereine Kaiserliche Akademie der deutschen Sprache,' 1874, reprinted in 'Reden, &c.,' Leipzig, 1886, vol. i. p. 141, &c. On the other side see Huxley in 'Critiques and Addresses,' ed. of 1890, p. 113, &c.

[2] The British Association, itself established somewhat on the model of the German "Naturforscher-Versammlung," founded by Oken and Humboldt (see *supra*, p. 238) in the year 1831, has become the model of the younger "Association française pour l'Avancement des Sciences," founded in 1872 under the presidency of Claude Bernard. It held its first public meeting at Bordeaux in 1874. In the opening addresses of the president, M. de Quatrefages, and the

secretary, M. Cornu, the elder sister in England is referred to. A characteristic passage in M. Quatrefages' address as regards the results achieved by the British Association is the following : "Grâce à elle une partie de la population a été transformée. Les fils de ces chasseurs de renards, qui, pour se délasser de leurs rudes passetemps, ne connaissaient que des joies également violentes et matérielles, sont aujourd'hui des botanistes, des géologues, des physiciens, des archéologues " ('Comptes Rendus,' Ière session, p. 40). Following the resolutions carried in 1885, the French Association amalgamated in 1886 with the older "Association scientifique de France," founded by Leverrier in 1864. See 'Compte Rendu de la 16me Session,' vol. i. p. 1, &c.

a systematic exploration of the heavens and the earth, the inanimate and the living world, could be undertaken. At the same time, the methods of measurement and calculation were submitted to closer study; new sciences were created by the application of these methods; and problems were attacked for the first time, with which, at the end of the century, the scientific world is still occupied. It was in France also that the discoveries of the laboratory were first applied so as to contribute to the revolution of arts and industries. In all its different expressions—in the production of works of classical perfection in substance and in form, in its application to the problems of life and society, and in its influence on general literature—we find the scientific spirit, as we know it, fully established in France in the beginning of the century. About three decades later we find this spirit domiciled in Germany, the study of the exact sciences having been gradually accepted at the German universities as an integral part of the university cycle. It there met the philosophical and classical spirit, which had organised the German university system and the teaching of the higher schools, and had revolutionised historical, especially philological, studies. What might have been wanting at times in French science, historical completeness and philosophical criticism, was added in Germany. Germany has in the course of this century not only become the country where the most faithful and exhaustive record is kept of the scientific labours of the whole world, but it has also become the country where mainly those problems have been attacked which lie on the borderland of natural science and philosophy, the problems of life and consciousness. Modern physiology, especially psychophysics, is claimed as essentially a German science.

Meanwhile England, where the introduction of the scientific spirit as an established canon of systematic and methodical research was later than in other countries, has all through this century, as before, continued to do pioneer work in many isolated branches of science : individual, as opposed to corporate effort, has here been rewarded by a succession of brilliant discoveries, which have revolutionised practical life or opened out new views into the hidden recesses of nature. For the want of organisations of research and teaching, such as other countries possessed, these ideas of English thinkers have frequently lain dormant or been elaborated by foreign talent; but this want of a recognised system, and of a standard course of study, has forced original minds into a closer communion with nature and with life, whence they have frequently returned to the laboratory with quite novel revelations. The largest number of works perfect in form and substance, classical for all time, belongs probably to France ; the greatest bulk of scientific work probably to Germany ; but of the new ideas which during this century have fructified science, the larger share belongs probably to England. Such seems to be the impartial verdict of history. During the second half of the century a process of equalisation has gone on which has taken away something of the characteristic peculiarities of earlier times. The great problems of science and life are now everywhere attacked by similar methods. Scientific teaching proceeds on similar lines, and ideas and discoveries are cosmopolitan property. So much more interesting must it be for those who have been born members of this international republic of learning to trace the way in which this confederation has grown up what have been the different national contributions to its formation, and how the spirit of exact science, once domiciled only in Paris, has gradually spread into all countries, and leavened the thought and literature of the world.

CHAPTER IV.

THE ASTRONOMICAL VIEW OF NATURE.

1.
The scientific spirit in the first and second half of the century.

So far I have only treated of the scientific spirit, or of the method of exact research, in a general way; showing how it was firmly established and developed in France, how it spread into Germany, and received there larger and more systematic application, and how in this country it gradually and almost imperceptibly grew out of the older experimental philosophy. This growth, as we have seen, took place partly under the influence of foreign science, but still more through the individual and un-aided labours of a small number of native intellects of the very highest order, to each of whom was for a time allotted the enunciation of some specially fruitful idea. The period referred to in this survey was mainly the first half of our century; in it were most clearly marked the characteristic differences between the three great civilisations of France, Germany, and England. A step further in time would lead into the midst of our own period—into the age which has largely reaped the benefits of those earlier labours, both in theory and in practice, fully realising in many directions the predictions and even the ideals of the pioneers of science.   One of these benefits, and perhaps that which to an external beholder marks the greatest difference between the first and the second half of the century, is the greatly increased intercourse which now exists as compared with the earlier years of our century.   This intercourse has reacted on the domain of thought, and produced that exchange of ideas which promotes more rapid progress.   It hardly belongs to the history of thought to analyse[1] the different steps by which the great change has been brought about.   Still, a very superficial glance will suffice to show how the work of bringing about an international exchange of ideas has been very characteristically divided among the three nations in which we are specially interested.   It was not in the interest of thought, of science, or of literature, but rather in that of commerce and of industry, that the modern facilities of intercourse and exchange were invented and introduced.[2]   We shall therefore expect to

2.
Science become international.

---

[1] The principal dates of the introduction of steam-engines and telegraphs for facilitating communication are as follows :—

1802. The tug Charlotte Dundas, built by Symington, was tried on the Forth and Clyde Canal.

1812. Henry Bell built the Comet with side paddle-wheels. It ran on the Clyde as a passenger steamer.

1829. George Stephenson's Rocket was tried on the Stockton and Darlington Railroad, which had been begun in 1821. In the year 1829 the Liverpool and Manchester Railway was inaugurated.

1838. The first steamboats, Sirius and Great Western, crossed the Atlantic.

1833. A comprehensive system of railways was planned by the French and Belgian Governments.

1835. The first German railway was opened between Nürenberg and Fürth. The first electric telegraphs for public use were almost simultaneously constructed in England, Germany, and the United States—the first successful line being probably that constructed by Wheatstone and Cooke between 1836 and 1840. The first Atlantic cable was begun in 1857, and after repeated failures, which were in the main corrected by the scientific investigations of William Thomson (Lord Kelvin), telegraphic communication with America was permanently established in 1866.

[2] This remark applies fully to the railway system, but scarcely to the development of the electric telegraph, which was first actually used for scientific purposes by Gauss and

find them originate mainly in that country in which
those larger spheres of practical work had grown un-
checked and flourished—in Great Britain and its extensive dependencies. To Germany, on the other side, with
its fully developed system of learning, we are indebted
mainly for the complete recording, registering, and analysing of the scientific labours of the whole world. To France

Weber at Göttingen in the year
1833. The documents referring to
this interesting application have
recently been published in H.
Weber's biographical notice of Wilhelm Weber, Breslau, 1893, p. 25, &c.
We read there that soon after 1830
Gauss had been occupied with reducing his magnetical measurements
to an absolute scale, having laid his
celebrated paper, "Intensitas vis
magneticæ ad mensuram absolutam
revocata," before the Göttingen Society in December of 1832. He had
induced Weber to take up similar
investigations at the Physical Institute, which was situated about a
mile distant from Gauss's Observatory. This distance was found to
be an inconvenience, and in order
to overcome it, the first longer telegraphic line in which galvanic currents were used, and which had
two wires, was carried overhead
between the two buildings, and the
instruments and signalling arrangements perfected in the years 1833
to 1836. Both Gauss and Weber
were well aware of the importance
of their invention for practical purposes. The former wrote to Olbers
on the 20th November 1833 : "I
do not know whether I have already
written to you regarding a magnificent arrangement which we have
made here. It is a galvanic chain
between the Observatory and the
Physical Institute, carried by wires
in the air over the houses, up the
Johannis tower and down again.
The whole length will be about

8000 feet. . . . I have devised a
simple arrangement by which I can
instantly reverse the direction of
the current, which I call a com-
mutator. . . . We have already
used this contrivance for telegraphic
experiments, which succeed very
well with whole words and short
sentences. . . . I am convinced
that by using sufficiently strong
wires one might telegraph instantaneously in this manner from
Göttingen to Hanover or from
Hanover to Bremen" (see Schering's address on the occasion of
Gauss's centenary, Göttingen, 1877,
p. 15, &c.) To Schumacher, 6th
August 1835, Gauss wrote as follows : "With a budget of 150
thalers [£22, 10s.] annually for
Observatory and Magnetic Institute together, really extensive trials
cannot of course be made. But
could thousands of thalers be be-
stowed thereon, I think that, for
instance, electromagnetic telegraphy
might be carried to a perfection and
to dimensions at which imagination
almost starts back." Gauss estimates that fifteen millions sterling
of copper wire would suffice to reach
the antipodes, and he says significantly, "I do not think it impossible to invent a mechanism by
which a despatch could be played
off almost as mechanically as a
musical-box plays off a tune when
it is once fixed on a roller" (see
'Briefwechsel zwischen Gauss und
Schumacher,' ed. Peters, vol. ii. p.
411, &c.)

we owe the first beginnings of a general and international system of units and measurements, which, like the common Latin tongue in former centuries, or like the universal languages of algebra or of music, enables us to express the results of scientific research in formulæ intelligible everywhere and at all times, without laborious translations and time-absorbing reductions.

The effect of these international labours has been to destroy the clearly marked differences of national thought. At least in the domain of science the peculiarities of the French, the German, and the English schools are rapidly disappearing. The characteristics of national thought still exist; but in order to find them in the present age we should have to study the deeper philosophical reasonings, the general literature and the artistic efforts of the three nations. These aspects of the thought of our century belong to later portions of this work. I hope there to take up many of the threads which I here break off, as for the present purpose they cannot be profitably continued. To separate the scientific work of the second half of the century according to countries and nations would lead to unnecessary repetition. The second half of the century sees everywhere in the domain of science the dying out of national restrictions—in every country the introduction of foreign methods and foreign models, foreign institutions and foreign apparatus. The establishment of an observatory or a laboratory in our age lays under contribution almost every civilised country in the world, and the most international of sciences—that of electricity— fixes its units by the names of discoverers of many countries.

3.
Disappearance of national differences.

I therefore look upon the spirit of exact research as thoroughly domiciled in the leading countries of Europe during the second half of the century, and intend in the sequel to explain more precisely the different views, the leading ideas, under which this research is everywhere conducted.　These leading ideas have themselves been more clearly brought out and recognised during this period.

4.
Special
scientific
ideas.

The narrow spirit of the Baconian philosophy which reigned in England, the vagueness of the philosophy of nature which reigned in Germany, during the earlier decades of the century, have disappeared in favour of the more comprehensive and the stricter methods taught by Lavoisier, by Monge, by Laplace, and by Cuvier in France. New ideas of extensive bearing have been added, and in the light of these the powers and the limits of science have been more correctly recognised.

To some of my readers well-known names will occur which might serve as guides to fix these leading ideas, under the influence of which the march of science has proceeded: Sir John Herschel, Auguste Comte, John Stuart Mill, and Whewell[1] have indeed done much to

5.
Philosophy
of science.

[1] Of these writings the earliest is Sir John Herschel's "Preliminary Discourse on the Study of Natural Philosophy," which appeared in Lardner's 'Cabinet Cyclopedia' in 1831.　The writings of William Whewell on the 'History' and 'Philosophy of the Inductive Sciences' were begun about the same time. They were planned to serve three distinct objects — to give, 1st, a philosophical history of astronomy, mechanics, physics, chemistry, and botany ; 2nd, an analysis of the nature of induction and the rules of its exercise ; and 3rd, to answer the question of applying inductive processes to other than material sciences — as philology, art, politics, and morals (see 'William Whewell,' by I. Todhunter, vol. i. p. 90). The 'History' appeared in 1837 in three volumes, a second edition in 1847, a third in 1857 ; the 'Philosophy' appeared in 1840 in two volumes, a second edition in 1847. In the course of its execution the original plan was not strictly adhered to—the scope of the History was enlarged considerably, and the

familiarise the unscientific public with the progress of
science and its canons of thought. And it would thus
appear natural to resort to their teaching and their explanations. But this is not the road I propose to follow.
Whewell's 'History of the Inductive Sciences,' being the
first attempt to compass a large subject, will, like
Montucla's earlier 'History of Mathematics,' always remain a standard work. It was, however, written at a
time when the tendency of modern scientific thought was

Philosophy was broken up into
different parts. Herschel stands
mainly on the ground of Bacon's
philosophy, whereas Whewell starts
with the remark that "Bacon only
divined how sciences might be constructed," but that "we can trace
in their history how their construction has taken place"; that "though
Bacon's general maxims still guide
and animate philosophical inquirers,
yet that his views, in their detail,
have all turned out inapplicable."
He accordingly aims at a "New
Organ of Bacon, renovated according to our advanced intellectual position and office" (Preface to 2nd ed. of the 'Philosophy,'
1847). In the exposition of his
views Whewell was greatly influenced by Kant's philosophy. He
thus searches for the fundamental
ideas which underlie all scientific
reasoning; for "besides facts, ideas
are an indispensable source of our
knowledge." The historical portions of Whewell's works have met
with great appreciation in England
and Germany even from those who,
like Herschel (see the review in the
'Quarterly,' June 1841) and Mill
(see 'Autobiography,' p. 208), could
not agree with his philosophy.
The latter has been eclipsed by
the bolder speculations of Auguste
Comte, whose 'Philosophie positive'
appeared in six volumes between the
years 1830 and 1842 in France.
Still more than Whewell did Comte
emphasise the necessity of learning
from the exact sciences how to
treat economical and social problems in a methodical manner.
Instead of the minute and frequently hesitating elaborations of
Whewell, we find in Comte the
bold generalisation of the three
stages of knowledge—the theological, metaphysical, and positive,—
which forms the groundwork of
"Positivism." Of more permanent
value than Whewell's and Comte's
philosophies are the investigations
of J. Stuart Mill, who in his 'System of Logic, Ratiocinative and Inductive' (1st ed., 1843), has laid
the foundation for all subsequent
treatises on this subject, and whose
thoroughgoing empiricism is being
more and more adopted by scientific thinkers. Like Whewell and
Comte, to whom he acknowledges
his obligations ('Autobiog.,' pp. 165,
209, &c.), his ultimate object was
to solve the question "how far the
methods by which so many of the
laws of the physical world have
been numbered among truths irre-
vocably acquired and universally
assented to, can be made instrumental to the formation of a similar
body of received doctrine in moral
and political science" (Preface to
1st ed.)

not as clear as it has become since, and the work has also been superseded by more detailed labours, especially of German historians.[1] The 'Philosophy of the Inductive Sciences,' by the same author, was written with the object of doing something towards determining the nature and conditions of human knowledge, and had thus a philosophical rather than a historical object in view. The same can be said of Mill's 'Logic,' of Comte's 'Philosophie positive,' and of more recent works—such as Jevons's 'Principles of Science.' They form an important section of the philosophical literature of our century, and on future occasions I shall frequently have to refer to their teaching. At present I am not about to investigate the eternal principles of correct reasoning, and the particular methods adopted, consciously or unconsciously, by scientific writers of all times. What I desire to do is, to enumerate and analyse briefly the changing ideas, the general views, under the guidance of which scientific work has progressed in the course of this century. No doubt the same object was before

[1] Besides the works on the history of the special sciences contained in the Munich Collection, 'Geschichte der Wissenschaften in Deutschland,' which in many instances is not limited to German science and learning, there is the unique 'Geschichte der Chemie,' by Hermann Kopp (Braunschweig, 4 vols., 1843-47), the 'Geschichte der Physik,' by Rosenberger (Braunschweig, 3 vols., 1882-90), and Häser's 'Geschichte der Medicin' (Wien, 1875-82, 3rd ed.) In addition to the numerous works of German specialists, I must mention as of the first importance and value the histories by the late Isaac Todhunter of the 'Theory of Attraction and Figure of the Earth' (2 vols., 1873), the 'Calculus of Variations' (1861), the 'Theory of Probability' (1865), and the 'Theory of Elasticity' (continued by K. Pearson, 2 vols. in 3 parts, 1886-93). They supply the want of a good history of modern mathematics, which does not exist. Lastly, the "Deutsche Mathematiker-Vereinigung" have published in their Jahrbuch valuable histories of special branches of mathematics—notably the 'Theory of Invariants' by Franz Mayer, and the 'Modern Theory of Functions' by Brill and Noether.

the mind of Whewell when, after writing his historical work, he attempted in the philosophical sequel to abstract the general ideas which have led scientific research; but it is instructive for our present purpose to note how, writing about the middle of the century, he hardly brought out any of those principles which in the course of its second half have turned out to be fruitful, and have almost become watchwords of popular science. In the year 1857, the date of the publication of the latest editions of Whewell's works, nothing was popularly known of energy, its conservation and dissipation,—nothing of the variation of species, and the evolution of organic forms,—nothing of the mechanical theory of heat or of that of gases—of absolute measurements and absolute temperature; even the cellular theory seems to have been popular only in Germany. And yet all the problems denoted by these now popular terms were then occupying, or had for many years occupied, the leading thinkers of that period. But we find no mention of them in Whewell's works.[1] So

6.
Whewell's
'History,
and 'Phil-
osophy.'

---

[1] The dates of the birth of these leading ideas of the second half of our century are approximately as follows :—

Absolute measurements were started by Gauss about 1830, and the scheme published in 1833 in his memoir, ' Intensitas vis magneticæ terrestris ad mensuram absolutam revocata.' They were extended to electrical phenomena by Weber in his 'Electrodynamische Maasbestimmungen,' 1846. The absolute scale of temperature was introduced by William Thomson in 1848.

The cellular theory was propounded by Schleiden in 1838, and extended to animal structures by Schwann in 1839 ; the term " protoplasm " was introduced by Mohl in 1846.

The mechanical theory of heat dates from Mayer's and Joule's determinations of the equivalent of heat in 1842 and 1843.

The doctrine of the conservation of energy dates from Helmholtz's memoir, ' Ueber die Erhaltung der Kraft,' in 1847 ; that of dissipation of energy from William Thomson's paper " On a Universal Tendency in Nature to the Dissipation of Mechanical Energy," 1852 ; it was prepared by Watt's and Poncelet's

little was the foremost champion of inductive thought able to discern the tendencies of his age : a warning to those who attempt to recognise the aims of contemporary thought.[1]

It is not, then, to the philosophical writers that I shall apply in order to trace the leading directions of scientific

definitions of horse-power and work (1826), which Whewell does not mention.

The mechanical theory of gases— not to mention the older specula- tions of Daniel Bernoulli — dates from Avogadro's and Ampère's hypothesis, published in 1811, "that all gaseous bodies, under the same physical conditions, contain the same number of units," from Herapath (1821) and Joule (1851). On Whewell's position with regard to the question of the origin and variation of species, then already ventilated by Lyell, see 'History of Induct. Sci.,' vol. iii. p. 489, &c. (3rd ed.), and Huxley's remarks in the 'Life of Charles Darwin,' vol. ii. p. 192, &c. Wallace's essay 'On the Law which has regulated the Introduction of New Species' was published in 1858 along with Dar- win's preliminary statement of his views.

We might form a whole catalogue of scientific terms, some of them by no means of recent origin, which are wanting in Whewell's books, but which now govern scien- tific progress : such are energy, work, action and efficiency, absol- ute measurement, to mention only physical terms. The general ideas upon which he himself lays some stress, such as those of polarity and symmetry, appear on the other hand to be vague generalisations, which have frequently led people astray.

[1] "It is a remarkable evidence of the greatness of the progress which has been effected in our time, that even the second edition of the 'History of the Inductive Scien- ces,' which was published in 1846, contains no allusion to the publi- cation in 1843 of the first of the series of experiments by which the mechanical equivalent of heat was correctly ascertained. Such a fail- ure on the part of a contemporary, of great acquirements and remark- able intellectual powers, to read the signs of the times, is a lesson and a warning worthy of being deeply pondered by any one who attempts to prognosticate the course of scientific progress" (Hux- ley in Ward's 'Reign of Queen Vic- toria,' vol. ii. p. 355). The same writer has pointed out how Au- guste Comte was still more un- fortunate in his opinions on con- temporary science. "What struck me was his want of apprehension of the great features of science ; his strange mistakes as to the merits of his scientific contempor- aries ; and his ludicrously erroneous notions about the part which some of the scientific doctrines current in his time were destined to play in the future" ("Scientific Aspects of Positivism," 'Lay Sermons,' 1891, p. 130). He then goes on to show how Comte treated the undulatory theory with contempt, extolled Gall, depreciated Cuvier, and spoke of the "abuse of microscopic in- vestigations" (ibid., p. 134).

thought in our century: their position towards this thought is indeed instructive, but it is frequently unsafe.

Philosophical reasoning either precedes or succeeds the labours of the scientific thinker; it rarely accompanies them. In the history of earlier times, during the first centuries of the modern period, we find some of the foremost philosophers, such as Descartes, Bacon, Leibniz, occupied in attempting to lay down the correct lines on which science should proceed, or to find general ideas which could serve as supreme principles of scientific truth. It is a rare thing to find that they have succeeded in either of these attempts. In more modern times, ever since Locke started on a different track, it has been, especially in this country, the endeavour of philosophers to abstract out of the existing volumes of scientific research the leading ideas which have proved so helpful, and to explain their origin, their bearing, and their value. Perhaps they have been more successful than their predecessors: it has, however, frequently happened to them, that whilst they were elaborately analysing some process of reasoning, or some prevailing scientific principle, science has meanwhile adopted some entirely different line, and presented an entirely unexpected development.

In this respect they resemble that school of historical politicians which in the middle of our century in Germany [1] attempted to read the signs of the times, and to

7.
Philosophy
and science.

---

[1] This is the school represented by the historians Dahlmann and Gervinus. A good account, with a somewhat severe criticism of the aims of this school, will be found in Karl Hillebrand, 'Zeiten, Völker und Menschen,' vol. ii. pp. 205-290. "The State and Literature had grown in Germany alongside of each other without coming into contact, the former active, reticent, modest, the latter declaiming, noisy, pretentious. It appeared as if all our life had become intellectual; Gervinus himself thought so and blamed us. In reality it was

prescribe the lines on which the desired unification of the
nation could be secured.   Events took their own course,
and the great statesman who was the central figure of the
new era of European history may be excused the scorn
with which he has sometimes treated these theoretical
politicians.

8.
Leading
scientific
ideas mostly
very
ancient.   The leading ideas which I select as marking the progress
of scientific research in our century have, with few excep-
tions, hardly been discoveries or inventions of this age.
Some of them are very old.   The ideas of attraction,
which in the hands of Newton and Laplace have led to
such remarkable results, are of great age, and were
familiar to the philosophers of Greece and Rome ; the
same can be said of the atomic theory, which in the
hands of Dalton became such a powerful instrument.
The principles of energy and its conservation can be
traced back to the writings of Newton and Leibniz, and
even to earlier thinkers.   The same may be said of the
modern ideas on heat, of the molecular theory of gases,
and even of Lord Kelvin's vortices ; whilst the views
which through Darwin have revolutionised the natural
sciences have been traced in the suggestions of much ear-

not so. When the professors turned
their backs on science in order to
turn to politics, they imagined politics were now only beginning :
with the wonted pride of learning
they saw in the administrative
class only labourers and clerks ; for
to them parliaments and freedom
of the press were identical with
politics. The mouthpiece of Germany was in the universities, as
that of France was at the bar;
they only heard each other : was
it therefore unnatural if they
thought the German professors
composed the German nation, as
the French lawyers formed the
French nation ? And indeed public opinion in Germany was that of
the professors. . . . The learned
newspaper writers imagined the
spirit of the age spake in them ;
no wonder that they overestimated
the importance of this spirit and of
this so-called public opinion " (ibid.,
p. 254).   See also Treitschke's
' Deutsche Geschichte,' vol. v. p.
408, &c.

lier writers.   Elaborate claims to priority have thus been
set up for persons to whom it is said the credit of modern
discoveries should be given.   I do not intend to contribute
to this controversial literature, except by a general remark,
which will explain how it has come to pass that ideas and
principles now recognised as useful instruments of thought
and research have only recently attained this importance,
while they have frequently been the property of many
ages of philosophical thought, and familiar even to the
writers of antiquity.   It is the scientific method, the exact
statement, which was wanting, and which raises the vague
guesses of the philosophical or the dreams of the poetic
mind to the rank of definite canons of thought, capable of
precise expression, of mathematical analysis, and of exact
verification.   Obscure notions of the attractive and repulsive forces of nature have floated before the minds of
philosophers since the time of Empedocles, but they did
not become useful to science till Galileo and Newton took
the first step to measure the intensity of those forces.
Lucretius's poem introduces to us the early speculations
on the atomic constitution of matter, but the hypotheses
of his school only led to real knowledge of the things of
nature when Dalton, following Lavoisier and Richter, reduced this idea to definite numbers; still more so when,
through the law of Avogadro and Ampère, and the calculations of Joule, Clausius, and Thomson, the velocities, the
number, and sizes of atoms became calculable and measurable quantities.   Descartes, and after him Malebranche,
filled space with vortices which were to explain the constitution of matter and the movements of its parts; but
the notion was abandoned and ridiculed till Helmholtz

and Thomson approached the subject with mathematical analysis and calculated the properties of vortex motion.

Heraclitus proclaimed, six hundred years before the Christian era, the theory that everything moves or flows; but not till this century was the attempt made to work out the definite hypothesis of Daniel Bernoulli, and to explain the properties of bodies, apparently at rest— the pressure of gases, or the phenomena of elasticity— by assuming a hidden motion of the imperceptible portions of matter. The same fate of lying dormant for ages attaches to the suggestive ideas of many thinkers. In every case the awakening touch has been the mathematical spirit, the attempt to count, to measure, or to calculate. What to the poet or the seer may appear to be the very death of all his poetry and all his visions—the cold touch of the calculating mind,—this has proved to be the spell by which knowledge has been born, by which new sciences have been created, and hundreds of definite problems put before the minds and into the hands of diligent students. It is the geometrical figure, the dry algebraical formula, which transforms the vague reasoning of the philosopher into a tangible and manageable conception; which represents, though it does not fully describe, which corresponds to, though it does not explain, the things and processes of nature: this clothes the fruitful, but otherwise indefinite, ideas in such a form that the strict logical methods of thought can be applied, that the human mind can in its inner chamber evolve a train of reasoning the result of which corresponds to the phenomena of the outer world. By such processes did Gauss and Leverrier succeed in tracing the lines in the heavens on which invisible

9.
Mathematical spirit.

stars were speeding through the universe; without them these objects of nature would probably never have been seen, and if seen, they would not have been recognised. Similar, and still more intricate, reasonings permitted Mendeléeff[1] to arrange in geometrical order the several elements or simple substances out of which matter is compounded, and to point to the vacant places on the chart, some of which have since been filled up by new discoveries. Thus it has also been shown that the ranges of temperature cannot be extended indefinitely in both directions—*viz.*, those of heat and cold—but that the latter possesses a zero point, representing the complete absence of motion.[2]

[1] The periodic arrangement of the elements, according to which, with increasing atomic or combining numbers, the same properties—such as density, fusibility, optical and electric qualities, and formation of oxides, &c.—recur in periods which are at least approximately fixed, so that they can be represented by curves, dates from the year 1869, when D. Mendeléeff and Lothar Meyer published almost simultaneously their classification of the elements. Newlands seems to have indicated some of these facts as early as 1864. Mendeléeff predicted the properties of a missing element, found to be those of scandium, which Nilson discovered ten years later. The same applies to the two other elements which were subsequently discovered by Lecocq de Boisbaudran (1878, gallium) and Winkler (1886, germanium), and in 1894 the newly discovered element argon was found to fill a vacant place in the plan.

[2] The zero point of temperature was originally a purely mathematical quantity suggested by the formula which gives the expansion of air in the air thermometer as dependent on the temperature. The ideal, not realisable, temperature at which, according to the formula, the volume of air would be nothing, was fixed by calculation at 459°·13 Fahr. or 272°·85 Centigrade. The real physical, not merely mathematical, meaning of the absolute scale of temperature with its zero point was only revealed when, through Carnot and Thomson, it was established that every degree of temperature has an assignable value for doing work, and when a scale of thermometry was suggested by Thomson (1848) in which every one degree had the same dynamical value, 100° in it corresponding to the 100° Centigrade in the air thermometer. It was then found that the two scales—that of the air thermometer and that measuring the dynamical value of temperature—agreed almost exactly. The number 273° Cent. thus acquired a physical meaning (see Clerk Maxwell, 'Heat,' 8th ed., pp. 49, 159, and 215). Another

By drawing curves on paper which correspond to the thermal properties of various substances, the conditions have been defined beforehand under which gaseous bodies like oxygen, hydrogen, nitrogen, or common atmospheric air can be reduced to liquid and solid bodies, upsetting the notions of the last generation, which looked upon these substances as permanent gases.[1] If the mathematical formula has killed, or failed to grasp, the true life of nature, that which to the poet and the philosopher will always be the feature of supremest interest, it has on the other side given birth to that new life of ideas which in our reasoning minds serve as the images of things

example of a purely mathematical quantity which, suggested originally by a formula, acquired later a physical meaning, is that of the potential function, used first by Lagrange as a simplification in calculating the forces of a disturbing planet, and termed by Laplace "à cause de son utilité, une véritable découverte" ('Méc. cél.,' v. livre xv. chap. i.) This function, which has the property that by a simple differentiation the component of the force in any direction is found, acquired a physical meaning as the quantity, the change of which measures the work required to move a unit of matter from one point to another (see Thomson and Tait, 'Natural Philosophy,' vol. i. 2, p. 29). Other examples of purely mathematical quantities which reveal physical properties are Hamilton's "characteristic function" (see Tait, "Mechanics," 'Ency. Brit.,' 9th ed., p. 749), Rankine's "Thermodynamic function," called by Clausius "Entropy" (see Maxwell, 'Heat,' pp. 162, 189): it measures the unavailable energy of a system.

[1] Thomas Andrews (1813-85) took up the experiments begun by Cag-niard - Latour in 1822, and explained how it comes about that a gas remains incondensable however great the pressure may be, provided the temperature exceeds what he termed the "critical temperature," which is different for different gases. He accompanied his statements, which were first published in the 3rd edition of Miller's Chemical Physics, by curves representing the behaviour of atmospheric air and of carbonic acid, the latter being a condensable gas, and he suggested in 1872 that the so-called permanent gases had a critical point far below the lowest known temperatures, and that this was the reason why their liquefaction had not yet been achieved. Two physicists, Cailletet and Pictet, took up these suggestions; after various trials they succeeded independently in 1877 in liquefying several of the permanent gases, notably oxygen and nitrogen. These have been followed by all the other permanent gases, including atmospheric air, of which large quantities can now be prepared in a liquefied form.

natural, and allow us to make them subservient to our purposes.

Whoever grasps the significance of the change which the exact or mathematical treatment of knowledge has worked in our life and thought, will readily place that name at the entrance of a history of modern thought, which is identified with a few simple mathematical formulæ, by which ever since his time the progress of science has been guided. Though belonging to an earlier period, the full meaning of Newton's work has only been recognised in the course of our century. In fact the Newtonian philosophy can be said to have governed at least one entire section of the scientific research of the first half of this period: only in the second half of the period have we succeeded in defining more clearly the direction in which Newton's views require to be extended or modified. Newton's greatest achievement was to combine the purely mechanical laws which Galileo and Huygens had established with the purely physical relations which Kepler—following Copernicus and Tycho—had discovered in the planetary motions, and to abstract in so doing the general formula of universal attraction or gravitation. Newton looked upon the motion of the moon round the earth, or the planets round the sun, as examples on a large scale of the motion of falling bodies—studied by Galileo—on the surface of the earth. Delayed in the publication of this simple rule of planetary motion through the absence of correct measurements, and through the necessity of inventing a new calculus by which the mathematical results of the formula could be ascertained, Newton did not publish his 'Principia' till 1687. The

10.
When first
introduced
into science.

11.
Newton's
'Principia.'
work, however, was conceived in the highest philosophic
spirit, inasmuch as the enunciation of the so-called law of
gravitation required the clear expression of the general
laws of motion.   In the first and second parts of the
work the discoveries of Galileo and Huygens were absorbed, generalised, and restated in such terms as have up
to our age been considered sufficient to form the basis for
all purely mechanical reasoning.[1]   In the latter part the
new rule, corresponding to Kepler's empirical laws, is
represented as the key to a system of the universe.   The
great outlines of this system are boldly drawn, and the
working out of it is left as the great bequest of Newton
to his successors.   At the end of the eighteenth century,

---

[1] The most recent historian of
the subject is Prof. Ernst Mach of
Prague, whose 'Mechanik in ihrer
Entwickelung, historisch - kritisch
dargestellt,' 2nd ed., 1889, I cannot
praise too highly. It has been
translated into English by M'Cor-
mack (Chicago and London, 1893).
Referring to Newton, he says:
"Newton has with regard to our
subject two great merits. Firstly,
he has greatly enlarged the horizon of mechanical physics through
the discovery of universal gravitation. Further, he has also completed the enunciation of the principles of mechanics as we now accept them. After him an essentially new principle has not been
established. What after him has
been done in mechanics refers to
the deductive, formal, and mathematical development of mechanics
on the ground of Newton's principles" (p. 174). "Newton's principles are sufficient without the
introduction of any new principle
to clear up every mechanical problem which may present itself, be

it one of statics or of dynamics.
If difficulties present themselves,
they are always only mathematical,
formal, not fundamental" (p. 239).
"All important mathematical expressions of modern mechanics were
already found and used in the age
of Galileo and Newton. The special names . . . have sometimes
been fixed much later. Still later
came the adoption of uniform
measures, and this process is even
yet incomplete" (p. 252). In this
country it is one of the great merits of Thomson and Tait's 'Natural Philosophy' that they "re-
stored" the teaching of mechanics
and placed it on the original foundations afforded by Newton's laws
of motion, in his own words, as
"every attempt that has been
made to supersede them has ended
in utter failure" (Preface), and,
though they "are only temporarily the best," there does not
exist, "as yet, anything nearly as
good" (Tait in article "Mechanics,"
'Ency. Brit.,' 9th ed., p. 749).

after many able mathematicians and observers had generally investigated the numberless problems contained in the 'Principia,' Laplace published his 'Exposition du Système du Monde,' followed in the course of the first quarter of this century by the 'Mécanique céleste';[1] and at the close of the present century the most learned astronomer of the age could say that the 'Principia' still formed the sole foundation of all investigations in that domain.[2]

It is interesting to see how in a simple formula the mathematician is able to condense an almost immeasurable volume of thought, bringing the theory and the observations of past ages to a focus from which new lines of thought diverge in many directions. Every mathe-

12.
The gravitation formula.

---

[1] The 'Exposition du Système du Monde' appeared, 1796, in 2 vols. 8vo: the first and second volume of the 'Mécanique céleste,' 1799, 4to; the third, 1802; the fourth, 1805; the last, 1825. Before publishing this work, which has been termed a second edition of the 'Principia,' Laplace had himself during thirty years assisted in dispelling the last doubts as to the sufficiency of the doctrine of universal gravitation to explain all cosmical phenomena; and he had especially brought the investigations of Clairaut, Euler, d'Alembert, Lambert, and Lagrange to a final result by publishing in successive memoirs between 1773 and 1786 the doctrine of "the stability of the system of the universe," based upon the invariability of the major axes and the periods of revolution of the planetary orbits. He and his predecessors also extended the solution of the problem "to find the orbit of two bodies, acting under the law of mutual gravitation," which was given by Newton in such a way that the action of one or more third (disturbing) bodies could be taken into account, dealing thus with the case of nature, which had in the first instance presented itself in treating of the complex motion of the moon. Laplace himself, who in numberless passages of his works recurs to the discoveries of Newton, announced the object of the 'Mécanique céleste' to be the treatment of astronomy "as a great problem of mechanics, from which it was important to banish as much as possible all empiricism," and to perfect it so as "to borrow from observation only the most indispensable data" ('Méc. cél.,' vol. i. introd.)

[2] The late Professor Rudolf Wolf of Zürich, whose 'Handbuch der Astronomie, ihrer Geschichte und Litteratur,' 2 vols., 1890-93, as well as his earlier 'Geschichte der Astronomie,' München, 1877, I warmly recommend.

matical formula which expresses the existing relations of natural things acts in a similar way, but probably few, if any, subsequent discoveries have given scientific minds so much fruitful work to do as the gravitation formula. An analysis of it will serve us as a guide through a very large portion of the scientific work of our period; it will serve also as an example of the great service which the mathematical mode of dealing with conceptions renders to the progress of science and of thought.

The so-called law of gravitation states that every two portions of matter, placed at a distance from each other, exert on each other an attractive force,[1] which depends on the masses of each, and on their distance from each other. The attractive force varies in the direct proportion of the mass of each, and in the inverse duplicate ratio of the distance. Three distinct lines of

[1] The gravitation formula gives no indication of the actual or absolute amount of the force in question; it only establishes a relation. It was fully three-quarters of a century after the publication of the 'Principia' that experiments were suggested in order to determine the actual magnitude of the force of gravitation—i.e., the constant c in the formula $f = c\dfrac{m.m'}{r^2}$. Michell in 1768 devised an apparatus, employed later (1797) by Cavendish, and Maskelyne made measurements towards the end of the last century. More and more accurate determinations were made all through the present century, and latterly by Prof. Boys. Few persons have an idea of the extreme feebleness of the force, which nevertheless, through the magnitude of the earth, acquires in our daily experience such formidable proportions. As it is desirable, in accordance with one of the principal scientific tendencies of our age, to place the knowledge of absolute physical quantities in the place of merely relative numbers, I mention here that the force with which two units of matter (i.e., 2 grammes) placed at unit distance (i.e., 1 centimetre) apart attract each other is such that they would approach each other with a velocity of nearly 7 hundred millionths of a centimetre in the first second of time. As a pound is a more familiar quantity, we may also say that two masses, each containing 415,000 tons of matter, and situated at a distance of one statute mile apart, will attract each other with the force of 1 lb. (see Sir R. S. Ball, 'Ency. Brit,' 9th ed., art. "Gravitation"). See also Sir R. S. Ball, 'The Story of the Heavens,' p. 106, and Prof. Boys in 'Nature,' vol. 50, p. 330, &c.

scientific research are involved and opened out by this statement.

First, There is the purely theoretical task of defining clearly what is meant by the different words which are used, and which in the formula are expressed in algebraic symbols. What is the definition of force, what of mass, what of distance? The 'Principia' give Newton's definitions.[1]

Second, The definitions must be given in such a way that they express definite measurable quantities; and in order to verify and apply the formula, methods must be devised for measuring these quantities as they occur in nature, and these measurements must be actually carried out.[2]

[1] It will be readily admitted that the definition of force as measured by change of motion, and the definition of mass as the quantity of matter, are definitions involving some difficulty. As to distance, it may be thought that this is a purely mathematical, not a physical quantity. So it would be if physical bodies were mathematical points, such as the planets in a first approximation may be considered to be. But in comparing the attraction of the earth upon a body at its surface with that on the moon, the dimensions of the earth could not be neglected, and the problem presented itself how the quantities of mass and distance, in the case of the earth and the body on its surface, had to be defined. It appears from a statement by Prof. Glaisher (see Rouse Ball, 'History of Mathematics,' p. 297, &c.) that the publication of the 'Principia,' containing the gravitation formula, was delayed, because Newton found it difficult to prove that in a sphere the different parts with their different distances from any point need not be considered separately, but that a quantity equal to the whole mass situated at the centre of the sphere may be substituted. Laplace showed a century later that this property of the sphere exists only for one decreasing function of the distance— viz., that of the inverse duplicate ratio. It exists likewise for that function which increases in proportion to the distance, but for none other (see 'Principia,' 1st ed., pp. 198, 200; 'Mécanique céleste,' 1st ed., vol. i. p. 143). Hitherto the delay in publishing the 'Principia' was (see Brewster, 'Life of Newton,' vol. i. p. 290) always attributed to the erroneous figure of the moon's distance from the earth, with which Newton had been reckoning, and which did not satisfy the gravitation formula.

[2] Up to the beginning of this century the merit of carrying out accurate measurements of astronomical constants is about equally divided between France and Eng-

Third, the formula is a mathematical expression, and, as such, can be subjected to purely mathematical analysis: this analysis may refer to purely algebraical processes of

land; the former country having supplied the means and organised many expeditions (under Richer, Picard, Cassini, La Condamine, Maupertuis, and others), the latter having invented and furnished the greater portion of the delicate instruments, through Newton, Gregory, Ramsden, Dollond, Harrison, and others. The latter was a matter of personal, the former one of organised, talent. England did not take any great part in the repeated measurements of the arc of the meridian till, towards the end of the eighteenth century (1785-87), the French astronomer Cassini de Thury presented to the Royal Society a memorial on the uncertainty in the difference of longitude of Greenwich and Paris, and proposed that the English and French mathematicians in concert should determine, by geodetic operations, the distance measured along an arc of parallel. This was assented to, and the late Astronomer Royal (G. B. Airy) claims that it "may be said that in this as in other grand experiments, though we began later than our Continental neighbours, we conducted our operations with a degree of accuracy of which, till that time, no one had dared to form an idea." Since the beginning of this century Germany has, through the accurate measurements of Gauss and Bessel, and through the famous establishments of Fraunhofer, Steinheil, Repsold, and others, taken a leading position both in the theory and practice of measuring. So far as gravitational astronomy is concerned, the United States of America seem at the end of this century to eclipse all previous performances. But if we owe to

English genius the invention of logarithms, the sextant, the reflecting and the achromatic telescope, the theodolite, and the chronometer, we owe to France the idea of an absolute system of measurements and the first approximation to it in the metrical system, which England has been tardy to adopt. A really absolute unit of measurement, as the ten-millionth part of the earth quadrant was intended to be—one which would be recoverable, if every actually existing pattern was destroyed—does not yet indeed exist; but the Government of the Revolution laid the foundation in 1790 of our present international decimal centigrade system. It does not appear that the idea of extending this system to all other forces and quantities in nature was then contemplated. A valuable contribution towards this desirable object was made by Fourier, who in his celebrated 'Théorie de la Chaleur' (1822, p. 152, &c.) laid down the doctrine of the "dimensions" of physical quantities which had to be measured and compared with each other. The first who reduced the measurement of other than purely mechanical phenomena to the standard of mechanical forces was Gauss (1832). In his investigations referring to the intensity of magnetic force at different points of the earth, he found it necessary to abandon the unit of weight, the gramme, and to adopt the unit of mass, inasmuch as the weight of the unit of mass varied at different points of the globe. He introduced the name "absolute" to signify that this standard is independent of local or relative influences (see

calculation, or to geometrical figures.   These geometrical figures represent on paper, and on a small scale, the curves or orbits of bodies in space and time, and can be interpreted as such.   Then, as in nature two bodies or portions of matter are never single gravitating points occurring alone, but are surrounded by the totality of existing things, the formula which reduces the action of gravitation to that of pairs of things, and to the elements of matter, requires to be extended to more than two—in fact to an infinity of elements.   The infinitesimal calculus teaches us how to deal with such a progression from finite numbers and quantities to infinite numbers; or from relations which refer to infinitesimal elements to finite measurable quantities.   We find very soon that our powers of calculation reach only a small way, and cover only a small extent of the ground which observation opens to our eyes. We are thus forced to deal with the element of error which creeps into our calculations; to be satisfied with approximations; [1] and instead of certainty, probability is

14.
Element of error.

Gauss, Werke, vol. v. pp. 85, 293, &c.)   Of Weber's electrodynamic measurements I shall speak later on. Absolute measurements were used by William Thomson (Lord Kelvin) as early as 1851, and owing mainly to his influence the present system was gradually established in the course of the following twenty years (see William Thomson, 'Popular Lectures and Addresses,' vol. i. p. 83, &c.)   Fourier's theory of dimensions was first brought prominently before the scientific and teaching world by Clerk Maxwell in his treatise on 'Electricity and Magnetism' (1st ed., vol. i. p. 2).   There also we meet for the first time with the use of astronomical magnitudes and relations by which the usual three units, time, mass, and distance, can be reduced to two.   This is also lucidly explained by Lord Kelvin (*loc. cit.*)   It has been followed up in detail in two interesting papers by W. Winter in Exner's 'Repertorium der Physik' (vol. 21, p. 775, and vol. 24, p. 471).

[1] The history of astronomical calculations since the time of Newton, when the theoretical basis was once for all laid, is a history of gradual approximations.   Mathematically a conic section is sufficiently defined if the position of the focus (the sun in our planetary system) and three positions of the moving star are known by observation.   But it was a long time before even tolerably complete methods of observation

the best we can attain to in our results.[1]   An entirely new branch of investigation springs up—*viz.*, the theory of error, the doctrine of probability, and the investigation

and calculation were invented to deal practically with the problem. Up to 1781, when the new planet Uranus was discovered by Herschel, the interest centred mainly in the determination of the orbits of comets, which were assumed to be parabolic. Halley was the first to calculate these by means of tentative methods given by Newton in the 'Principia.' After 1781 the necessity arose of determining closed orbits, and a first attempt was made to do so by assuming circular orbits (neglecting the ellipticity) and neglecting the inclination of the plane of the orbit to that of the earth. But in the first year of this century neither the parabolic nor the circular figure of the orbits seemed to answer in the case of the new planet Ceres, nor could the inclination of the orbit be neglected. It required all the skill of Gauss to tackle the entire, unabbreviated problem, and this was done in his fundamental work 'Theoria motus corporum cœlestium.' As the 'Principia' form the foundation of all physical, so does the 'Theoria motus' of all calculating astronomy. A similar fundamental work which should take the next important step, solving generally the problem of the motion of a body which is attracted from more than one fixed or movable centre (the problem of three bodies), would mark the next great era in calculating astronomy. Hitherto this problem has only been treated under the assumption that the third attracting body disturbs the real orbit which has been calculated. The necessity of solving the problem of three bodies has made itself felt in the theory of the moon and other satellites, which stand under

the influence of the main planet as well as the sun, and where therefore the ellipsis of Kepler cannot even be taken as a first approximation. And here again the necessity of taking into account the volume and the figures of the attracting bodies still further complicates the problem. On them depend the precession of the equinoxes and the irregularity of the precession known under the name of nutation.

[1] According to Wolf ('Handbuch der Astronomie,' vol. i. p. 128 *sqq.*) the merit of having first considered the best methods of dealing with errors of observation belongs to Picard (1670) and Roger Cotes ('Aestimatio errorum in mixta mathesi,' 1722). The former seems to have first used the apparently so obvious rule of taking the arithmetical mean of a number of observations, the latter introduced the notion of attributing to each observation its value or weight. Cotes accordingly found that the centre of gravity of a number of weighted points distributed over a plane coincided with the position of greatest probability. Gauss suspected that Tobias Mayer had already employed modern methods in his calculation of long series of observations, and he himself used what is termed after Legendre the "method of least squares" as early as 1795. It was not published till 1806 by Legendre, in his memoir 'Nouvelles méthodes pour la détermination des orbites des comètes.' Gauss published his methods in 1809 in the celebrated 'Theoria motus corporum cœlestium.' This method of finding the most probable result when a larger number of equations is given than unknown quantities

of the degree of approximation which we can attain to. And this does not only refer to the methods of calculation which we adopt,—is not only a consequence of the limits of our mathematical powers; this element of error attaches likewise to our actual observations, to the imperfection of our senses and of our instruments. The many sources of mistake and inaccuracy which surround us may either combine to produce an absolutely useless result, or may be adroitly adjusted so as very largely to destroy each other.[1] The arrangement of instruments of observation and calculation, so as to minimise our errors, is a special branch of science. Before the time of Newton few minds

is the same as that of finding the centre of gravity of a number of weighted points. This centre has the property that the sum of the squares of its distances from these points is a minimum. After the method had been introduced, Laplace and Gauss independently tried to prove it by a variety of considerations. These have not always been accepted as conclusive, though it is remarkable that very different ways of attacking the problem all lead to the same result, and that the rule is confirmed by actual trials on a large scale. It has been shown that the method of least squares in the case of a series of observations of one and the same quantity is equal to taking the arithmetical mean,—a process which recommends itself to common-sense, though it is not easy to prove it mathematically to be the best. On the whole, the calculus of probabilities and the so-called law of error are attempts to put into figures and mathematical formulæ a few common-sense notions, and it is interesting to see to what complicated processes of reasoning a combination of these simple notions may lead. The literature of

the subject, belonging almost entirely to this century, is very large, Laplace and Gauss heading the list. Encke has summarised the scattered discussions of Gauss and Bessel in his memoir on the subject, reprinted in Taylor's 'Scientific Memoirs' and in the 2nd vol. of Encke's 'Abhandlungen,' Berlin, 1888. De Morgan, Airy, and Jevons ('Principles of Science,' vol. i.) in England have done much to popularise the subject, and Bertrand ('Calcul des Probabilités,' 1888) has very fully discussed the principles of the whole matter and shown up the weak points. The application of the calculus to statistics will occupy us in a future chapter.

[1] Not only has every instrument its constant errors, but even every observer himself has what is called a personal equation—i.e., he is subject to constant errors of observation, dependent on the peculiarity of his sense organs, or his temperament, &c. This was hardly recognised at the beginning of this century, when Maskelyne, the Astronomer Royal, dismissed an assistant whose observations showed a constant difference from his own.

were occupied with the many researches indicated here. But as the contents of the 'Principia' became familiar and intelligible to men of science, a large army of workers, collected from all sides, had within the first century after its publication accumulated a great mass of research. It is the glory of the old French Academy of Sciences, in spite of the opposition to Newton that ruled there for some time, to have in all earnest taken up his great bequest, and to have made such a summary possible as was given by Laplace in the two works above referred to. To Laplace belongs also almost exclusively the merit of having recognised the importance which attaches in all human science to the existence of error, and of having founded the theory of probability. The element of error cannot be eliminated from our observations and our reasonings : the only true scientific method is to measure and study it.

15. Laplace and Newton.

The gravitation formula of Newton not only brought precision and definiteness into scientific work in the three directions mentioned above—it not only produced strict definitions of the fundamental notions of dynamics, promoted accurate measurements of physical quantities, and inaugurated a new literature in pure mathematics ; but it had, as all other great generalisations have had since, a very far-reaching influence on scientific thought in other ways. There always have been, and always will be, several distinct interests which induce men to study nature. Some are driven to it by curiosity, or a pure love of nature. To those who belong to this class the end of the study of nature is to describe and to portray the objects which surround us, to see and know them

16. Several interests which promote science.

better. It would seem as if to such minds the scientific formula, the so-called law of nature, must be distasteful, and probably useless. Nevertheless the scientific view, of which the mathematical formula is an extreme expression, has reacted, though not always beneficially, upon the labours of those who confine themselves to observation and description; it has given to their efforts general interest and encouragement, indicated new directions, and frequently opened new fields. Thus the new formula of Copernicus and Galileo gave a great impetus to stargazing, which was greatly increased by the almost contemporary invention of the telescope. The new theory required the rotation of the planets, and led to minute observations of their phases, and to the discovery of the satellites of Jupiter and the ring of Saturn. Variable stars were incidentally discovered by Tycho, and the long-neglected comets received greater attention. Bernoulli attempted, and Halley actually carried out, the calculation of the return of a comet. Still later—in fact, not before the end of the eighteenth or the beginning of the present century—came the turn for reliable observation of meteors and auroras; for as late as 1790 the 'Décade philosophique,' as well as the Paris Academy and many learned persons, ridiculed the authentic reports of the fall of meteors, and Chladni's classical dissertation on the stone of Pallas.[1] It seems as if the purest love of

[1] When in the year 1790 the municipality of Juillac in Gascony submitted a report, signed by more than 300 eyewitnesses, to the Paris Academy, on a fall of stones which had there taken place, one of the editors of the 'Décade philosophique' remarked that it would be better to deny such incredible things than to enter into any explanations. Bertholon could not help pitying a community which had such a foolish *maire*, and remarked in the 'Journal des Sciences utiles': "How sad it is to find a whole municipality attesting formally by protocol popu-.

17.
Insuffici-
ency of mere
observation.
nature, the greatest devotion of the observer and the
collector, lead only a little way in finding out the hidden
paths of natural things or the behaviour of natural objects; and however grateful we must be to those pioneers
of knowledge who with unrewarded patience amass the
material for later theorists, it is to the classification of a
Linnæus, to the arrangements of a Cuvier, to the theories
of a Darwin, to the measurements of a Bradley and a
Herschel, most of all to the formulæ of a Newton or a
Gauss, followed by the calculations of their pupils, that
we are indebted for a real grasp, for a comprehensive
knowledge, of great masses of natural phenomena.

18.
Practical
interest.
Next to the pure love of nature, the desire to apply
natural knowledge, and to make it useful for practical
purposes, has rendered in return great services to science.
The Royal Society and the Royal Institution had both
from their infancy a large admixture of the practical
spirit. These were founded, more even than the academies
abroad, to a great extent upon the desire to make knowledge useful.

The Governments of England and of France promoted

lar fables which are only to be pitied !
What can I add to such a protocol ?
The philosophical reader will himself suggest what to say when he
reads this authentic proof of an
evidently wrong fact, of a phenomenon which is physically impossible" (Wolf, 'Geschichte der Astronomie,' 1877, p. 697 *sq.*) Chladni
published his essay on the large
mass of iron found by the traveller
Pallas in Siberia in the year 1794,
and, in spite of adverse criticisms,
followed it up by a catalogue and
an atlas of meteoric stones, suggesting that they were of cosmic

origin. Fortunately, a remarkable
fall of stones, accompanied by
meteoric phenomena, took place in
1803 not far from Paris, at l'Aigle
in the department de l'Orne, and
Biot was commissioned by the
Academy to proceed to the district and examine the case. In the
'Relation,' &c., which he read before
the Institute, he established the
fact that a meteor exploded in the
district, and that at the same time
a fall of many thousand stones,
weighing about 20 tons, took place
(Biot, 'Mélanges scientifiques et
littéraires,' vol. i. p. 15 *sqq.*)

the study of the "mechanics of the heavens" by offering large prizes for scientific and practical means of determining the longitude at sea. The lunar theory, which has occupied the attention of the greatest mathematicians since Newton—of Euler, Clairaut, and Tobias Mayer in the last century; of Burckhardt, Plana, and Hansen, of Delaunay and Adams, in the present century—was an outcome of this. It still engages the attention of scientific minds, involving as it does all the most delicate astronomical calculations, whilst for practical nautical purposes the moon has ceased to be the great timekeeper, and has since 1763 been replaced by the wonderful chronometers of Harrison and his successors. A similar stimulus both to abstract scientific research and to the perfection of the practical instruments of measurement was given in this century by the development of submarine telegraphy: in this case both sides of the problem, the scientific and the practical, were attacked, and carried to a high degree of perfection by one and the same mind [1]—

[1] William Thomson's (Lord Kelvin's) investigations and inventions, which made submarine telegraphy at long distances commercially practicable, refer mainly to the overcoming of the "embarrassment" occasioned by the property (discovered by Werner Siemens, 1849, and investigated by Faraday, 1854) which submerged cables possess of "retaining a quantity of electricity in charge along the whole surface." In 1854 Thomson made a full theoretical examination of this phenomenon, showed how it depended on the length, the electric resistance, and the electrostatic capacity of the line, and gave a mathematical formula, with practical examples of the retardation of the signals and the gradual increase of the strength of the electric current at the receiving end of long submarine cables ("On the Theory of the Electric Telegraph" and other papers, reprinted in the 2nd vol. of 'Math. and Phys. Papers,' 1884). The importance of constructing delicate instruments for registering feeble signals, and of a method for reducing the time of single signals, became evident through these theoretical investigations. The mirror galvanometer was first used in 1858 on the first Atlantic cable, and afterwards on the successful cables of 1865 and 1866. It was followed by the spark-recorder, which led to the syphon-recorder (1867-70), which

an almost unique instance of the combination of abstract reasoning and practical inventiveness. An almost equally important problem, having both scientific and practical interest, arising out of the Newtonian gravitation formula, is the problem of the tides. Here also the first suggestions towards a theory were given in the 'Principia,' whereas the first attempt at a solution is contained in Laplace's great work. A closer approximation was reached by Sir W. Thomson in his extensive theoretical and practical use of Fourier's mathematics.

I shall have frequent opportunity to refer to the beneficial and fructifying influence which practical problems have exerted on scientific thought;[1] in fact, in spite of

has since been in use in submarine telegraphy. The best account of these discoveries and inventions is to be found in Lord Kelvin's own papers, a good summary being given in his short article in Nichol's 'Cyclopedia,' reprinted as No. 82, vol. ii. p. 138.

[1] How much science owes to the practical interests of navigation can be seen by a glance at the subjects contained in the third volume of Lord Kelvin's 'Popular Lectures and Addresses.' The Tides, Deep-Sea Sounding, Cable-Laying, and Terrestrial Magnetism all furnish important practical as well as highly abstract theoretical problems, the solution of which demands new instruments and new methods of calculation. The phenomena of the tides and those of terrestrial magnetism are intimately connected with two of the most refined mathematical theories which this century has developed. The former was first attacked by the so-called equilibrium theory—the problem being to find the figure of equilibrium of a rotating ellipsoid covered with water under the influence of various attracting forces. Laplace, followed by Airy and Thomson, showed how it is much more a question of dynamics than of statics, and that it resolves itself into the analysis and subsequent synthesis of a number of periodic movements, dependent upon the several periodic changes of the rotation of the earth and the revolutions of the moon round the earth and the sun. A general method of dealing mathematically with the superposition of several periodic changes had been invented by Fourier in the early part of this century, and it was this which, especially in the hands of Lord Kelvin and his brother—the late Prof. James Thomson—led to the harmonic analysis of tide motion and the subsequent invention of tide-predicting apparatus (see the above volume, p. 177 *sqq.*) The observation of the magnetism of the earth is connected with great improvements in the theory and construction of the mariner's compass, suggested and carried out by

the great reciprocal influence which science has gained in
the course of this century over practical life, I am still
doubtful whether scientific thought has, at the end of
our century, as yet balanced the debt which it owes to
practical inventors. It is instructive, for instance, to
consider how much, in the hands of Rumford, of Sadi
Carnot, of Hirn, and of Rankine, science has learnt from
the steam-engine, and to reflect whether from all the
theoretical insight gained any really radical improvement of the steam-engine—still one of the most imperfect
machines—has resulted.[1]

Lord Kelvin; and it has in another direction led to remarkable
scientific results in the hands of
Gauss, who between the years 1830
and 1840 brought the theory almost to perfection. Here again
the physical phenomenon required
for its treatment a special mathematical analysis, which Gauss greatly furthered in his 'Allgemeine
Lehrsätze in Beziehung auf die im
verkehrten Verhältnisse des Quadrats der Entfernung wirkenden
Anziehungs- und Abstossungs-
Kräfte' (1840). This is a mathematical investigation of the Newtonian
gravitation-formula. Gauss followed
out the theories of Laplace and Lagrange simultaneously with Green,
whose now celebrated memoir on
the subject remained long unknown
(see *supra*, pp. 231, 247). The mathematical theory showed that in a
sphere containing a certain amount
of attracting (magnetic) matter an
ideal distribution on the surface of
the sphere can be found which
takes the place of the real but unknown distribution in the interior,
and that if through observation the
necessary data are supplied, the
magnetic condition of any point
on the surface can be foretold with
great approximation. As an ex-

ample, Gauss foretold from the
imperfect data at his command
the position of the south magnetic
pole. In 1840 Capt. Sir James Ross
approached it sufficiently to show
the correctness of the calculation.
The theoretical investigations in
connection with magnetic attraction and with tidal movements
have remodelled the methods of observation of the phenomena themselves, the older methods having
proved to be in many ways insufficient. A full account of Gauss's
labours here referred to will be
found in E. Schering, 'C. F. Gauss
und die Erforschung des Erdmag-
netismus,' Göttingen, 1887.

[1] I refer in this matter to two
addresses delivered recently—one
by Prof. Unwin ('Electrician,' vol.
35, pp. 50 and 79) on "The Development of the Experimental
Study of Heat-Engines"; the
other by Prof. Lodge on "The
Second Law of Thermodynamics"
('Electrician,' vol. 35, p. 80 *sqq.*)
From a perusal of these papers one
gains the impression that science
has been more successful in teaching us why the steam-engine is so
wasteful a machine than in showing how it can be greatly improved.
It is interesting to hear that "al-

19.
Focalising
effect of
mathemati-
cal formulæ.
The mathematical formula is the point through which
all the light gained by science passes in order to be of
use to practice; it is also the point in which all knowledge gained by practice, experiment, and observation must
be concentrated before it can be scientifically grasped.
The more distinct and marked the point, the more concentrated will be the light coming from it, the more un-
mistakable the insight conveyed.   All scientific thought,
from the simple gravitation formula of Newton, through
the more complicated formulæ of physics and of chemistry, the vaguer so-called laws of organic and animated
nature, down to the uncertain statements of psychology
and the data of our social and historical knowledge, alike
partakes of this characteristic, that it is an attempt to
gather up the scattered rays of light, the diffused knowledge, in a focus, from whence it can be again spread out
and analysed, according to the abstract processes of the
thinking mind.   But only where this can be done with
mathematical precision and accuracy is the image sharp
and well defined, and the deductions clear and unmis-
takable.   As we descend from the mechanical, through
the physical, chemical, and biological, to the mental,
moral, and social sciences, the process of focalisation
becomes less and less perfect,—the sharp point, the

most all the present difference between the best steam-engine and
the worst is some 5 or 6 per cent"
(Lodge).   Prof. Unwin sums up by
saying : "Since 1845 purely scientific men, scientific experimenters,
and practical engineers have all
been engaged in the study of the
steam-engine.   I do not believe
that any one of the three can
claim all the credit for the improvement of the steam-engine to
the exclusion of either of the
others. . . . Representing perhaps
rather the scientific than the practical interest, I do not think that
the mathematical and physical researches of which I have tried to
give an account have had no influence on the practical business of
the engineer."

focus, is replaced by a larger or a smaller circle, the contours of the image become less and less distinct, and with the possible light which we gain there is mingled much darkness, the source of many mistakes and errors. But the tendency of all scientific thought is towards clearer and clearer definition; it lies in the direction of a more and more extensive use of mathematical measurements, of mathematical formulæ.

There is probably no science which has come so perfectly under the control of this kind of mathematical expression as has astronomy since the time of Newton or of Laplace, and, we may add, there exists probably no mathematical formula which has stood the test of application to existing phenomena so long and so thoroughly as the gravitation formula of Newton. It possesses two unique properties which no other formula possesses—so far as we can now see—it is universal[1] and it is accurate.[2] These

---

[1] The law of gravitation can be called the first and most general physical law or statement of universal application. The laws of motion may be called mechanical or dynamical statements. Both the law of gravitation and the laws of motion describe facts, and have been found by experience; but the laws of motion contain no physical constant — i.e., no quantity which requires to be fixed and measured by observation, and the absolute value of which has for us at present no ulterior meaning. The law of gravitation has one physical constant, the universal gravitation constant (see p. 320). As it measures what we call matter, it need not be determined, and its actual determination, which has been accurately made only in recent times, has not in any direction advanced our general physical knowledge. For all practical purposes of physics the unit of mass is a weight, just as for all commercial purposes gold is the standard of value. The astronomical view permits us to go a step further and express the mass of a pound of matter in units of time and space, and the political economist may seek for a real standard of value—for instance, an article of food like wheat. Other fundamental physical laws or general statements involve other physical constants, as we shall see later on.

[2] The accuracy of the so-called laws of nature, or, more correctly, of the expressions which science gives to the laws of nature, is a very important question. Little is said on this point in the ordinary text-books. It is only in very

two properties of the gravitation formula have been brought
out by a long line of investigations, carried on with the
view of substantiating or of refuting the formula. They
mark the development of whole sciences, the foundation
of quite novel branches of research. I propose briefly to
follow up these developments.

20.
Matter and
force mathe-
matically
defined.

Common-sense has never had any difficulty in knowing
what matter and force are, or in defining them for the
purposes of practical life. But it took thousands of years
to find a definition of these quantities which could serve
as the basis of exact measurement, and permit calculations of results into which both factors entered in varying

recent publications that attention
is sufficiently drawn to the fact
that very few mathematical formulæ in physics or chemistry are
more than approximations. The
law of gravitation is one of the few
mathematical expressions which,
besides being universal, have stood
the most rigorous tests as to accuracy. A most interesting attempt
to prove the inaccuracy of Newton's law was made, but speedily
abandoned, by Clairaut, one of
the earliest Newtonians in the old
Academy of Sciences. Clairaut
began about 1743 to study the
lunar theory in the light of Newton's system, which Madrin before him had already despaired
of reconciling with the facts of
observation. When he himself,
on calculating the annual motion
of the moon's apogee (or farthest
point in its orbit round the
earth), found only half the value
which observation furnished, he was
tempted in his communication to
the Academy of November 1747 to
suggest that the Newtonian formula might require a correction for
great distances. This suggestion
was followed, as Lalande tells us,
by a veritable scandal in the learned
world. Buffon, for purely metaphysical reasons, objected to this
infringement of the simplicity of
the laws of the universe. The
opponents of Newton's system had
a short triumph, which however
was speedily reversed when Clairaut, putting a greater precision
into his calculations by taking
inequalities into account which he
had previously neglected, explained
to the Academy in May 1749 that
he had succeeded in reconciling the
movement of the moon's apogee
with the law of attraction according to the inverse square of the
distance. From that time the
Newtonian theory, to which only
shortly before mathematicians like
Euler had been won over, reigned
supreme. See Lalande in the 4th
volume of Montucla's 'Histoire
des Mathématiques,' p. 67, &c.
Euler's merits in solving many
problems in physical astronomy were
so great that the Academy procured permission from Louis XV. to
receive him as a *surnuméraire*, the
eight places granted to external
members being all occupied.

quantities and in varying combinations. That a smaller quantity of matter in motion could produce the same action as a larger which was moving slowly, or even apparently at rest, and acted only by what is termed its dead-weight, was a well-known phenomenon; but it was only within the half-century which preceded the publication of the 'Principia' that, through the labours of Galileo and of Huygens, mathematical definitions and simple formulæ were laid down, and generally accepted, which gave the means of accurately measuring and calculating the phenomena of moving bodies and the combination of forces. These labours resulted in a definition of matter which, translated into the language of our day, says that matter is that which moves and is capable of resisting any change of motion. Motion is a measurable quantity. For its measurement we require the measurement of space and time, and the well-known relation of both —*viz.*, velocity.

The above formula therefore says that matter is measured by the resistance it offers to change of motion or of velocity. And correspondingly force is that which is capable of producing change of motion, or velocity in matter, and it is measured by the amount of change it produces. Given a definite, though unknown, force, portions of matter—*i.e.*, masses—can be compared by the resistance they offer to the change of their motion; the smaller the change the larger the mass or quantity of matter. Given a definite, though unknown, quantity of matter, forces can be measured by the different changes they produce in the motion—*i.e.*, the velocity—of this quantity; they are greater or smaller in the proportion

of the change of velocity which they produce. One of
the great difficulties which stood in the way of the fixing
of these very simple mathematical relations and definitions was the fact that all matter with which we can
experiment is under the influence of a constant but unknown force, that which makes it fall if not supported.
It was only by freeing themselves from the effect of this
constant force, or by balancing it, that philosophers
gradually arrived at the conception and definition of
mass, or quantity of matter, as something independent
of its weight.   It was reserved for Newton to show and
define the exact relation which weight bears to the other
properties of matter defined and measured by his predecessors.   By doing so he added a new definition, a new
means of measuring the quantity of matter or its mass,
showing at the same time to what extent the popular
measure of matter—*i.e.*, its weight—could be accurately
used for scientific purposes.   Again, to express it in the
language of our day, Newton showed that matter is not
only that which offers resistance to change of motion,
but also that which causes change of motion in other
portions of matter : it is not only the object on which
force spends itself, it is the seat of this force, and the
degree in which it can change motion in other portions
of matter is proportional to the degree in which it
resists the change of its own motion—in other words,
the gravity or weight of matter is proportional to its mass
or inertia, and is not dependent on any other difference,
whether of size or of quality.   This second universal
property of matter, which brought out more clearly the
reciprocity of all mechanical, and subsequently of all

21.
Weight and
mass.

physical actions, is, however, dependent on the mutual distances of the particles of matter, and can therefore be altered, but can as little as the existence of matter itself be removed. This view of Newton's explained or described clearly [1] the phenomena of moving and falling

[1] The distinction between an explanation and a description of the facts of nature has been slowly developed in the course of modern thought. Probably Leibniz was the first to insist on it, and to maintain in the abstract that all description of nature would be mechanical, but that the explanation or interpretation of nature must be spiritual. But the first practical instance of this important distinction is really to be found in Newton's philosophy. In many passages of the 'Principia,' and especially in the 'Optics,' the double view of the problems of philosophy is clearly indicated. The principles of science since the time of Newton are general facts, established by experience and put into mathematical language, admitting of constant verification by observation and by the deductions of the calculus. These principles are not the ultimate causes, but only a concise description of some of the phenomena of nature. These principles Newton calls mathematical—referring to measurable quantities —and distinguishes them from the philosophical principles] ('Princ.,' 1st ed., p. 401). Especially as regards gravitation, Newton explains many times that he uses this term not as an explanation, but only as a mathematical description of the force with which bodies approach each other, whatever the cause of this phenomenon may be, which he leaves others (called with some irony metaphysicians) to determine ('Optics,' query 31). That

Newton, besides giving the precise mathematical principles of all future dynamical science, indulged also in further speculations, which he put into the form of queries and advanced with hesitation and merely tentatively, gave his opponents ample opportunity to attack the doubtful and uncertain statements in his philosophy. Instead of studying and understanding the mathematical truths of the 'Principia,' they attacked the doctrines which were fragmentarily put forward in the queries to the 'Optics' or added in the general scholium at the end of the second edition of the 'Principia.' Roger Cotes in his preface to the second edition of the 'Principia,' and Clarke in his correspondence with Leibniz, pointed out the difference between Newton's descriptive and calculating and the older or metaphysical philosophy. They were, however, more interested in disproving the atheistical consequences of which Newton's philosophy had been accused than in clearly insisting on the fundamental difference between mathematical and metaphysical principles—i.e., between the exact and the philosophical views of nature. And in Bentley's Boyle lectures, delivered in 1692 and 1693, the principles of Newton's philosophy were specially brought forward to refute atheism, an undertaking which Newton himself supported in his contemporary correspondence with Bentley, published half a century later, in 1756.

masses, not only at a point on the surface of our earth, where the force of gravity can be considered to be constant, but all through the universe, where it varies with the distances of the moving masses.

22. Gravitation not an ultimate property of matter. The Newtonian formula of gravitation was not at once accepted by philosophers as a correct statement of the facts of nature.[1] It appeared to limit the existence of

---

[1] The philosophy of Descartes, which then reigned on the Continent, seemed in many ways to hinder the acceptance of Newton's doctrines. Descartes had taken a great step in advance in philosophical teaching; he had placed mathematics at the head of his doctrine; he had opposed the older metaphysical methods, and he had, through his application of algebra to geometry, made great progress towards a mechanical description of phenomena. But he had not separated the description from the interpretation of nature. Philosophy and science remained united, the mathematical formulæ were only a new kind of metaphysics, incapable without observation of making any real advance in the knowledge of nature. The facts of geometry which are required for an application of analysis are the well-known axioms of Euclid. An application of analysis to dynamics requires a knowledge of the laws or fundamental properties of motion. These were not correctly and completely known to Descartes; Newton placed them at the head of his mathematical philosophy of nature. A further application to physical phenomena required a knowledge of some general physical fact: such was supplied by Newton in the gravitation formula. The laws of motion and gravitation once admitted as facts, there was plenty to do for mathematics. Not so with Descartes. In his philosophy the basis of facts was too narrow and indefinite, and had to be supplemented by metaphysical suppositions and deductions. The field for mathematical reasoning not being sufficiently prepared and wide enough, Descartes had speedily got back again into metaphysical reasoning. In fact the doctrines of Newton, in which mathematical and philosophical deductions had for the first time been successfully separated, encountered on the Continent the doctrines of Descartes, in which mathematical and philosophical deductions were hopelessly mixed up. On one point especially the two views seemed to clash. Descartes had by metaphysical considerations tried to define what matter is. Newton had postponed the answer to this question, but had defined mathematically two properties of matter—*viz.*, inertia and gravitation. Descartes' metaphysical considerations had led to the conception that matter and extension were identical, that space therefore could not be empty. Newton, occupying himself not with matter in the abstract, but only with moving observable matter, had established the general law of gravitation, leaving it undecided whether the apparent vacuum existing between visible bodies was really empty or full. For the deductions from the law of gravitation it might in the first instance be considered empty. Thus on this question about space

matter to certain changing places in an empty space, and to attach the forces of nature likewise to this distribution of matter. This was hardly the intention of the author himself, who saw in the so-called law of gravitation not a final explanation, but only a description of the phenomena of nature—notably of the larger phenomena. That behind the mathematical formula there may be conditions which are capable of further analysis, —that the larger or molar phenomena of moving bodies are made up of their smaller or molecular movements, was well known to Newton. For before he approached the great laws of the universe he had been occupied with investigations which led him into the minutest phenomena, those of light and colour. To him, indeed, are owing some of the observations and methods by which subsequently the greatest and the smallest measurements of natural objects have been carried out. But in exact science the deeper philosophical meanings disappear where the strict mathematical deductions point to definite conceptions, mark certain fixed paths of research, and promise definite results. The eighteenth century gradually settled down to a wholesale adoption of the gravitation theory—looked upon space as empty, upon matter as subject to a definite though changing distribution in space, and upon the forces of nature as attached to certain moving centres, between which only a mathematical, but no intelligible physical, connection

—whether it was empty or full— the two doctrines came into conflict. That Newton's position was not a final, but only a provisional one, was overlooked ; he was accused of introducing again the occult quali- ties of the scholastic philosophy, and a great fight was started against his views in the Academy of Sciences, where Descartes' philosophy reigned supreme.

could be traced.[1] What to some contemporaries of Newton, and even to Newton himself, seemed an absurdity—that action could take place at a distance [2]—became through

[1] Voltaire, who did not dive very deep into the teachings of Newton, gives a graphic description of the different opinions then current in English and French learned circles. In his 'Lettres sur les Anglais,' written about the time of the death of Newton, after having discoursed on Quakerism, the Church and Government, on vaccination, Bacon and Locke, he devotes four chapters to the philosophy of Newton, which he contrasts with that of Descartes. "Un Français qui arrive à Londres trouve les choses bien changées en philosophie, comme dans tout le reste. Il a laissé le monde plein, il le trouve vide. Paris on voit l'univers composé de tourbillons de matière subtile, à Londres on ne voit rien de cela. Chez nous c'est la pression de la lune qui cause le flux de la mer ; chez les Anglais c'est la mer qui gravite vers la lune. . . . Chez vos Cartésiens tout se fait par une impulsion qu'on ne comprend guère ; chez M. Newton c'est par une attraction dont on ne connait pas mieux la cause. . . . Descartes assure encore que l'étendue seule fait la matière, Newton y ajoute la solidité" (lettre xiv.)
[2] "You sometimes speak of gravity as essential and inherent to matter. Pray, do not ascribe that notion to me ; for the cause of gravity is what I do not pretend to know" (Newton's 2nd letter to Bentley, 17th January 1692-93). "It is inconceivable that inanimate brute matter should, without the mediation of something else, which is not material, operate upon and affect other matter without mutual contact, as it must be, if gravitation, in the sense of Epicurus, be essential and inherent in it. And this is one

reason why I desired you would not ascribe innate gravity to me. That gravity should be innate, inherent, and essential to matter, so that one body may act upon another at a distance through a *vacuum*, without the mediation of anything else, by and through which their action and force may be conveyed from one to another, is to me so great an absurdity that I believe no man, who has in philosophical matters a competent faculty of thinking, can ever fall into it. Gravity must be caused by an agent acting constantly according to certain laws; but whether this agent be material or immaterial, I have left to the consideration of my readers" (3rd letter to Bentley, 5th February 1692-93). And in the fifth answer to Leibniz (published after Leibniz's death) Clarke says : "That the sun attracts the earth . . . —that is, that the earth and sun *gravitate* towards each other, or tend towards each other, with a force which is in a direct proportion of their masses, . . . and in an inverse duplicate proportion of their distances, and that the space betwixt them is void—that is, has nothing in it which sensibly resists the motion of bodies passing transversely through : all this is nothing but a phenomenon or actual matter of fact, found by experience. That this phenomenon is not produced *sans moyen*—that is, without some cause capable of producing such an effect—is undoubtedly true. Philosophers therefore may search after and discover that cause, if they can ; be it mechanical or not mechanical. . . . The phenomenon itself, the attraction, gravitation, or tendency of bodies towards each other, and the laws or proportions

a century of confirming thought, observation, and calculation an adopted axiom, and the accepted formula of all physical explanations. For a time, indeed, the exact formula of gravitation seemed liable to some correction, but gradually the apparent anomalies disappeared, and even in our century none of the many attempts to modify the gravitation formula, to look upon it as merely an approximation, or to go behind it and find some more general relation from which it could be deduced, have been generally useful or acceptable.[1] It still stands there as the only universally accepted mathematical expression which corresponds to a general physical property of natural objects.

Two different lines of thought combined to give the formula of Newton a still wider importance than its author primarily intended, or than it has been found possible to maintain in the course of further inquiry. The first was the ancient philosophical idea of attraction, which, without being mathematically defined and practically useful, had nevertheless, from the dawn of Greek speculation

of that tendency, are now sufficiently known by observations and experiments. If this or any other learned author can by the laws of mechanism explain these phenomena, he will not only not be contradicted, but will, moreover, have the abundant thanks of the learned world. But in the meantime, to compare gravitation, which is a phenomenon or actual matter of fact, with Epicurus' declination of atoms seems to be a very extraordinary method of reasoning" (§§ 118-124, Leibniz's 'Philosophische Schriften,' by Gerhardt, Berlin, 1890, vol. vii. p. 439 *sq.*)

[1] A very complete account of these different attempts will be found in the writings of C. Isenkrahe, 'Das Räthsel von der Schwerkraft,' Braunschweig, 1879; "Euler's Theorie von der Ursache der Gravitation," in 'Zeitschrift für Mathematik und Physik,' vol. xxvi.; 'Ueber die Fernkraft,' Leipzig, 1889; "Ueber die Zurückführung der Schwere auf Absorption," in 'Abhandlungen zur Geschichte der Mathematik,' vol. vi., Leipzig, Teubner, 1892. See also as bearing on this subject, Paul du Bois-Reymond, 'Ueber die Grundlagen der Erkenntniss in den exacten Wissenschaften,' Tübingen, 1890.

and all through ancient and mediæval philosophy, figured as one of the occult causes or forces which regulate the behaviour of living and dead matter.   That the force of

attraction alone would result in an accumulation of all matter in one body was of course recognised, and a second arbitrary and occult force—that of repulsion—was introduced as a counteracting or balancing agent.

In Newton's system of the universe the balancing force was found to be that of an inherent initial motion which matter, in consequence of its mass or inertia, maintained in addition to the motion due to gravitation.   If motion and inertia were able to account for the apparent repulsion of bodies at a distance, it might be that they could also account for their apparent attraction.   This idea, though expressed about the time when the Newtonian gravitation formula was established, did not meet with serious attention till far on in our century other lines of thought led to similar views.[1]   The phenomena of attrac-

[1] Newton himself seems to have looked for a mechanical explanation of gravitation.   Long before the publication of the 'Principia' he laid before the Royal Society a paper containing "a hypothesis explaining the properties of light" by the assumption of an "ætherial medium, much of the same constitution with air, but far rarer, subtiler, and more strongly elastic" (Letter to Oldenburg, January 25, 1675-76, given in Brewster's 'Memoirs of Sir I. Newton,' vol. i. p. 390 *sqq.*), which might explain magnetic and electric phenomena, as well as those of gravitation, and especially light.   And in a letter to Robert Boyle, of 28th February 1678-79 (Brewster, vol. i. p. 409), he reverts to this subject.   Having,

however, in the course of the next decade found it more useful to work out the mathematical conclusions to be drawn from the phenomenon of gravitation, which was a fact and not a hypothesis, he abandoned the metaphysical part of the subject, the question how gravitation was to be explained, "finding" (as Maclaurin says in his account of Newton's discoveries) "that he was not able, from experiment and observation, to give a satisfactory account of this medium and the manner of its operation in producing the chief phenomena of nature." And in his letter to Boyle, as well as in a later one to Halley (20th June 1886, Brewster, vol. i. p. 439), he carefully distinguishes between the results of the 'Principia' and

tion and repulsion at a distance rather received additional weight and importance when, following Newton's cosmical measurements, Cavendish and Coulomb, towards the end

the mere framing of hypotheses and conjectures, for which he professes to have little fancy, though "the heads of some great virtuosos run much upon hypotheses"; and he describes his earlier speculations as "guesses which I did not rely on." In fact, the elaboration of the theorems contained in the 'Principia' marks the transition from the metaphysical to the exact or scientific treatment of natural phenomena. Before Newton showed the far-reaching consequences, the unexpected grasp of a simple mathematical formula in combining facts apparently disconnected, no one could have suspected that such would be possible, and it is not to be wondered at that when once philosophers realised the power of such formulæ, an opposite movement set in through which mathematical processes were extolled at the expense of experiment and observation on the one side, and of philosophical reasoning on the other. Newton himself never fell into this error. He knew well the importance of observation, and he retained to the end of his life a great interest in the philosophical or metaphysical problems which lay beyond or behind the mathematical statement; he carefully distinguished between the *vis gravitatis* and the *causa gravitatis*. Two other great thinkers, second only to Newton himself, took up a similar position to the law of gravitation. Whilst firmly believing in it, they considered it to be not an ultimate law of nature, a *causa occulta*, but believed that it must be possible to derive it from some mechanical properties of matter. The one was older than Newton. It was Huy-

gens (1629 - 95) who through his analysis of centrifugal forces (1673) had done so much to pave the way for Newton's own work. In 1690, after having paid a visit to England in order to become more intimately acquainted with Newton's work, he published at Leyden his 'Discours sur la Cause de la Pesanteur,' a treatise which was little noticed at the time, and in which he is supposed to have revived the vortices of Descartes. Those who have carefully examined it (Fritsch, 'Theorie der Newton'schen Gravitation,' &c., Königsberg, 1874; and Isenkrahe, 'Das Räthsel von der Schwerkraft,' p. 87, &c.), find that Huygens reverted to his conception of a material fluid, an ether, such as he had suggested for the explanation of optical phenomena, "which surrounds the earth up to very great distances, which consists of the minutest particles, which fly about in the most different ways in all directions with tearing velocity"— an anticipation surely of Lesage's "ultramundane corpuscles." The other great thinker who, whilst firmly believing in Newton's law, sought for a mechanical explanation of it, was Leonhard Euler (1707-83). In his ether theory, to which he reverts frequently, he made an attempt to explain the various physical agencies, among them gravitation (1743, in his 'Dissertatio de Magnete,' which received in 1744 the prize offered by the Paris Academy), by the pressure of the ether. He admits the difficulty of the problem, but insists upon the necessity of finding a mechanical cause for gravitation. See Isenkrahe in 'Zeitschrift für Mathematik und Physik,' vol. xxvi. ; but

24.
Electrical
and mag-
netic action.
of the last century, subjected the less universal terrestrial phenomena of magnetic and electric action to exact measurements, finding that a formula corresponding to the gravitation formula described them with surprising accuracy, with this remarkable difference, that here not only attractive but also repulsive forces, following the same mathematical relations as to mass and distance, came into play. To these confirmatory discoveries must be added the measurement of the intensity of radiations which proceed from centres, such as those of light and heat, made by various philosophers during the latter half of the last century. Newton, and his great successor Laplace more than a century after him, both favoured the emission or emanation hypothesis of light, and it was thus natural to fasten upon the analogy which existed between the intensity in which radiation, gravitation, and electric and magnetic action change with the distance from their respective centres. All these agencies came thus under the general conception of forces emanating from fixed centres, and spreading through space, in the proportion of the superficial area of the spheres described around their centres with increasing radii—i.e., decreasing or becoming diluted in the ratio of the squares of these radii or distances. These analogies were indeed recognised to be very imperfect, inasmuch as light and radiant heat occupy a measurable time to spread from their centres, whereas the time occupied by the force of gravitation is

25.
Law of
emanations.

especially Miething, ' L. Euler's Lehre vom Aether,' Berlin, 1894. In the course of this century the mechanical theory of gravitation, including the attempts of Lesage, Euler, Huygens, and Newton himself, has again received attention through Faraday's, Maxwell's, and Hertz's electric theories, and Wm. Thomson (Lord Kelvin) has especially studied the ideas of Lesage. Of this more later on.

either exceedingly small or this force is propagated instantaneously through the greatest cosmical distances which come under our notice. Then, again, light and radiated heat spend themselves as they meet with reflecting or absorbing bodies, whereas gravitation does not seem to be affected by intervening or screening bodies.[1]

[1] It is now known that this screening effect exists likewise in magnetic and electric action. In the formula which expresses the action at a distance of magnetic, electrical, and ponderable masses, viz., $f = \mu \, \frac{m.m'}{r^2}$, the older view— previous to Faraday's researches— considered m and m' the masses (ponderable or imponderable), and the distance r to be variable, μ a constant, corresponding to the gravitation constant. As stated above, the gravitation constant is, so far as we know, a real constant—i.e., it is not affected by the nature of the medium which fills the space intervening between m and m', the attractive masses. Faraday doubted this; but leaving gravitation—"as a relation by some higher quality" —aside, he directed his efforts to the testing of the validity of this view as regards electric and magnetic action. He found that μ is not a real constant, but dependent on the nature of the medium and the objects which intervene between the magnetic and electric masses. These researches, which are probably the first step in the direction of gaining by observation some notion of the mechanical manner in which action at a distance is brought about, begin with the year 1837 (see 11th series of 'Experimental Researches in Electricity,' No. 1252). The result was that the "specific electric induction for different bodies" was established, contrary to the ideas of Poisson and others ('Exper. Res.,' No. 1167), and the word "dielectric" invented to denote the "action of the contiguous particles of the insulating medium" (No. 1168). From this point he was led a step farther, to "expect that all polar forces act in the same general manner"—viz., by contiguous particles. Faraday, however, is careful to remark that by contiguous particles he means those "which are next to each other, not that there is no space between them" (No. 1665).

In 1838 Faraday was still doubtful whether magnetic action was similar in this respect to statical electric action; but he thought it probable that it was "communicated by the action of the intervening particles" (No. 1729), and in pursuing this line of thought, in spite of many unsuccessful trials, he at last saw his ideas realised, discovered the magnetisation of light, and invented the term "diamagnetic" to describe "a body through which lines of magnetic force are passing, and which does not by their action assume the usual magnetic state" (1845, 'Exper. Res.,' No. 2149). At the end of the 19th series of researches he says: "In former papers (1838) I proposed a theory of electrical induction founded on the action of contiguous particles, . . . and I then ventured to suggest that probably . . . magnetic action was also conveyed onward in a similar manner. At that time I could discover

Nevertheless, the fact that gravity, radiation, and electric and magnetic action appear as central emanations, decreasing with the square of the distance,—two properties which lend themselves to mathematical and geometrical representation,—seemed to pave the way for further generalisations. All forces in nature were put down as central forces, either attractive or repulsive, and if not following the Newtonian formula, still dependent on the distance according to some mathematical expression. For nearly a century theoretical physics were occupied in working out the mathematical formulæ expressive of these ideas, and Laplace himself promoted these attempts by the weight of his great authority. We do not possess the final views on this point with which the great mathematician intended to complete the last edition of his ' Exposition du Système du Monde '; but some of the later chapters of this work, treating of gravitation and molecular attraction, show us clearly in which direction he looked for progress in theoretical physics.[1]

26.
Molecular
action.

no peculiar condition of the intervening or diamagnetic matter ; but now that we are able to distinguish such an action; . . . now that diamagnetics are shown not to be indifferent bodies, I feel still more confidence in . . . asking whether it may not be by the action of the contiguous or next succeeding particles that the magnetic force is carried onward," &c. (No. 2443). Faraday also made repeated experiments with the view of determining how the force of gravitation is communicated, believing as little as Newton did in an *actio in distans*, and he was wont to quote Newton's words on this matter, referring also to Euler's ether theory (No. 3305).

[1] In the fifth edition of the ' Exposition du Système du Monde ' Laplace had suppressed these chapters, and had announced his intention " to unite the principal results of the application of analysis to phenomena depending on a molecular action differing from universal attraction" into a special treatise which should form a sequel to the ' Exposition,' &c. This project was never carried out (see "avertissement au sixième édition de ' l'Exposition ' "). The success which attended Laplace's attempts to explain double refraction and aberration of light (following Newton's suggestions in the ' Principia ' and ' Optics ') as well as capillary phenomena (following Haukesbee) left no

The great prominence given by Laplace to the gravitational explanation of all natural phenomena, the fact that all the observable movements of the universe, the shape and size of the moving masses, and the orbits they describe, as well as many phenomena observable on the surface of our globe, such as the aberration and refraction of light, the phenomena of the tides, of atmospheric pressure, and some of the more important molecular properties of matter, could be perfectly or approximately described, calculated, and predicted by gravitation or analogous attractions, gave to what we may call—following a hint of Clerk Maxwell's—the astronomical method [1] of con-

doubt in his mind that such phenomena "are owing to attractive and repulsive forces between molecule and molecule" ('Expos.,' 6me éd., p. 328). He saw in molecular attraction the cause of the solidity of bodies, of chemical affinities, and of the properties of chemical saturation, which Berthollet had developed about that time ('Expos.,' p. 360); he thinks it likely that the law of molecular attraction is the same for all bodies, and he finally dwells on the question whether the attraction of gravity and molecular attraction could be united under one common law or expression (p. 363), and throws out the idea that thus the phenomena of physics and astronomy might be brought under one general law, adding, however, significantly, "Mais l'impossibilité de connaître les figures des molécules et leurs distances mutuelles, rend ces explications vagues et inutiles à l'avancement des sciences."

[1] "Cavendish, Coulomb, and Poisson, the founders of the exact sciences of electricity and magnetism, paid no regard to those old notions of 'magnetic effluvia' and 'electric atmospheres' which had been put forth in the previous century, but turned their undivided attention to the determination of the law of force, according to which electrified and magnetised bodies attract or repel each other. In this way the true laws of these actions were discovered, and this was done by men who never doubted that the action took place at a distance, without the intervention of any medium, and who would have regarded the discovery of such a medium as complicating rather than as explaining the undoubted phenomena of attraction. . . . Ampère, by a combination of mathematical skill with experimental ingenuity, first proved that two electric currents act on one another, and then analysed this action into the resultant of a system of push - and - pull forces between the elementary parts of these currents. . . . Whereas the general course of scientific method then consisted in the application of the ideas of mathematics and astronomy to each new investigation in turn, Faraday seems to have had no opportunity of acquiring a technical knowledge of

27.
The astro-
nomical
view.
Cosmical,
molar, and
molecular
phenomena.
sidering nature a great impetus. As we have seen, it was entirely an outcome of Newton's great discovery.

It is sometimes useful to distinguish between cosmical, molar, and molecular phenomena; it is, however, well to note that this distinction is a popular or practical, not a scientific one. The question, in how far pure magnitude affects the appearance and relations of the parts or elements of which the universe is composed, is indeed of great scientific interest, but it has not yet received a definite answer. In the meantime we can use the term cosmical for such magnitudes of space, mass, or time as far transcend our own powers of direct measurement by the foot-rule, the balance, and the timepiece, and still more, our powers of direct action : those dimensions compared with which our own homes and actions absolutely disappear. We will call molar those masses which we can handle directly, those dimensions in which we build our own homes and pass our own lives. And we will call molecular those sizes and masses which on the other side are so small that the utmost powers of the microscope and the dividing machine fail to make them directly visible, still less tangible or manageable for our active powers. The lines which limit these three regions are indeed neither fixed nor fixable; the middle region, which

mathematics, and his knowledge of astronomy was mainly derived from books. . . . Thus Faraday was debarred from following the course of thought which led to the achievements of the French philosophers, and was obliged to explain the phenomena to himself by means of a symbolism which he could understand, instead of adopting what had hitherto been the only tongue of the learned " (Clerk Maxwell, " Action at a Distance," 'Proceedings of the Royal Institution,' vol. vii. Reprinted in 'Scientific Papers,' Cambridge, 1890, vol. ii. p. 317 *sq.* Cf. also vol. i. p. 156). Du Bois-Reymond uses the term "astronomical knowledge" in a somewhat wider sense in his discourse "Ueber die Grenzen des Naturerkennens" ('Reden,' vol. i. p. 120).

we may call our own home, seems to be extending through improved means of seeing and handling; still every one has a vague notion, and science has supported this notion, that there are certain limits, marking the immeasurably large and the immeasurably small, which we cannot transcend. Now it is a question of great scientific interest to what extent mere enlargement, such as the microscope makes familiar to us, would essentially alter the behaviour and appearance of things natural. Would the planetary or stellar systems, reduced in size many million times, present an aspect similar to the view we here enjoy of the inanimate matter on the surface of our earth, and would the molecular structure of microscopic objects, many times enlarged, differ essentially from that aspect? Our present knowledge would lead us to say they would essentially differ. Certain phenomena or modes of motion seem, so far as we know, essentially characteristic of the molecular, others of the molar, others again of the cosmical world.[1]

[1] Laplace has made a significant remark on this point. See 'Exposition du Système du Monde,' 6 éd., p. 319 *sq.*: "La loi de la pesanteur réciproque au carré des distances . . . est celle de toutes les émanations qui partent d'un centre, telle que la lumière; il paraît même que toutes les forces dont l'action se fait apercevoir à des distances sensibles, suivent cette loi: on a reconnu depuis peu, que les attractions et les répulsions électriques et magnétiques décroissent en raison du carré des distances, en sorte que toutes ces forces ne s'affaiblissent en se propageant, que parcequ'elles s'étendent comme la lumière; leurs quantités étant les mêmes sur les diverses surfaces sphériques que l'on peut imaginer autour de leurs foyers. Une propriété remarquable de cette loi de la nature est que si les dimensions de tous les corps de cet univers, leurs distances mutuelles et leurs vitesses, venaient à augmenter ou à diminuer proportionellement; ils décriraient des courbes entièrement semblables à celles, qu'ils décrivent, et leurs apparences seraient exactement les mêmes; car les forces, qui les animent, étant le résultat d'attractions proportionelles aux masses divisées par le carré des distances, elles augmenteraient ou diminueraient proportionellement aux dimensions du nouvel univers. On voit en même temps, que cette propriété ne peut appartenir qu'à la loi de la nature. Ainsi, les apparences des mouvements de

28.
Special
interest
attached
to molar
dimensions.

And we cannot but be struck by the fact that only those dimensions which we call molar appear to be the abode of living and conscious beings. The cosmical world has, so far as we know, no inhabitant which can behold it in the same way as man beholds this planet, and the same obtains so far as we are acquainted with the molecular world. So far as our knowledge goes and is likely ever to reach, a special importance or dignity will therefore always belong to molar dimensions and masses. The process by which we try to picture to ourselves in tracings and models, constructed in molar dimensions, the behaviour and appearance of cosmical as well as molecular masses will always recommend itself, not only as the most practical, but likewise as the most interesting and plausible, for only by this procedure do these unreachable worlds become amenable to direct observation and to the processes of experiment in the physical laboratory. It seems *prima facie* that the wealth of phenomena and the variety of different kinds of motion decrease as we ascend into the cosmical, or as we descend into the molecular world, giving way in the former to essentially uniform, though to many times multiplied modes of motion, and disappearing in

---

l'univers sont indépendantes de ses dimensions absolues, comme elles le sont, du mouvement absolu, qu'il peut avoir dans l'espace ; et nous ne pouvons observer et connaître que des rapports." This is easily seen. For if in the formula $f = \dfrac{m \cdot m'}{r^n}$, the dimensions be all multiplied by K, we get the new formula $F = K^{6-n} \times \dfrac{m \cdot m'}{r^n}$, and the acceleration of a body moving round

a centre like the sun would be $\dfrac{F}{K^3 m'} = K^{3-n} \times \dfrac{m}{r^n}$, which is only K times the acceleration $\dfrac{m}{r^n}$, if $n = 2$. In another passage Laplace repeats the above statement in slightly different words : "L'univers réduit successivement jusqu'au plus petit espace imaginable, offrirait toujours les mêmes apparences à ses observateurs" (p. 440). That this would not apply to molecular attractions or repulsions is evident.

the latter in stable and self-repeating averages. Possessed therefore, as we seem to be, of the greatest wealth and variety of observations and notions, we may—perhaps erroneously—conclude that we can grasp the simpler cosmical and molecular movements and phenomena by starting from molar, physical, or mechanical models.[1]

[1] English naturalists have always excelled in this line of investigation, whereas foreign scientific literature has been rich in purely mathematical deductions from formulæ which contained no *construirbare Vorstellung*. And it is interesting to note that both lines of thought go back to Newton. Whereas Newton himself believed in the possibility of a mechanical explanation or representation of the gravitation formula, the second edition of the 'Principia' by Cotes can be looked upon as sanctioning the view that gravitation is an ultimate quality which must be accepted as such; and as it was the second edition through which Newton's ideas became largely known on the Continent, it is not surprising that he was there accused of reintroducing the *qualitates occultæ* of the older metaphysics, which Descartes and others had successfully banished. Clerk Maxwell says ("Action at a Distance," 'Scient. Pap.,' vol. ii. p. 316): "The doctrine of direct action at a distance cannot claim for its author the discoverer of universal gravitation. It was first asserted by Roger Cotes in his preface to the 'Principia,' which he edited during Newton's life. According to Cotes it is by experience that we learn that all bodies gravitate. We do not learn in any other way that they are extended, movable, or solid. Gravitation, therefore, has as much right to be considered an essential property of matter as extension, mobility, or impenetra-

bility. And when the Newtonian philosophy gained ground in Europe, it was the opinion of Cotes rather than that of Newton that became most prevalent." In fact, philosophers could be divided into two classes—those who took the fact of gravity or the wider idea of a universal attraction as a beginning, and drew from this beginning all the possible mathematical and experimental consequences which they could think of; and those who, whilst admitting this process as a legitimate one, thought it necessary to go behind the assumed beginning and find a still more hidden mechanical reason for this admitted property. To the latter class belonged Newton himself, Huygens, Euler, and in modern times notably Faraday and his followers; to the former class belonged Daniel Bernoulli, who wrote to Euler, 4th February 1744, referring to the ether theory of the latter: "Moreover, I believe both that the ether is *gravis versus solem* and the air *versus terram*, and I cannot conceal from you that on these points I am a perfect Newtonian, and I am surprised that you adhere so long to the *principiis Cartesianis;* there is possibly some feeling in the matter. If God has been able to create an *animam* whose nature is unknown to us, He has also been able to impress an *attractionem universalem materiæ*, though such is *attractio supra captum*, whereas the *principia Cartesiana* involve always something *contra captum*" (see

29.
Geometrical
axioms.

I may, in passing, mention here that in the course of our century certain views have been put forward in pure mathematics, or rather in geometry, which make it conceivable, if not probable, that our ideas of space might not apply to immeasurably small or to immeasurably large dimensions.[1] Should the future progress of thought

Miething, 'L. Euler's Lehre vom Aether,' p. 30). In quite recent times a similar position has again been taken up by Paul du Bois-Reymond in his essay "Ueber die Unbegreiflichkeit der Fernkraft," in the 'Naturwissenschaftliche Rundschau' (vol. iii. No. 14), and in his posthumous work, 'Ueber die Grundlagen der Erkenntniss in den exacten Wissenschaften' (Tübingen, 1890), in which he adds action at a distance as a third "ignorabimus" or unknowable problem to the two given in his brother Emil's address, "Ueber die Grenzen des Naturerkennens" (1872, reprinted in 'Reden,' vol. i. p. 105). On the Continent, about thirty years ago, the fruitlessness of pursuing this problem seemed generally admitted. Helmholtz in 1847 speaks of the initial assumption "that all actions in nature are to be reduced to attracting and repelling forces, whose intensity depends merely on the distance of points mutually acting on each other" (*actio in distans*), and Du Bois-Reymond repeats this in 1871 in his address. But it is significant that Helmholtz, who (through his memoir on vortex motion in 1858) gave such an impetus to the mechanical explanations of molecular forces, modified his views on this point (see his address on Magnus, 1871, 'Vorträge und Reden,' vol. ii.); accordingly in the reprint of his memoir of 1847 he has accompanied it with some significant remarks on the necessity of that initial assumption (1881, 'Wissen-

schaftliche Abhandlungen,' vol. i. p. 68).

[1] Reimann was probably the first to give expression to this line of thought. His memoir on this subject, "On the Hypotheses which lie at the Foundation of Geometry," bears the date 1854. It was read before the Philosophical Faculty of Göttingen in the presence and at the request of Gauss, on whom it made a profound impression (see the biographical notice on Reimann by Dedekind, attached to Riemann's 'Gesammelte Werke,' Leipzig, 1876). The memoir was not published till after Riemann's death in 1867. In England the late Prof. Clifford introduced the subject to the Cambridge Philosophical Society in 1870: "The axioms of plane geometry are true within the limits of experiment on the surface of a sheet of paper, and yet we know that the sheet is really covered with a number of small ridges and furrows, upon which these axioms are not true. Similarly although the axioms of solid geometry are true within the limits of experiment for finite portions of our space, yet we have no reason to conclude that they are true for very small portions ; and if any help can be got thereby for the explanation of physical phenomena, we may have reason to conclude that they are not true for very small portions of space" (see Clifford's 'Mathematical Papers,' p. 21. Compare also his lectures on "The Philosophy of the Pure Sciences" in 'Lectures and Essays,' vol. i. p. 295 *sqq.*)

or observation bring forward any indications that the idea is not only a theoretical possibility, but an actual reality, then the mode of thought now so successfully used—*viz.*, that of transferring phenomena belonging to molar dimensions, and exemplified in the physical laboratory, into cosmic or molecular space by a process of enlarging or of reducing—would become inapplicable. Mathematics indeed would not fail, but our ordinary geometry and the physical model and mechanism would fail: we should probably still be able to calculate, though not to represent, those phenomena of immeasurable dimensions.

As it is, the first great example of calculating and predicting the phenomena of an unreachable world was Newton's successful attempt to explain the movements of the moon, and other cosmical bodies, by using the phenomena of falling bodies on the surface of the earth described by Galileo and Huygens ; and he was rewarded by the discovery of a universal law of attraction, which would probably never have been discovered by experiments carried on within molar dimensions, the mass of the earth being so immeasurably greater than that of any molar masses under our control.   It quite escapes our observation that in the action and reaction of the falling stone the immensity of the earth's mass is compensated by the vanishing distance through which the earth moves when attracted by the stone.   Thus the astronomical view came to the rescue of physical or molar experiments, helped to explain them, and indicated the manner in which cosmical forces could be measured even on the surface of the earth.   The pendulum experi-

30.
Difficulty of measuring gravitation directly.

ments of Richer, Halley, and many others, the measurements of the arc of the meridian, and Cavendish's and Maskelyne's experiments, were some of the direct results of the discovery.

It was natural that, having explained the cosmical, and subsequently many terrestrial phenomena, successfully by the formula of attraction, Newton himself, and still more Laplace and his school, should have attempted the explanation of molecular phenomena by similar methods.

31. Astronomical view of molecular phenomena.

The astronomical view spread into molar and molecular physics. Newton himself made use of the notion of molecular attraction [1]—*i.e.*, of attraction existing only at

[1] In the fourteenth section of the first book of the 'Principia' Newton is, however, careful to speak always of "attractio vel impulsus," leaving it open to the reader to form his own opinion whether it is an action at a distance or a "vis a tergo," a push. He says also that the particles of light approaching solid bodies with a definite velocity are bent, "quasi attracti in eadem (*i.e.*, corpora)." And in the twenty-third query to the first Latin edition of the 'Opticks' (1706) he says: "May not the small particles of bodies have certain virtues, powers, or forces by which they act at some distance, not only on the rays of light, reflecting, refracting, or inflecting them, but also on each other, producing various natural phenomena? For it is sufficiently known that bodies mutually act on each other through the attraction of gravity and through magnetic and electric virtue. And these examples show what is the order and reason of nature, so that it becomes very probable that there may be other attractive forces. For nature is very similar and agreeing to her-self. Through what efficient cause these attractions are brought about I do not inquire here. What I here call attraction may well be produced by an impulse or in some other way unknown to us. I take this word attraction here in this way, that it be understood merely to mean some universal force with which bodies try to approach each other, whatever cause this force may have to be attributed to. For from the phenomena of nature it behoves us first to be taught which bodies attract each other, and what are the laws and properties of this attraction, before we inquire by what efficient cause this attraction is brought about. The attraction of gravity and of the magnetic and electric virtue extend to sufficiently large distances, so that they fall under the notice of the vulgar senses; but it may be that there are others which are contained in such narrow limits that they have so far escaped all observation." And he goes on to speak of the deliquescence of some salts and of chemical combinations of finely powdered substances. And further on in the same query, after

very small distances—to explain the refraction and inflection of light passing from empty space, or from the

referring to attractive forces acting only at small distances, he proceeds : "And as in algebra, when the positive quantities disappear and cease, negative quantities begin ; so in mechanics, where attraction stops, there a repelling force must come in. But that such a force exists, seems to follow from the reflection and inflection of the rays of light. For the rays are repelled by bodies in both these cases, without the immediate contact of the reflecting or inflecting body. And if all this is so, then the whole of nature will be very simple and similar to herself ; performing all the great motions of the heavenly bodies by the attraction of gravity, which exists between all those bodies, and almost all the smaller motions of their particles through some other attracting and repelling force, which exists mutually between those particles" ('Optice,' MDCCVI., p. 341). The suggestions of Newton regarding forces of molecular dimensions were taken up by other contemporary writers and experimentalists, and the 'Philosophical Transactions' during the early years of the last century contain several memoirs touching on this subject, notably by John Keill (1708), who refers to Newton's 'Opticks,' and enlarges, as does also John Freind ('Prelectiones Chymicæ'), on the usefulness of the idea of molecular attraction in explaining chemical and physiological phenomena. In the later editions of the 'Opticks,' evidently in consequence of the elaborate experiments of Hauksbee, Newton enters more fully into the question of molecular, especially capillary, action ; and his last query, No. 31, is quoted by Laplace in his 'Théorie

de l'Action capillaire,' which forms the supplement to the tenth book of the 'Mécanique céleste.' I may here mention that as some confusion exists in the different editions of the 'Optics' regarding the numbering of the "Queries," it is best to refer to Horsley's Collected Edition of the Works of Newton, where the latest English edition is reprinted, and all the variations and additions noted from the first (English) edition through the subsequent ones. The first edition breaks off with query 16 ; the first Latin one with query 23, and this was in later editions numbered 31, a number of new queries being inserted, Nos. 18 to 24, referring to the "probability of a medium more subtle than air" and the "mechanical efficient of gravity," This was added "to show" (Newton's words in preface dated 16th July 1717) "that I do not take gravity for an essential property of bodies, . . . choosing to propose it by way of a question, because I am not yet satisfied about it by way of experiments." We may note that this was written a few years after the second edition of the 'Principia' was published by Cotes, whose preface did a good deal to occasion the misunderstanding regarding Newton's views on gravitation as a primary quality of matter. From his correspondence with Cotes, edited by Eddleston (1850), we know that Newton is composing the "Scholium generale," which is added to the second and later editions of the 'Principia,' had intended to say "much more about the attraction of the small particles of bodies," but that on second thoughts he abandoned this intention (p. 147).

atmosphere, into or in the neighbourhood of solid bodies. He conceived light to be a material substance, consisting of minute particles, propelled in straight lines from the luminous centres. These small particles, when arriving at or near the surface of transparent bodies, came under the influence of an attraction from the substance of such bodies, and Newton succeeded in showing that for rays of light which fall on transparent surfaces at an angle, the path of the ray in the body would be deflected according to the rule experimentally determined by Snell, and published by Descartes. This application of the idea of attraction, or action at a distance, to very small or molecular dimensions, required a modification of the gravitation formula. The first who took an important step farther in this direction was Francis Hauksbee. Between the year 1709 and 1713 he made a series of experiments on what is called capillary action. His experiments were discussed by Newton in the later editions of the 'Opticks,' and followed by those of Dr Jurin in 1718. Hauksbee, Newton, Jurin, and subsequent writers, like Clairaut, all attributed these and similar phenomena to molecular attractions, and Laplace showed that for the mathematical treatment of the subject a knowledge of the exact law (corresponding to the Newtonian law of molar attraction) was unnecessary, but that it was necessary and sufficient to assume the existence of an attraction of the molecules of bodies, which decreases very rapidly as their distances increase, " so as to become insensible at the smallest distances perceptible by our senses." [1] The phenomena of atmos-

32.
Capillary
action.

---

[1] See 'Mécanique céleste,' vol. iv. (1805), Supplement, p. 67. See also p. 2 : " J'ai cherché, il y a long- temps, à déterminer les lois d'attraction qui représentent ces phénomènes : de nouvelles recherches

pheric refraction as well as those of cohesion and adhesion of bodies—*i.e.*, the attraction of particles of the same or of different matter under what is commonly called contact or at distances which we call in science molecular—were thus submitted to calculation, and the results brought largely into harmony with experience.[1] The problem presented itself and occupied natural philosophers all through the last century, whether a more general law of action at a distance could be found which comprised the phenomena of molecular as well as of molar attraction.

The most celebrated attempt in this direction is that of the Jesuit Roger Boscovich, who in 1758 published an elaborate treatise on this subject.[2]

33. Boscovich's extension of the Newtonian formula.

---

m'ont enfin conduit à faire voir qu'ils sont tous représentés par les mêmes lois qui satisfont aux phénomènes de la réfraction, c'est-à-dire par les lois dans lesquelles l'attraction n'est sensible qu'à des distances insensibles ; et il en résulte une théorie complète de l'action capillaire."

[1] The terms insensible and imperceptible, which are commonly used in these discussions, must be taken with caution. It is now known that, though not directly perceptible or sensible, the distance through which molecular action takes place is measurable. Plateau in Belgium (1843 and following years) and Quincke in Germany (1868) made experiments on independent lines, and came to very similar results. The distance of molecular action appears to be about the twenty thousandth part of a millimetre. See Clerk Maxwell's article on Capillary Action in the 9th edition of the 'Ency. Brit.,' reprinted in 'Scientific Papers,' vol. ii. ; also Violle's 'Cours de Physique,' German edition, vol. i. p. 591, &c., and p. 639.

[2] Roger Joseph Boscovich, of the Society of Jesus (1711-87), took up the ideas thrown out by Newton in the last query to the 'Opticks,' and published in 1758 at Vienna an elaborate treatise with the title 'Theoria Philosophiæ Naturalis redacta ad unicam legem virium in Natura existentium.' A second edition was published at Venice in 1763. His speculations begin with the year 1745, when he hit upon his general view that all forces in nature can be reduced to the action of indivisible and inextended atoms, endowed with inertia and with a mutual force which at vanishing distances is repulsive, which at insensible distances alternates according to some mathematical formula between repulsion and attraction, and, finally, at sensible distances becomes identical with Newton's force of gravitation. The general form of the curve which exhibits this action at a distance is given, and the algebraical formula discussed, in the Supplement. But it was, of course, impossible to define the law any further. The

Though many of the views contained in this treatise were really the same as those embraced by a large school of Continental mathematicians till far into this century,

whole treatise is really more of a philosophical than a mathematical or experimental investigation. A large portion is taken up in defending his view against possible objections, and in showing how it agrees with or differs from the philosophies of Leibniz and Newton. Whilst this treatise represents in general a view largely held by Continental philosophers of nature, it does not contain any new mathematical methods such as the ' Principia' contained before and Laplace's 'Mécanique céleste' later, nor does it contribute any experiments such as those works likewise contained and suggested to others. In fact, it is more a metaphysical than an exact treatise, and as such has exerted no lasting beneficial influence on the progress of science. "The eighteenth century made a school of science for itself, in which for the not unnatural dogma of the earlier schoolmen, 'matter cannot act where it is not,' was substituted the most fantastic of paradoxes, *contact does not exist.* Boscovich's theory was the consummation of the eighteenth - century school of physical science. This strange idea took deep root, and from it grew up a barren tree, exhausting the soil and overshadowing the whole field of molecular investigation, on which so much unavailing labour was spent by the great mathematicians of the early part of our nineteenth century. If Boscovich's theory no longer cumbers the ground, it is because one true philosopher required more light for tracing lines of electric force " (Sir William Thomson's Lecture before the Royal Institution, May 1860. Reprinted in ' Papers on

Electrostatics and Magnetism,' 2nd ed., 1884, p. 224). Nevertheless it is extraordinary to note that Boscovich's theory was more popular among British than among Continental physicists. In France the book seems to have been little appreciated, although Boscovich was well known through his optical and astronomical researches (see Montucla's ' Histoire des Mathématiques,' vol. iii. p. 490, vol. iv. p. 188) ; and his differences with d'Alembert were notorious. But French science was then occupied less with metaphysical theories than with mathematical analysis and experimental research. In Germany the book remained unknown, probably because Euler's authority favoured an opposite theory. In this country, however, the theory is often referred to from the time of Priestley (' History of Optics ') to Faraday ("On the Nature of Matter," ' Phil. Mag.,' 1844, vol. 24), and more recently Thomson (Lord Kelvin). The last has probably more than any other living writer of similar eminence referred to Boscovich, whose theory he considers suggestive, and we are indebted to him for the first serious attempt to establish by actual calculation the real capabilities of the Boscovich atoms in explaining the properties of chemical molecules, their stability and degree of saturation (see the Report of the British Association at Liverpool, 1896). In Scotland Boscovich's theory was fully discussed in a posthumous article on "Corpuscular Forces " by John Robison, Professor of Natural Philosophy at Edinburgh, and published by Brewster in the 1st volume of Robison's ' System of Mechanical Philosophy '(Edinburgh,

the book was almost completely forgotten on the Continent.[1] No real progress has indeed been made in the explanation of physical phenomena by the application of

1822). His 'Elements of Mechanical Philosophy' (Edinb., 1804) betray, according to Dugald Stewart, "a strong and avowed leaning to the theory of Boscovich" (Works by Hamilton, vol. v. p. 107). The theory probably found favour, among other reasons, because it seemed to give support to the prevalent corpuscular theory of light, which Euler opposed, as he did simple action at a distance. In the Scotch school of philosophy, of which Dugald Stewart was the most popular exponent, Boscovich was well known. Stewart refers to him frequently (Works by Hamilton, vol. ii. pp. 50, 107, 110, 343 ; vol. iii. p. 233 ; vol. v. p. 93 *sqq.* ; vol. vii. p. 173 *sqq.*) He quotes Priestley, Robison, and James Hutton as followers of Boscovich, whilst his own adherence is certainly very qualified, and he makes a very pertinent remark in his Introduction to the 'Elements of the Philosophy of the Human Mind' (1792) : "I cannot help taking this opportunity of remarking that if physical inquirers should think of again employing themselves in speculations about the nature of matter, instead of attempting to ascertain its sensible properties and laws (and of late there seems to be such a tendency among some of the followers of Boscovich), they will soon involve themselves in an inextricable labyrinth, and the first principles of physics will be rendered as mysterious and chimerical as the pneumatology of the schoolmen" (vol. ii. p. 50). Boscovich seems to have been fond of tracing mathematical curves to represent all kinds of processes, such as the intellectual advancement of the age, and he shows

graphically that this was declining (Dugald Stewart's quotation in his 'Dissertation,' Works, vol. i. p. 499).

[1] When Fechner published the first edition of his 'Atomenlehre' (1st ed., Leipzig, 1855; 2nd ed., 1864), he does not seem to have known of Boscovich's treatise (see p. 229 of the 2nd edition), and it was similarly unknown to the Dutch meteorologist Buys Ballot, whose curves of the attracting and repelling forces of matter agree almost exactly with those of Boscovich (see 'Fortschritte der Physik,' 1849, p. 1 *sqq.*; also Rosenberger's 'Geschichte der Physik,' vol. iii. p. 536 *sqq.*) In French scientific literature the treatise of Boscovich is mostly ignored—the 'Grande Encyclopédie' does not even give its title. In fact, French science does not consider itself beholden to the celebrated Jesuit for what I call the astronomical view of matter. See St Venant in 'Comptes Rendus,' vol. 82, p. 1223: "Plusieurs auteurs, soit anglais, soit allemands, dans ses œuvres qui sont du reste d'une haute portée, . . . se sont pris à condamner vivement, sous le nom de *théorie de Boscovich*, non pas son idée capitale de réduction des atomes à des centres d'action de forces, mais la loi même, la loi physique générale des actions fonctions des distances mutuelles des particules qui les exercent réciproquement les unes sur les autres. Et ils attribuent ainsi au célèbre religieux *l'erreur grave* où sont tombés, suivant eux, Navier, Poisson et nos autres savants, créateurs, il y a un demi-siècle, de la mécanique moléculaire ou interne. Or cette loi blâmée, cette loi qui a été, mise en œuvre aussi par Laplace, &c., et

Boscovich's or similar formulæ, though the idea of action
at a distance between the minute particles of matter underlies the theories by which Poisson, Navier, Cauchy,
Lamé, and others calculated the effect of elastic forces in
solid bodies, or the phenomena of light passing through
transparent and crystalline substances. A different school
of physicists, starting from ideas of a different kind, with
which we shall become acquainted hereafter, have shown
that specific notions as to the molecular structure of bodies
are not required in order to deal with the phenomena
referred to. Nevertheless, the idea of action at a distance
governing the movements of immeasurably small, as it
seemingly does those of immeasurably large masses in
nature, received a great support by the development of
two other branches of science, which belong essentially to
the history of the present century.

34. Coulomb's measure-ments.
The sciences of electricity and magnetism can be said
to have originated with Coulomb's accurate measurements with the torsion-balance. With this instrument
he measured the attracting and repelling forces of
bodies, electrified or magnetised, by comparing them
with the mechanical forces required to twist a metallic
wire. In this way he fixed what have ever since his
time been termed the units of electricity or magnetism,
reducing these quantities to the same system of measurement with which we measure the masses or inertia of

35. Extended by Gauss and Weber.
moving bodies. His methods were adopted and modified and greatly perfected by Gauss and Weber—the

prise par Coriolis et Poncelet pour
base de la mécanique physique,
n'est autre que celle de Newton lui-
même, comme on le voit non seulement dans son grand et principal
ouvrage, mais dans le scholie général de sa non moins immortelle
'Optique.'"

former applying them to the measurement of the magnetic forces of the earth, the latter to that of the forces exerted by currents of electricity—*i.e.*, by electricity which is not at rest but in motion. As I have already stated, the measurements of Coulomb confirmed the prevalent notion that action at a distance, varying inversely as the square of the distance, and directly in the proportion of the quantities of the acting substance, was a universal formula or law of nature.[1] The idea

[1] Coulomb's exact measurements of the attraction and repulsion at a distance of electrified bodies and of magnets were published during the years 1784 to 1789 in seven memoirs presented to the Paris Academy of Sciences. They are conveniently collected, together with some other memoirs of Coulomb, Poisson, and others on kindred subjects, in the first volume of the 'Collection de Mémoires relatifs à la Physique,' published in 1884 by the Société française de Physique. Coulomb made use of the torsion-balance and the proof-plane, the actions of which he carefully examined. He confirmed the law, which had been vaguely or approximately expressed by various writers before him, that electrified bodies act on each other with a force which is proportional to the inverse square of their distances. This he did by direct measurements of the repulsion of small electrified bodies in the torsion-balance (1785, 1st Mémoire). He then extended his measurements by an indirect method to the action of electrified bodies of larger size and to magnets (2nd Mémoire). He also defined what is meant by quantity and density of electricity and magnetism, and showed how these could be measured and how the action of electrified bodies and magnets depended on the more or less of these quantities. Coulomb's researches contain experiments of great delicacy. Although the laws which bear his name appear so simple when written down, the phenomena they represent are most complicated, as in the case of electricity the effect of electrical influence, called by Faraday induction, and in the case of magnetism the presence of the earth's magnetism, and the fact that we have never to do with one kind of magnetism but always with two states, destroys all chance of exhibiting experimentally the simple case represented by the mathematical formula. It was therefore necessary to consider this formula as being merely a convenient description of the elementary action of supposed isolated quantities of electricity and magnetism, and by a process of summation to deduce mathematically the actual effects for such cases of interaction as are actually observable in the laboratory. It was especially the phenomena of the distribution of electricity on the surface of electrified bodies of simple shape and the distribution of magnetic forces in the neighbourhood of magnets which had to be calculated and measured. In physical astronomy a similar course of reasoning and observation combined had verified

of mass, which in the Newtonian formula meant merely the quantity of matter, had indeed to be enlarged, and to the attracting forces had to be added those of repulsion; still, though physically the phenomena were entirely different, the mathematical expression which ruled the two electric and the two magnetic quantities, usually termed fluids, looked very much like the Newtonian gravitation formula: it betrayed philosophers into thinking they possessed an explanation where really they had only a measurement and a description.[1]

Newton's elementary law of gravitation, Laplace as it were summing up the evidence in his great work. What Laplace did for Newton was done by Poisson for Coulomb's elementary law of electric and magnetic action, and on a still larger scale by Gauss, who worked out the mathematical theory and applied it to the case of the magnetic distribution on the earth's surface. In England, already before Coulomb's researches were published, Cavendish had, likewise by a combination of experiment and calculation, established the elementary formulæ and properties of electrical phenomena. See note to the following page.

[1] The exact measurements of Coulomb and the mathematical analysis of Poisson and Gauss superseded the vaguer discussions on the nature of electricity and magnetism which were very frequent before that period, just as the mathematical principles of Newton and Laplace drove into the background the discussion on the nature and cause of gravity. Coulomb himself does not profess to settle the controversy carried on between the two schools of which Dufay and Franklin can be considered as the principal representa-

tives—*viz.*, whether there existed two electric fluids or only one. Coulomb judged the rival views simply as to their usefulness in describing and measuring phenomena: "Comme ces deux explications n'ont qu'un degré de probabilité plus ou moins grand je préviens, pour mettre la théorie . . . à l'abri de toute dispute systématique, que dans la supposition des deux fluides électriques je n'ai d'autre intention que de présenter avec le moins d'éléments possibles, les résultats du calcul et de l'expérience, et non d'indiquer les véritables causes de l'électricité" ('Collection de Mémoires,' vol. i. p. 252). He had previously, in 1777, rejected the theory of vortices to explain magnetic phenomena: "Il semble qu'il résulte de l'expérience que ce ne sont point des tourbillons qui produisent les différents phénomènes aimantains, et que, pour les expliquer, il faut nécessairement recourir à des forces attractives et répulsives de la nature de celles, dont on est obligé de se servir pour expliquer la pesanteur des corps et la physique céleste" (vol. i. p. 8). And in 1789 he is still more cautious: "Pour éviter toute discussion, j'avertis . . . que toute hypothèse d'attraction et de répul-

The extension and confirmation which the Newtonian attraction formula had thus gained in the minds of many seemed to be entirely upset by a series of discoveries in which electrical, and subsequently magnetic, phenomena played an important part. These were, the discovery of galvanic electricity by Galvani in 1791 and by Volta in 1800; of the physiological and chemical effects of this form of electricity, especially by Davy (1806); of the magnetic effect of moving electricity by Oersted in 1820; of the connection of heat and electricity by Seebeck in 1822; of induction by Faraday in 1831—*i.e.*, of the action of electric currents and magnets in generating other electric currents or magnetic effects in bodies which are moving in their neighbourhood; and, finally, of diamagnetism by Faraday in 1845.

Many of the celebrated men with whose names the modern discoveries in electricity are identified, and amongst them notably Davy and Faraday, were not brought up in the mathematical school of the Continent,[1] in which

36.
Davy and
Faraday.

sion suivant une loi quelconque ne doit être regardée que comme une formule qui exprime un résultat d'expérience " (vol. i. p. 297).

[1] To these must be added the name of Cavendish (1731-1810), whose electrical researches, in which he anticipated many of Coulomb's results, proceeded on entirely different lines from those of the Continental school. He proved —in or before 1773—from the fact that a small globe situated in the hollow of a large electrified globe and communicating with it showed no signs of electricity, that electric attraction and repulsion must be inversely as the square of the distance. In his published and post-

humous papers (edited by Maxwell in 1879 under the title of ' The Electrical Researches of the Hon. Henry Cavendish ') he anticipated, as Maxwell has shown, many later investigations of British and Continental writers. He had a clear notion of electrical capacity, of potential and of electrical resistance, he anticipated Ohm's law— *i.e.*, the proportionality between the electro-motive force and the current in the same conductor. He studied the properties of dielectrics, and "not only anticipated Faraday's discovery of the specific inductive capacity of different substances, but measured its numerical value in several substances "

the astronomical view of phenomena had been established and strengthened mainly by a development of the Newtonian philosophy. They belonged to another school, which approached that great field of research from the purely experimental side,—mainly, so far as Davy was concerned, from the side of chemistry, which, dealing with the qualitative, not merely the quantitative, properties of matter, was at that period almost entirely thrown

(Maxwell's Introduction to the 'Researches,' p. xlix *sqq.*) Cavendish's electrical work seems to have remained unnoticed abroad. Cuvier, who fully appreciates him as a pioneer in modern chemistry, does not refer to his electrical researches, and in Continental works his name is hardly mentioned in connection with electrical science. He, however, clearly belongs to the same lineage as Davy and Faraday, whose breadth of experimental observation somewhat prevented them from fully assimilating the results of Coulomb and his school, which moved in narrower but more precise lines. If Cavendish was unknown abroad as an electrician, Coulomb was little known in England. Whewell, who did more than any other to make known the researches of the mathematical school (see his article in the 'Encyclopædia Metropolitana,' 1826, and his British Association Report, 1835), could state in the first edition of his 'History of the Inductive Sciences' (1837) that "the reception of the Coulombian theory has hitherto not been so general as might have been reasonably expected from its very beautiful accordance with the facts which it contemplates" (3rd ed., vol. iii. p. 28). He then refers to the experiments of Snow Harris. These experiments, as well as those of

Faraday, carried on about the same time, dealt largely with the properties of dielectrics and of what we now call the electric field, a subject almost entirely neglected by the mathematical school of that period. It was not till 1845 that William Thomson (Lord Kelvin) cleared up the whole subject in a memoir, "On the Mathematical theory of Electricity in Equilibrium" (see 'Reprint of Papers,' &c., p. 15). He there refers to the fact that "many have believed Coulomb's theory to be overturned by the investigations" of Snow Harris and Faraday, and he therefore proposes to show that "all the experiments which they have made having direct reference to the distribution of electricity in equilibrium are in full accordance with the laws of Coulomb, and must therefore be considered as confirming the theory" (p. 18). He thus brought together the two independent lines of research and thought, the mathematical and the experimental, represented by the school of Gauss and Weber abroad, and by Faraday in England, and suggested those further researches of which Maxwell's 'Treatise on Electricity and Magnetism' is the great exponent. See the preface to this work, p. xi, &c., 1873; also Maxwell's 'Scientific Papers,' vol. ii. pp. 258, 302, 304.

upon experimental research.[1]   Chemistry had only just entered the list of the exact sciences, by the use of the balance, largely owing to Lavoisier and his followers.

[1] Although Faraday's 'Experimental Researches in Electricity' (1831-52) contain mostly what chemists would call "qualitative" investigations and only few exact "quantitative" measurements — forming in this respect a very remarkable contrast to Weber's 'Electrodynamische Maasbestimmungen' (1846-78)—it is important to remark that one of the methods for exact measurement of the electric current—*viz.*, by the chemical decomposition of compounds —was established by Faraday in 1833 and 1834. He showed that whenever decomposition took place the quantities decomposed were in proportion to the amount of electricity flowing through the circuit and in proportion to the chemical equivalents. Owing to the want of a clear definition of quantity and intensity of current, Berzelius opposed this view of Faraday's as illogical, confounding the quantity of substance decomposed with the force required to set it free. Clearer definitions and accumulated experience have confirmed Faraday's law, which is now looked upon as one of the best established general facts of chemical and electrical science. Somewhat earlier than Faraday, Georg Simon Ohm established (1827, 'Die galvanische Kette, mathematisch bearbeitet') the proportionality of the quantity of electricity passing through a circuit with the electromotive force in the same conductor, introduced the notion of electrical resistance, and showed how this varies as the length and inversely as the thickness of the same conductor, and is different in different conductors. The accuracy of Ohm's law, though elaborately tested by Fechner and confirmed by Pouillet, was frequently doubted; in France it met with tardy recognition, and in England some of the most important researches—such as those of Faraday—were carried on without reference to it. In the first edition of Whewell's History it is not mentioned. When the second edition was published (1847), Ohm had received the Copley Medal of the Royal Society (1841), and Wheatstone had besides in the year 1843 drawn attention to the clear definitions which Ohm had introduced. The opinion has been expressed that Ohm found his law by theoretical considerations based on analogy with the flow of heat in conductors, and that he subsequently proved it experimentally. The publication of Ohm's collected papers by Lommel ('Gesammelte Abhandlungen,' Leipzig, 1892), however, disproves this opinion ; as his experimental measurements had during 1825 and 1826—not without some initial mistakes—led him to the well-known expression of the relations of the different quantities (see Lommel's Introduction, p. vii). Whereas in Germany it was a purely scientific interest—that, namely, of subjecting physical phenomena to mathematical calculation—which induced Ohm, Gauss, and Weber to devise instruments and methods for exact measurement, it was in England mainly the practical requirements of telegraphy which created the desire for clear definitions and exact methods. With these requirements in view Wheatstone invented his instruments and drew attention to the definitions of Ohm. See his Bakerian Lecture for

Yet the great variety, more than the exact measurement
of phenomena, attracted the attention of natural philosophers in this new field. And when through Davy, Berzelius,
and Faraday in different ways the importance of electric
action in chemical processes became established, it was
natural that from this school an entirely different view of
electrical and magnetic phenomena should emanate : we
may term it—in opposition to the astronomical—the physical view of phenomena.   This view, which, as the astronomical view had done, found later on its expression in a
mathematical formula, will occupy our attention in a subsequent chapter.   It has in the course of the second half
of the century very largely expelled the other and rival
view from the domain of molar and molecular physics.
But the astronomical view, with its largely developed
mathematical apparatus, was not easily defeated : it was

37.
Ampère and
Weber de-
velop the
astronomi-
cal view.
quite able to grapple with even such complicated processes
as the discoveries of Oersted and Faraday had revealed.
In the opinion of many Continental thinkers it won its
greatest laurels when, under the treatment of Ampère in
France and of Neumann and Weber in Germany, the
perplexing interactions of magnets, diamagnets, and

1843 ('Philos. Transactions,' 1843,
p. 303, &c.) : "An energetic source
of light, of heat, of chemical action,
and of mechanical power, we only
require to know the conditions under which its various effects may
be most economically and energetically manifested to enable us
to determine whether the high expectations formed in many quarters
of some of these applications are
founded on reasonable hope or on
fallacious conjecture."   Forty years
later Lord Kelvin, in his address

"On the Electrical Units of Measurement" (1883 ; see 'Popular
Lectures and Addresses,' vol. i. p.
76), could still speak of the comparatively recent date at which
"anything that could be called
electric measurement had come to
be regularly practised in most of the
scientific laboratories of the world,"
whereas such measurements had
then been for many years "familiar
to the electricians of the submarine
cable factories and testing sta-
tions."

electric circuits—the phenomena of electro-magnetism, diamagnetism, and induction—were all resolved into elementary processes of attraction and repulsion, and summed up in a formula which looked like an extension of the Newtonian gravitation formula, revealing the mysterious influence of molecular forces.

" Oersted had found that an electric current acts on a magnetic pole, but that it neither attracts it nor repels it, but causes it to move round the current. He expressed this by saying that the electric conflict acts in a revolving manner. The most obvious deduction from this new fact was, that the action of the current on the magnet is not a push-and-pull force, but a rotary force, and accordingly many minds began to speculate on vortices and streams of ether, whirling round the current. But Ampère, by a combination of mathematical skill and experimental ingenuity, first proved that two electric currents act on one another, and then analysed this action into the resultant of a system of push-and-pull forces between the elementary parts of these currents." [1]

Weber in Germany took up the work where Ampère had left it.[2] One of his objects was to combine the

---

[1] Clerk Maxwell "On Action at a Distance" ('Scientific Papers,' vol. ii. p. 317).

[2] Weber's interest was twofold. The primary object was to put accurate quantitative data in the place of merely qualitative descriptions or mere estimates of phenomena. He had then already published, together with his brothers (see *supra*, p. 196, note 3), two works in which in a similar way exact research has taken the place of inexact description. The first was his experimental investigation of wave-motion ('Die Wellenlehre auf Experimente gegründet,' 1825), the other the still more delicate attempt to treat a physiological phenomenon, the mechanism of the organs of locomotion, on exact mechanical principles (1836). This rare gift of exactness, invaluable at all times, but almost unique at that time in Germany, where philosophical vagueness was only too common, attracted the notice of Gauss, who brought Weber to Göttingen in 1830 after

different electric phenomena—those of electricity in the state of rest, called statical effects; those of electric currents on each other, the dynamical results; and those of electric conductors in a state of motion, the phenomena of induction—in one general and fundamental formula or law. He had before him Coulomb's electrostatic formula, Ampère's electro-dynamic formula, and a more general one established by Franz Neumann, which described and embraced not only the phenomena discovered by Oersted, but also those of moving conductors discovered by Faraday. It is not necessary here to enter into the details of the investigations, experimental and mathematical, by the aid of which Weber succeeded in establishing his very remarkable and seemingly all-embracing formula. Two remarks, however, present themselves, bearing upon the history of thought and the value of precise mathematical expressions. The first is, that as the gravitation formula necessitated a series of the most careful definitions and measurements of physical quantities, and the invention of accurate instruments and methods of measurement, so the first and probably the most valuable performances of Weber were his ingenious apparatus, and the careful measurements by which he

38.
Weber's fundamental measurements.

the death of Tobias Mayer. Gauss introduced Weber to his own exact measurements of terrestrial magnetism, and from hence Weber's own line of thought led through the phenomena of magneto - induction (discovered by Faraday in 1831) and terrestrial magneto - induction (1832) to electro - dynamics, the science which Ampère had created in the years 1820 to 1823. In 1846 Weber speaks in the introduction to the 'Electro-dynamische Maas-

bestimmungen' of the endeavour to determine natural phenomena according to number and measure, expressing surprise that this has not yet been done in electro-dynamics, and then proceeds to describe his "electro-dynamometer," an instrument used by him for many years. With this instrument he then, further, proceeds to confirm Ampère's formula for the action at a distance of the elements of electric currents.

fixed the elementary conceptions and quantities with which he operated. All his researches were comprised under the very significant title "electro-dynamical measurements." As such they remain a great monument of ingenuity and unparalleled accuracy.[1] The second

[1] Gauss had, some years before Weber commenced his electrical researches, introduced the idea of an absolute measure of other than mechanical forces—*i.e.*, following up the definition of force in the Newtonian laws of motion, that it is the cause which brings about a change of motion, he suggested that every physical force can be measured by the velocity it imparts to a movable body of measurable mass, the quantity of mass being in the same locality measured by its weight ; and he applied this to the measurement of magnetic forces. In applying the same idea to the measurement of electric currents, Weber came at once upon the circumstance that the forces exerted by an electric current can be measured in two ways—*viz.*, by the action they have upon magnets or by that which they have on other electric currents. Now by a familiar conception, electricians look upon a current of electricity as measurable by the quantity of electricity which flows through a section of the circuit in a given unit of time, this quantity of electricity being measurable in the same way as Coulomb measured the action at a distance of charged bodies. Should it then be possible to carry out this latter measurement of an electric current, a comparison between the electro-magnetic and the known electro-static units of electricity would become possible. Faraday had already, in 1833 and 1834, made estimates of the numerical relation of the quantity of electricity in a current, measured by its chemical or electro-magnetic effects, and of the same quantity if produced by an electrical machine. These estimates were more than twenty years later, in 1856, reduced to accurate measurements by Weber and Kohlrausch. Through these measurements, which confirmed the enormous numbers which are revealed when we compare electricity at rest and electricity in motion, Weber finished the series of accurate measurements, reduced to an absolute or mechanical standard, which had been begun by Gauss in 1833. It was soon recognised of what practical importance these data must be to electricians. Accordingly the British Association at their meeting at Manchester in 1861 appointed a committee, on the suggestion and under the presidency of Sir William Thomson, called the "British Association Committee of Electrical Standards." "This committee worked for nearly ten years through the whole field of electromagnetic and electro-static measurement, until in its final report, presented to the Exeter meeting in August 1869, it fairly launched the absolute system for general use" (Thomson, 'Popular Lectures and Addresses,' vol. i. p. 84). In recognition of Weber's great merit in first introducing this system into electrical science and practice, the name "Weber" had been selected by Latimer Clark for the unit of current. In the final fixing of the units in Paris in 1881 other units than those previously in use were adopted, and to avoid confusion the names were somewhat differently

point I wish to urge is, how in those days the Newtonian formula was taken as the great model of a law of nature, and how the researches of Coulomb, Poisson, Ampère, and Weber stand in logical connection with the theory of gravitation. Let us see what Weber himself says on this subject:[1] "After the general laws of motion had fur-

chosen. This explains the fact, deplored by Weber's friends and admirers, that his name has dropt out of the list of terms now adopted throughout the civilised world. (See Wiedemann, 'Die Electricität,' Braunschweig, 1885, vol. iv. p. 906, &c.) Recently Prof. Lodge has suggested the introduction of the names of Weber and Gauss to denote some of the derived units in the electrical measurements. See Brit. Assoc. Report, 1895, p. 197 n.

[1] Weber's theoretical conception of the nature of electric action at a distance is mixed up with his exact measurements of electrical quantities, though these can be stated without making use of his theoretical conceptions. It is the nature of the absolute system of measurement that it establishes numerical relations based upon a small number of original units (space, time, and mass, or space and time alone, see note to p. 323 above) which are universally intelligible. Whatever, therefore, the theoretical views may be which led the investigation, in the end these are eliminated in the system of original (primary) and derived (secondary) units. But Weber's theory commands attention for its own sake as the furthest stage to which the gravitational view of phenomena, provisionally introduced by Newton, has been pushed. It has been extolled and condemned, according to the favour with which the purely mathematical treatment of phenomena has been received.

In the school of Laplace this purely mathematical treatment quite obscured all other views which did not minister to it. Thus Laplace remained to the end an adherent of the emission or corpuscular theory of light, and opposed the ideas of Young and Fresnel, who developed the dynamical view. In order to make the cosmical view of nature useful for the explanation of molecular phenomena, two distinct and definite conceptions, contained in the gravitation formula, had to be modified and enlarged. The conception of matter, which in physical astronomy is limited to gravitational matter, had to be extended so as to bring into calculation what was then called imponderable matter, such as light, heat, and electricity. And the law of gravitation, which defines the purely attractive property of ponderable matter, had to be modified so as to embrace also the repulsive action observable in a certain class of phenomena. Coulomb had shown that ponderable matter charged with electricity followed the same formula for attraction and repulsion as gravitating bodies did : he simply adopted the two-fluid theory of electric matter. Poisson developed the mathematics of fluids, actuated by repelling forces depending on the inverse square of the distance. Oersted showed the action of electric currents on magnets ; and Ampère showed that magnets can in their action be supplanted by electric currents. Laplace very early satisfied himself that

nished a foundation, there remained in physics mainly the investigation of the laws of interaction of bodies; for without interaction bodies would for ever remain in that state of rest or motion in which they happened to be.

these actions of ponderable matter, in which electricity was flowing, could be reduced to an action at a distance proportional to the inverse square of the elements of the electric circuits. When Faraday showed that a current of electricity under certain conditions induced in conductors in its neighbourhood other currents, this was explained by saying that the electric fluid exerted not only pondero-motoric but also electro-motoric action at a distance. Not only did electrified matter act on other electrified matter, but electricity as a fluid acted on electricity itself. Weber adopted, for the purpose of putting these apparent actions into mathematical language, and for finding an elementary law of the ultimate particles of electric matter out of which by summation the observable data might be calculated, the hypothesis of Fechner, according to which in an electric current the two electric fluids were moving with equal velocity in opposite directions. It then became evident —looking at the phenomena discovered by Oersted, Ampère, and Faraday — that the electro - static formula of Coulomb required to be supplemented by an additional term, if the mutual action was to be determined not only for the case of equilibrium and rest, but also for that of relative motion. The additional term, depending on this relative motion, had to be found. (See 'Electrodynamische Maasbestimmungen,' vol. i. p. 102). From this starting-point, and with this definite problem in view, Weber undertook a series of most valuable measurements. No doubt can exist as to the lasting importance of these measurements. Any theoretical conception which produces in its application such results must hold a prominent place in the history of scientific thought. And the very fact that, unlike Boscovich and other purely metaphysical theorists, Weber undertook to fix by experiment the actual constants or numerical quantities which his abstract formula contained, led to much enlargement of actual knowledge. I will mention only one of the most interesting points in his elaborate researches. I stated above that it took a whole century after the discovery of the law of gravitation before the gravitation constant was approximately fixed, but that for the progress of physical astronomy this was of little importance, gravity being a universal property of matter. Still such a constant exists, because we possess another definition of matter —viz., inertia or mass. The constant in Coulomb's law cannot be determined in a similar manner, as the property of attraction or repulsion defines for us ultimately the numerical quantity of electricity. We have—so far—no other ultimate absolute measure of electricity. But in Weber's law it was the quantities of electrical matter which acted on each other not only according to their distances, but also according to their relative motion or their velocities. A second constant thus entered into his formula, and this constant established a relation between electricity at rest and electricity in motion. This constant was a velocity, and, if determinable, it revealed a constant of nature in

All changes of these states, and all phenomena dependent thereon, are therefore consequences of these interactions. But bodies exert such mutual actions when in contact as well as from a distance, and it was evident that a beginning had to be made with the latter in order to gain a clue for the investigation of the former; this being especially needful whenever the spatial relations of bodies escape observation, as is the case with bodies which are in contact. And so it has really happened, inasmuch as a beginning was made by examining the mutual action of cosmic bodies—*i.e.*, with the phenomena of gravitation. To this first field of research—*viz.*, the phenomena of gravitation—there was then added the investigation of electric and magnetic interactions, as next to gravitation these are the only actions which take place from one body to another at measurable distances,—these actions being themselves measurable. Now for a long time Newton's doctrine of gravitation furnished the leading idea for nearly all theories of electricity and magnetism, till a new clue was gained through Oersted's and Ampère's discoveries

the form of a velocity. It had for Weber a theoretical as well as a practical meaning, for it enabled him to effect a connection between the electro-magnetic and the electro-static or absolute system of measurements. When he succeeded in measuring this quantity, it was found that the figure for the constant, which meant a velocity, was practically the same as that for the velocity of the propagation of light. Weber himself does not seem to have attached any physical meaning to this coincidence : later he and Kirchhoff remarked that under certain conditions an electrical wave-motion might take place in an electrical conductor, and that the velocity of the propagation of this would coincide with that of light (see Kirchhoff in ' Annalen der Physik und Chemie,' 1857; and Weber, ' Electrodyn. Maasbest.,' 1864). It was reserved for Clerk Maxwell to point to the real physical interpretation of Weber's constant. Of this I shall speak in a later chapter (see Maxwell's memoir ' On Physical Lines of Force,' 1862, reprinted in ' Scientific Papers,' vol. i.)

regarding the equivalence of closed electrical currents with magnets.   This led, first, to the reduction of all magnetic effects to the action of electrical currents; and, secondly, to the enunciation of a fundamental law of the interaction of two elements of electricity in motion.   A third leading idea was that of reducing the interaction of all bodies to that of the mutual action of pairs of bodies.   This idea could in general be considered as well established and confirmed by experience on a large scale." [1]

This leads me to another and a final remark on the view of natural phenomena, first introduced by Newton's gravitation formula, which has been so successful in the calculation of all the movements of cosmic bodies, and which in the eyes of such a great authority as Laplace contained the clue to an explanation also of molar and molecular phenomena.[2]   This view calculates

39. Necessity of developing the infinitesimal methods.

[1] 'Electrodynamische Maasbestimmungen,' 1878, p. 645.

[2] Although Weber followed the lines so deeply impressed upon the whole of Continental thought by the labours of Laplace and his school, it does not seem that he held the same exalted opinion of the value of any mathematical formula as did Laplace. Though he looked upon his electro-dynamic law as well established by experiment and valuable in guiding further research, he was fully impressed with the fact that all such formulæ are merely provisional. Thus he says in the first part of his researches, written in the year 1846 : "It seems to follow that the immediate interaction of two electrical particles does not depend upon these alone, but also upon the presence of third bodies. . . . It is conceivable that the forces comprised in the discovered fundamental law may be partly the forces which two electrical particles exert indirectly on each other, and which therefore depend on the intervening medium. . . . The general law for the determination of the acting forces might perhaps be yet more simply expressed by taking the intervening medium into account, than has been possible without it in the fundamental law now established. The exploration of the intervening medium, which might afford an insight into many other matters, can alone give an answer to this question. . . . A hope now exists that it will be possible, in several new ways, to gain some information as to the neutral electric fluid which pervades everything.   Perhaps in

the actions of large masses and complicated systems of
bodies by a process of summation from the interaction of
units placed in the simplest relation—that of two and
two, pushing or pulling each other in a straight line.
Now, in consequence of the great distances at which we
are placed from the heavenly bodies, these appear to us
as mere points, and the observation of their movements,
their orbits, and their periods enabled astronomers like
Kepler, and mathematicians like Newton, to gain by mere
observation and subsequent calculation an idea of the
elementary rule which masses, considered to be concentrated in points, follow in their motion in a connected
system. The next step was to see how these elementary
actions would add up in cases where the dimensions of
the moving bodies were not vanishingly small in comparison with their distances. The infinitesimal methods,
invented in the age of Newton, and developed by him
and others into a special calculus, came to the aid of
mathematicians, and enabled them to calculate from
elementary data the motions and phenomena of extended
bodies and systems of bodies. These could afterwards
be actually measured, thereby confirming the elementary
formulæ and assumptions which had formed the basis of
those calculations. As already remarked, this process

other bodies, which are not conductors, there exist, not currents,
but only vibrations, which may in
future be observed by the methods
indicated above. Further, I need
only point to Faraday's recent discovery of the influence of electric
currents on the vibrations of light,
which makes it probable that the
all-prevading neutral electric medium itself constitutes the all-prevading ether which contains and pro-
pagates luminous vibrations, or at
least that the two are so intimately
connected that the observation of
luminous vibrations may afford some
information regarding the properties of the neutral electric medium."
He then refers to Ampère's own
suggestion in this direction. ('Electrodynamische Maasbestimmungen,'
Part I., p. 169.)

of confirmation occupied a long period, during which it became more and more satisfactory and complete. In fact, so great has the coincidence of calculation with observation turned out to be, in all problems of physical astronomy, that no astronomer at the end of this century doubts that the gravitation formula alone will suffice to explain all anomalies which still exist in great number in the movements of cosmic bodies—such, for instance, as the moon.

40.
The Newtonian formula
the basis of
physical
astronomy.

Moreover, in the whole wide range of physical and chemical, not to speak of other natural phenomena, there is probably no instance of a simple mathematical relation having been applied to so large a field of facts, found so trustworthy a guide, and been so unfailingly verified.

And yet the very extent of this field must not blind us to the fact that for the explanation of molecular [1]

---

[1] This is indeed not to be wondered at when we consider that in all molecular and molar phenomena such a variety of elements and forces come into play that it is impossible to isolate any special quantities as we do when from the cosmic point of view we lose sight of everything except mass, time, and distance—i.e., the elementary factors of our system of measurement. In the phenomena of electricity, for instance, it is merely by a process of mental abstraction, which has no counterpart in the observable phenomena, that we speak of electrical masses, be they one or two; of fluids; of elements of currents, which in nature cannot exist alone; of velocities of a something which as yet cannot be clearly defined. Any mathematical formula can under such conditions be merely tentative, and the preciseness of it must not hide from us the fact that it is based upon hypothetical relations and artificial definitions. This was, for the gain of scientific thought, very clearly brought out in the theoretical discussions which followed upon Helmholtz's critical examination of Weber's and kindred formulæ, and is well expressed by Carl Neumann: "Electrical matters"—if such there be—"never exists alone, but only in combination with ponderable matter." Any law like that of Weber can therefore be merely a "particular," not a "fundamental" or "universal" law, for it refers merely to a small portion of the properties, forces, and relations of electric and ponderable matter, leaving others—as, for instance, those between electricity and heat, electricity and light,

phenomena, or even for such processes as happen continually under our eyes and our hands, this universal law of gravitation has practically done nothing. The action of gravitation alone between masses which we can manipulate directly is so weak that it takes the very finest instruments to detect it at all, and at molecular distances it is so immeasurably small that it is hardly conceivable how it can explain the existence of those enormous forces with which we here have to deal.[1] If

&c.—more or less in the dark (see 'Mathematische Annalen,' vol. xi. p. 323). From a philosophical point of view these discussions, in which many other eminent leaders of scientific thought took part, are of great interest and importance, as they bear upon the value of mathematical formulæ in physical research, upon the definition of laws of nature, the extent of their applicability, the correct lines of future research, the use of analogies in the formation of physical theories, &c. I therefore refer here to the literature of the subject: Tait, 'Sketch of Thermodynamics' (1868, pp. 57, 76); Thomson and Tait, 'Natural Philosophy' (1st ed., p. 311); Carl Neumann, 'Die Principien der Electrodynamik' (Tübingen, 1868); Helmholtz in various memoirs from 1872 onwards, all collected in 'Wissenschaftliche Abhandlungen' (vol. i. pp. 545, 636, 774, &c.) and in 'Vorträge und Reden' (vol. ii. Faraday Lecture); Carl Neumann, 'Mathematische Annalen' (vol. xi. p. 318). See also Riecke on 'Wilhelm Weber' (Göttingen, 1892), and Clerk Maxwell, 'Electricity and Magnetism,' (vol. ii. last chapter); 'Elementary Treatise on Electricity' (p. 51).

[1] An interesting speculation as to whether the Newtonian formula of gravitation is capable of explaining cohesion and capillary attraction will be found in Thomson's (Lord Kelvin's) paper to the Royal Society of Edinburgh (1862), and in his lecture before the Royal Institution (1866), on Capillary Attraction, both reprinted in the first volume of 'Popular Lectures and Addresses.' He there shows that if we combine Newton's law with the assumption of an ultimate heterogeneousness of matter,—as is demanded in the so-called atomic theory used in chemistry,—the mass of ultimate portions of matter at vanishing distances, or what is called in contact, may give rise to molecular forces of attraction of any magnitude; since the Newtonian attraction depends on two data—the distance and the density (or mass) of attracting particles. He concludes by saying that "it is satisfactory to find that, so far as cohesion is concerned, no other force than that of gravitation need be assumed" (p. 63). It does not seem that this view, which was also held by Sir John Herschel, is generally adopted by physicists (see Todhunter and Pearson, 'History of the Theory of Elasticity,' vol. i. p. 418, &c.; vol. ii. art. 1650). Another interesting speculation arose out of the discussion over Weber's law. One of the objections started by Helmholtz against Weber's law was that, under certain conditions,

for the purpose of discovering the forces which exist in the universe between cosmic bodies we had been confined to experiments in the laboratory, as we are in all other departments of physics and chemistry, it is very doubtful whether this universal law of gravitation would ever have been discovered. And yet it stands there as almost the only formula universally applicable to all matter throughout the visible and tangible universe.

41.
The Newtonian formula
unique as to
universality
and accuracy.

In the foregoing pages I have sometimes spoken of this great discovery of Newton, on which is based the astronomical view of nature, as a formula, sometimes as a law. A formula is merely the expression in definite terms of certain relations of measurable quantities. By a law we are apt to understand something more—*viz.*, the statement of some fundamental, all-pervading property of the things of nature, which, so far as we are concerned, is final.[1] Whether the human mind is at all

---

this expression would give an infinite value for the force between electrical particles in motion. Weber replied that the same argument could be used against the gravitation formula, and hinted at the possibility that a correction might have to be added to the Newtonian formula to make it applicable to molecular distances ('Electrodyn. Maasb.,' 1871, p. 60). This idea was taken up by several Continental mathematicians (see Isenkrahe, 'Das Räthsel von der Schwerkraft,' p. 33, &c.; Paul du Bois-Reymond, 'Ueber die Grundlagen der Erkenntniss,' p. 50; Tisserand, 'Comptes Rendus,'September 1872).

[1] Helmholtz says, referring to Weber's so-called law: "If we are to consider Weber's law as an elementary law, as an expression of the ultimate cause of the phenomena to which it refers, and not merely as an approximately correct expression of facts within narrow limits, then we must demand that, if applied to objects of the largest imaginable dimensions, it should give results which are physically possible" (1873, 'Wissenschaftliche Abhandlungen,' vol. i. p. 658). This sentence raises a philosophical question as to the demands which we can legitimately expect to be satisfied by any so-called law of nature expressible in the symbols of human thought, be these words or algebraic signs. I venture to think that nowadays, and largely in consequence of discussions similar to those carried on over Weber's law, physicists do not any longer expect to find laws of that general and fundamental character which the words given above describe.

capable of finding out the ultimate properties of things, is a question which has been answered in opposite ways. But whatever the answer may be to this philosophical question, the further and more modest question can be raised, Does the gravitation formula express one of those universal facts which we have to accept as final, beyond or behind which we cannot penetrate? Opposite answers have been given to this question. But it stands very much in the same position in which Laplace left it when he said:[1] "The extreme difficulty of the problem referring to the system of the universe obliges us to have recourse to approximations, which leave room for the fear that the neglected quantities may have a sensible influence on the results. As soon as mathematicians by observation became aware of this influence they returned to their analysis: by rectifying the same they have always found the cause of the observed anomalies; they have determined the laws of these, and frequently they have outrun observation by discovering irregularities which had not yet been observed. The lunar theory, the theory of Saturn, of Jupiter and his satellites, offer many examples of this kind.[2] Thus we may say that nature herself has helped in perfecting the astronomical theories founded upon the

42. Is the Newtonian formula an ultimate law?

43. Laplace's opinion.

---

[1] Exposition du Système du Monde,' 6th ed., p. 318.

[2] Tisserand, in discussing the difficulties which still beset the lunar theory, and after referring to the "prix Damoiseau" offered by the Academy of Sciences for an essay on this subject, says ('Bulletin astronomique,' 1891, vol. viii. p. 501): "La théorie de la lune se trouve arrêtée par la difficulté que nous venons de développer; déjà à l'époque de Clairaut la gravitation universelle paraissait impuissante à expliquer le mouvement du périgée; elle triomphera encore du nouvel obstacle qui se présente aujourd'hui, mais il reste à faire une belle découverte."

principle of universal gravitation. This is, in my opinion, one of the greatest proofs of the truth of this admirable principle. As to this principle, is it a primordial law of nature? Is it only a general effect of an unknown cause? Here the ignorance in which we are as to the ultimate properties of matter stops us, and removes all hope that we shall ever be able to answer these questions in a satisfactory manner."

In the meantime, as I have tried to show, the clue afforded by this principle has led physicists by strict analysis, by observation, by cleverly arranged experiments as well as by guesses drawn from analogy, to the discovery of many unknown phenomena, to the fixing in mathematical language of interesting relations, and in general to a large extension of the field of natural knowledge. No wonder that a principle which has done, and is still doing, such valuable service in physical astronomy should have done much to establish the astronomical view of nature.[1] As one of the latest representatives of physical science abroad has said, " The present generation

---

[1] This view was concisely put by Poisson at a time when the corpuscular theory of the imponderables —light, heat, and electricity—still reigned supreme in the Continental school: "Toutes les parties de la matière sont soumises à deux sortes d'actions mutuelles. L'une est attractive, indépendante de la nature des corps, proportionnelle du produit des masses, et en raison inverse du carré des distances : elle s'étend indéfiniment dans l'espace, et produit la pesanteur universelle et tous les phénomènes d'équilibre et du mouvement qui sont du ressort de la mécanique céleste. L'autre est attractive et répulsive ; elle dépend de la nature des particules et de leur quantité de chaleur ; son intensité décroit très rapidement quand la distance augmente, et devient insensible, dès que la distance a acquis une grandeur sensible " ('Journal de l'École polytechnique,' cahier xx, p. 4, 1831). See also Clerk Maxwell, 'On the Equilibrium of Elastic Solids' (1850, reprinted in 'Scientific Papers,' vol. i. p. 30), where a similar assumption is stated as the basis of the mathematical theories of Navier, Poisson, Lamé, and Clapeyron.

is still more or less accustomed to think in the manner of
Newton's view of nature, in which the supposition of
forces acting at a distance appears as the most simple
view: we feel it difficult to step out of this circle of
ideas."[1]   Nevertheless, the country itself which produced

[1] Kundt, 'Die neuere Entwicklung der Electricitätslehre' (Berlin,
1891, p. 35). This habit is probably more marked on the Continent
than in England. In this country
the later developments of Laplace's
astronomical view of nature have
remained unknown except to a few
scientific specialists. Through Faraday's influence, and in consequence
of the backwardness which the
English school of science exhibited
early in the century in assimilating
Continental ideas (see p. 232, note),
theoretical views on electricity as
well as on other forms of energy
were formed and taught more in
conformity with experimental observation. I am not aware that
Weber's theory was expounded in
any English text-book or handbook
before Maxwell referred to it as the
view to which Faraday and he himself were opposed. In fact, the
astronomical view of molecular
physics is almost entirely of foreign
growth. In England "action at a
distance" is now stigmatised as a
pernicious heresy (Tait, 'Properties
of Matter,' 2nd ed., 1890, Introduction) or as unthinkable (O. Lodge,
'Modern Views of Electricity,'
1892, p. 386, &c.) Abroad weighty
authorities have pronounced against
the astronomical view of nature as
final or even helpful in the present
stage of physical and chemical
science. Helmholtz, who was
trained in it, gradually emancipated himself, probably under the
influence of physiological studies ;
so did Kirchhoff, who in his lectures
on Electricity (edited by Planck,
1891) hardly mentions Weber's law,

though he had previously, in 1857,
based an elaborate and valuable
investigation upon it ('Ueber die
Bewegung der Electricität in Dräh-
ten,' 'Gesammelte Abhandlungen,'
p. 131, &c.) Still more marked is
the aversion to the attitude or
habit of thought which belongs to
the astronomical view of nature on
the part of those who approached
physical problems from the side of
chemistry. Hittorf (quoted by
Lehmann, 'Molecularphysik,' vol. ii.
p. 456) explains the opposition of
Berzelius to Faraday's electrolytic
law and to his other results from
the fact that they stood in direct
opposition to that view "which at
the end of the last century had
been introduced into chemistry
through the success of Newton's
law in astronomy, and under the
influence of Laplace on Lavoisier
and Berthollet," and sees the importance of his own laborious
researches in the demonstration
"that the mysterious potential
energy cannot in the case of un-
combined chemical substances be
explained by the work of attractive
forces," and "that a confession of
ignorance in such matters is more
conducive to progress than the assertion that every process in nature
is essentially a phenomenon of attraction in the Newtonian sense."
Of Ostwald's endeavours to liberate
theoretical views in chemistry from
the tyranny of the older hypotheses
I shall have frequent occasion to
speak. His discourse 'Die Energie
und ihre Wandlungen' (Leipzig,
1888) contains an expression of
opinion similar to those quoted here.

the author of this the astronomical view of nature has
also been the birthplace of a different manner of regarding physical phenomena.   It will be the object of a future
chapter to trace the origin and growth of what I propose
to call the physical view of nature.   We shall then learn
how the germs of this different view can be traced even
in the writings of Newton.   But before I take up this
subject I must deal with another and independent way
of regarding nature which very largely supplemented the
astronomical view.   If the Newtonian gravitation formula
is the basis and principle of physical astronomy—of our
knowledge of cosmic phenomena—the view I am now
going to explain has been equally useful in building up
another most important science of modern times—the
science of chemistry.

44.
Opposition
to the astro-
nomical
view of
nature.

CHAPTER V.

THE ATOMIC VIEW OF NATURE.

1.
Recapitula-
tion.

IN the last chapter I have shown how, under the influence of the Newtonian philosophy, the ancient but indefinite ideas of Attraction and Repulsion acquired a definite meaning, and how—at least so far as cosmical phenomena are concerned—the Newtonian Gravitation formula was made the foundation of very successful explanations [1]

[1] I use the word explanation in conformity with the popularly accepted meaning of the term. It is, however, well to remark here that, in the course of our century and greatly owing to the influence of the exact scientific spirit, a change is being gradually introduced into language, which will assist in conveying more correct views as to the objects of science. In England the metaphysical interest has been so long banished from scientific literature, the part also which experiment and observation have played has been so great, that misunderstandings as to the real objects of science have been less frequent than abroad, especially in Germany, where the metaphysical or philosophical interest still largely pervades scientific literature, though metaphysics themselves may be on the decline. There the definition of the science of mechanics (now more usually termed dynamics in this country), given by Kirchhoff in his 'Vorlesungen über mathematische Physik' (vol. i. p. 1), has marked quite an epoch in the philosophy of the exact sciences. This definition is as follows : " Mechanics is the science of motion ; we can assign as its object : to describe completely and in the simplest manner the motions which occur in nature." Inasmuch as a large school of natural philosophers consider that it is the object of all exact sciences to give a mechanical explanation of natural phenomena, it would follow that the object of all science is to reduce the phenomena of nature to forms of motion, and to describe these completely and in the simplest manner. We may feel some reluctance in assenting at once to this definition. Still an analysis of

of nature. Towards the end of the last century, and all through the present one, this view of things natural, which I have called the Astronomical view, has exerted a great fascination over scientific minds: especially in the mathematical schools of France and the Continent it has been a leading idea in scientific thought. It has been extended into molar and molecular physics, and has in these led to some very extraordinary and ingenious theories. In England, this astronomical view of Nature has, in the course of the present century, been received

what has been done since Newton in real science will probably convince us that the definition is safe and sufficient. It means the analysis of phenomena as to their appearance in space and their sequence in time. Both can, in consequence of the small number of elementary relations on which arithmetic, geometry, and dynamics are built up, be reduced to —or described in—a small number of elementary terms or conceptions, the alphabet of all science. To show how in every instance the terms of this alphabet are to be put together, in order to correspond to any phenomenon, is all the explanation we can give. Objections have been raised to Kirchhoff's definition by Du Bois-Reymond ("Göthe und kein Ende," in 'Reden,' vol. i. p. 434), inasmuch as it does not define the difference between the descriptive (historical) and the exact (mathematical) sciences of nature; but the difference is really maintained if we demand a complete description. Natural history only affords an incomplete description. The only complete description is that afforded by a mathematical formula in which the constants are supplied by observation. This permits us to calculate those features or phases of phenomena which are hidden from our observation in space or in time. An objection to the view which identifies physics with mechanics, seems implied in Mach's remarks contained in the last chapter of his very thoughtful book 'Die Mechanik in ihrer Entwickelung' (Leipzig, 1889). According to his view, the aim of exact science is not necessarily to give mechanical explanations or descriptions of phenomena, inasmuch as temperature, electric potential, &c., are just as simple elements of natural phenomena as mass and motion. It seems, nevertheless, that exact measurements are only possible in the data of time and space. Assuming that a complete and simple description—admitting of calculation—is the aim of all exact science, it is evident how much and how little we may expect from science. We shall not expect to find the ultimate and final causes, and science will not teach us to understand nature and life. The search after ultimate causes may perhaps be given up as hopeless; that after the meaning and significance of the things of life will never be abandoned: it is the philosophical or religious problem.

with less favour, although it was entirely owing to
Newton's gravitation formula that it ever obtained its
great influence, the labour of Continental men of science
being very largely spent in two directions: first, in drawing the purely mathematical consequences of Newton's
formula—in this they have met with increasing success,
unparalleled by that in any other domain of science;
and secondly, in extending the principle of Newton, by
experiment and analogy, into other departments.   In some
of these, very remarkable results have been achieved; but
nevertheless at the end of the century no extension or
analogue of the Newtonian gravitation formula has been
generally accepted, and it still stands there as almost
the only firmly established mathematical relation, expressive of a property of all matter, to which the progress of more than two centuries has added nothing,
from which it has taken nothing away.   The value,
however, of all those partial attempts in another direction has been enormous; for with the aim of applying,
extending, or modifying a rigorous mathematical formula, those philosophers have carried out a series of
the most exact observations and measurements of physical quantities, very greatly extended our knowledge of
natural phenomena and their mutual relations, and
founded that general system of physical measurement
which is now universally adopted.   The names of Gauss
and Weber stand out prominently as leaders in this
work.   I shall have to come back to this point later
on, after I have shown that other views of nature
besides the astronomical have also led up to it, and
placed it in similar prominence.

About a century after the publication of the 'Principia,' which, by propounding the gravitation formula, raised the ancient and indefinite notion of Attraction to the rank of a useful and rigorously defined expression, another favourite theory of the ancient philosophers [1] was similarly elevated to the rank of a leading and useful scientific idea.

Although no mathematical relation equal in value and definiteness to the gravitation formula marks the introduction of the Atomic theory in Chemistry, it nevertheless owes its success to similar qualities—*viz.*, to the fact that it led natural philosophers to make definite measurements, and put exact research in the place of vague reasoning.

2. Atomic theory.

The atomic theory, usually associated with the name of Dalton, is, however, not nearly as much the historic property of that great man as gravitation is that of Newton, for whereas the latter gave the fullest generalisation that can so far be safely made, the atomic

---

[1] Ancient philosophers have furnished us with three distinct abstractions which have survived, and which, put into definite mathematical language, have led exact research in physics and chemistry in modern times — the theory of Attraction and Repulsion, the Atomic Theory, and the Kinetic Theory, or the notion that everything is motion. Of these three theories the second was most developed in antiquity ; Lucretius's great poem on the nature of things being really a treatise on the subject, in which the atomic view is placed in the centre, the two other ideas being likewise largely utilised. The historians of ancient philosophy trace these abstract or leading ideas back to the earlier Greek thinkers. Thus Heraclitus of Ephesus is credited with having first taught that everything is in motion. Empedocles of Agrigentum made use of the notions of Attraction and Repulsion, poetically represented as Love and Hatred, to explain the action of his elements ; and Democritus of Abdera is universally considered to be the true founder of the atomistic theory, which was adopted and developed in the School of Epicurus, and very fully explained by the Roman poet. A very good analysis will be found in Lange's 'History of Materialism' (English translation by Thomas, 3 vols.), in which also the historical connection with modern thought, especially through Bacon, Gassendi, and Hobbes, is clearly brought out.

theory has been gradually defined and variously modified in the course of this century, and is still in a somewhat unstable condition.   We are also bound to attach
the greatest importance to the preliminary step taken
by Lavoisier, who is even more justly called the father
of modern chemistry than Kepler is called the father
of modern astronomy.

3.
Lavoisier.

The exact claims of Lavoisier to this important place in
the history of chemistry have been variously stated:[1]

[1] Continental writers are pretty
unanimous in dating modern chemistry from the time of Lavoisier
(1743-1794).   In this country there
has been less unanimity, the names
of Black, of Cavendish, of Priestley,
even of Robert Boyle, having occasionally been put forward.   The
fact that Lavoisier did not sufficiently acknowledge his indebtedness to some of his English contemporaries has given occasion in
some quarters to depreciation of his
merits.   It cannot be upheld that
he was the first formally to express
the doctrine of the indestructibility
or conservation of matter, as this
idea underlay many experimental
researches before his time; nor
that he was the first to refer to
the balance as the ultimate test
of chemical facts.   The assertion
that he first introduced the idea
of two different kinds of matter,
ponderable and imponderable, is
also questionable, and still more
so his claim to having discovered
oxygen, the composition of water
and of atmospheric air, the combus-
tibility of the diamond, and other
special facts.   His fame rests upon
a much broader basis, and has
been most clearly investigated and
settled by Hermann Kopp in his
'Entwickelung der Chemie in der
neueren Zeit' (München, 1873).

In this excellent work the author
somewhat modifies the view he
took in his earlier 'Geschichte der
Chemie' (Braunschweig, 1843, especially vol. i. p. 274, &c.), and sums
up Lavoisier's merit in the following words (p. 145): "His contemporaries could dispose of the same
inherited and much new material,
but not one of them understood
how to build up out of this material
and his own independent researches
a chemical system, the reception of
which should form the starting-
point for all future improvement
of this science.   Lavoisier has the
whole merit of having achieved
this.   He added to his own recognition of the correct views the work
of procuring recognition for them
from others.   He imparted his own
matured views to those who represented chemistry at the end of the
last century. . . . We must measure
his greatness not merely by his
own insight but also by the resistance which he had to overcome
in other chemists who clung to
the older theory.   These achievements are great enough not to require the exaggeration with which
they have occasionally been announced, and not to be touched by
attempts on the other side to minimise them."

there is however no difference of opinion on this point,
that since his time, and greatly through his labours, the
quantitative method has been established as the ultimate
test of chemical facts ; the principle of this method being
the rule that in all changes of combination and reaction,
the total weight of the various ingredients—be they elementary bodies or compounds—remains unchanged. The
science of chemistry was thus established upon an exact,
a mathematical basis. By means of this method Lavoisier,
utilising and analysing the results gained by himself and
others before him, notably those of Priestley, Cavendish,
and Black, succeeded in destroying the older theory of
combustion, the so-called phlogistic theory.[1] From a

[1] This result was announced in
1777 to the Paris Academy, and
the demonstration completed in a
memoir of 1783. "He closes this
latter memoir with the expression,
that his object had been to bring
forward new proofs of his theory
of combustion of 1777, and to
prove that Stahl's phlogiston was
something purely imaginary,—that
without it facts could be more
easily and more simply explained
than with it ; he did not expect
that his views would be at once
accepted, . . . time would have
to confirm or to reject the opinions
he had developed, but already he
recognised with satisfaction that un-
prejudiced students of the science,
unbiassed mathematicians and physicists, believed no longer in phlogiston as Stahl viewed it, and that
they considered the whole doctrine
more as a hindrance than as a helpful scaffolding in erecting the edifice
of science " (Kopp, 'Entwickelung,'
p. 202). This and the further remark of Kopp that it was the
mathematicians who took up Lavoisier's views (see *supra*, p. 115,

note 2) are significant signs of the
introduction of the mathematical,
the measuring, spirit into chemistry.
Few ideas which once exerted so
great and lasting an influence on
science as that of phlogiston, have
so entirely disappeared from our
text-books, and it is interesting to
note that those whose researches
were guided by it were not so far
from grasping a valuable truth
as has been supposed. This theory,
elaborated by Stahl, a contemporary of Newton and Leibniz
(1660-1734), was the first attempt
to co-ordinate a great mass of observations, to bring the phenomena
of chemical change under one common principle. Phlogiston was
the thing the migration of which
gave rise to chemical change, and
as the most obvious changes were
exhibited in the processes of combustion, " Phlogiston " or " Brenn-
stoff" was the name which suggested itself as most suitable for
this principle. Chemical changes
were not to be measured so much
by the resulting change of weight
as by the readiness with which

scientific point of view, the principal defect in this theory was, that its explanations could not be subjected to any strict and exact numerical verification. Whenever an element enters into our operations which has either no weight or a negative weight, and thus evades exact determination and control, explanations and observations become vague and uncertain.

In the time of Lavoisier, and pre-eminently through his exertions, this vague and unmeasurable principle phlogiston was eliminated from the laboratory and the textbooks : quantities took the place of indefinable qualities, and numerical determinations increased in frequency and accuracy. The vague phlogistic theory, which contained a germ of truth, but one which at that time could not be put into definite terms, had helped to gather up many valuable facts and observations : these were collected and restated in a new and precise language. It has been said that every science must pass through three periods of development. The first is that of presentiment, or of faith ; the second is that of sophistry ; and the third is that of sober research. Liebig states the case somewhat

4.
Phlogistic
theory.

substances enter into chemical reaction ; and the mobility or inertness of chemical substances was to be measured by the presence or absence of a definite something. A hundred and fifty years after Stahl, science had so far advanced, that besides the change of weight or mass, the change of the power of entering into chemical combination could also be measured, and the term "potential energy" was introduced to describe many of those properties and processes which Stahl had fastened upon, when he, as the pioneer, undertook to co-ordinate chemical phenomena. If Stahl considered phlogiston to be a substance, though he did not inquire into its mass or ponderable property, the question might be put again, whether "energy" is not to be considered after all as a substance. Cf. Tait, 'Properties of Matter' (2nd ed., introduction, especially p. 5 *sqq.*) ; 'Recent Advances of Science,' introduction ; also Clerk Maxwell, 'Electricity and Magnetism' (last chapter) ; Ostwald, 'Chemische Energie' (Leipzig, 1893, p. 41).

more correctly when he says: "To investigate the essence of a natural phenomenon, three conditions are necessary: We must first study and know the phenomenon itself, from all sides; we must then determine in what relation it stands to other natural phenomena; and lastly, when we have ascertained all these relations, we have to solve the problem of measuring these relations and the laws of mutual dependence—that is, of expressing them in numbers. In the first period of chemistry, all the powers of men's minds were devoted to acquiring a knowledge of the properties of bodies; it was necessary to discover, observe, and ascertain their peculiarities. This is the alchemistical period. The second period embraces the determination of the mutual relations or connections of these properties; this is the period of phlogistic chemistry. In the third period, in which we now are, we ascertain by weight and measure and express in numbers the degree in which the properties of bodies are mutually dependent. The inductive sciences begin with the substance itself, then come just ideas, and lastly, mathematics are called in, and, with the aid of numbers, complete the work." [1]

As Galileo, Huygens, and Newton, by a series of brilliant investigations and theories, such as those of the pendulum, the fall of bodies, finally of universal gravitation, established the usefulness of the mathematical treatment of physical phenomena, so Lavoisier and his school proved the correctness and usefulness of their views by the new theory of combustion, as consisting in the combination of a special body or element called oxygen with other bodies

5.
Theory of
combustion

---

[1] 'Familiar Letters on Chemistry,' translated by Blyth, 4th ed., London, 1859, p. 60.

or elements. A very large field of research—all on the
lines pointed out by the new school—was opened out. But
the age for a further application of mathematical reasoning came much more slowly in chemistry than in physical
science.

The latter had at least one great department, in which
a small number of factors, all admitting of mathematical
accuracy—those of distance, mass, and motion—sufficed
to explain the phenomena, at least if viewed from a great
distance. This science is the physics of the heavens, the
science of cosmic phenomena. On this earth—in physical
and still more in chemical phenomena—the matter stood
very differently. Here we have not to deal with a few
measurable quantities only. A large number of elements
or factors, of which only very few can be accurately
measured, combine to make up what we called in the last
chapter molar and molecular phenomena. In the study
of inanimate nature, astronomy—the mechanics of the
heavens—deals with the simplest relations ; chemistry—
the science of the changes which bodies undergo when
being combined or separated—deals with the most complicated side of reality. Physics occupy an intermediate
position, and thus we can also trace in the history of
physical research the twofold influence of the astronomical
method of inquiry on one side, and the chemical on the
other.

But the general rule, that in chemical changes the
weight of all the constituents put together never changes,
was not the only numerical relation which came to the
aid of students of nature, when they, at the end of the last
century, betook themselves to exact measurements and

determinations.   That rule is indeed the foundation of all work in the laboratory, the principle which decides the degree of accuracy attained in every analysis, and which not infrequently is the only method of determining the presence of some undiscovered constituent.[1]   Not long

[1] The revolution in chemistry at the end of the last century manifests itself in nothing more than in the various distinct problems, corresponding to different courses of scientific thought and different interests, which have guided chemical research since that time.   The first definite object was the search after the real elements, the attempt to decompose the existing substances of nature into their ultimate constituents.   This interesting occupation somewhat pushed into the background the theoretical investigations regarding the forms of the combinations of the various elements into compounds, still more the study of chemical affinity.   A second definite object was the development of the theory of combustion which Lavoisier propounded, and the confirmation or refutation of the idea according to which oxygen occupied almost as important a position in chemical reactions as phlogiston had done before.   A third definite object was the development of analytical chemistry, the systematic and methodical use of the balance.   So far as the first branch of this pursuit was concerned, Lavoisier's catalogue of the elements was still very incomplete ; it contained thirty-three members, including light and heat, and twenty-three of the substances which now figure in the list of the seventy elements enumerated in the text-books ; the alkalies and earths were still considered to be simple bodies.   A great addition to our knowledge in this department came

through Davy's decomposition of soda and potash.   And after his proof of the elementary nature of chlorine the oxygen theory of Lavoisier had also to be greatly modified.   "Through a series of most important investigations, he rose in the beginning of this century to such eminence, that he was then considered to be the first representative of chemical science.   With great experimental ability he combined a singular freedom from all the theoretical doctrines which were recognised in his age" (Kopp, 'Entwickelung der Chemie,' p. 451).   In this he resembled Dalton and Faraday and other natural philosophers in this country, on whom theoretical notions formed in the Continental schools had little or no influence.   Qualitative analysis was less indebted to Lavoisier than other branches of the science were.   In fact, it was more at home in Sweden and Germany, where the interests of mineralogy and metallurgy promoted it.   Bergmann and Scheele in Sweden, Klaproth in Berlin, were the forerunners of Berzelius and of the Berlin school of analysts.   In this country Black and especially Cavendish had carried out some important quantitative determinations, the accuracy of which seems very far behind modern standards (see Kopp, 'Geschichte der Chemie,' vol. ii. p. 70, &c., 1844).   It was the introduction of the notion of chemical equivalence, a term used already by Cavendish, which furnished the ultimate test for accuracy and revolutionised quantitative analysis.

6.
Rule of fixed
proportions.

before the age of Lavoisier, another general conception had been introduced into chemical research; this was the rule of definite proportions—*i.e.*, the fact that substances, whether simple or compound, combine only in definite proportions of their weight, and that the numbers marking these proportions are characteristic of every definite chemical substance. It took some time, nearly a century, before this idea, which arose through the examination of neutral salts and the determination of the quantities of acids and alkalies which were wanted to effect mutual saturation, became clear; before the rule of definite proportions was generally established, becoming a guide for chemical analysis. It is interesting to note how the vaguer terms of chemical affinity and elective attraction, of chemical action, of adhesion and elasticity—mostly borrowed from other departments of science where they had definite meanings—gradually disappeared, when by the aid of the chemical balance each simple substance and each definite compound began to be characterised, and labelled with a fixed number. Nevertheless, even at the beginning of this century, eminent chemists were still so much engaged in discussing the rival claims of the old phlogistic, and the modern theory of combustion, of Berthollet's chemical equilibrium, of the so-called dynamical and the electro-chemical views of phenomena, that the first methodical attempt actually to fix these numbers—*i.e.*, to give a table of chemical equivalents—remained unnoticed.[1]

[1] The history of chemistry early in this century furnishes a good example of the sway which theoretical views exercised over the minds of investigators. Berthollet, who began by critically examining Bergmann's doctrine of chemical affinities, was evidently much influenced by the mathematical theory of attraction, and by the mechanical laws of equilibrium, which formed so prominent a subject of investigation in the

The merit of having made this attempt belongs to one who approached chemistry entirely from the mathematical side, who wrote the first chemical book with a title pointing directly to measurements, but who perhaps spoilt his work by giving way to the fascination which regular numerical and geometrical arrangements have again and again exercised over philosophical inquirers. Jeremias Benjamin Richter—a name possessed of no popular celebrity—published in 1792 to 1794, in three parts, his " Stœchiometry, or the art of measuring chemical elements." [1] From his data, Fischer calculated in 1802 the

7.
J. Benjamin
Richter.

writings of Laplace and his school. Chemical affinity was to be co-ordinated with what he called astronomical attraction ; both were to be ultimately the same physical property ; they acted differently, because in the case of gravitation the dimensions were so large, that the form, distances, and peculiar properties of the molecules had no influence. It was an attempt to introduce the astronomical view of matter into molecular physics, and to base chemistry upon this view. Berthollet adhered to the corpuscular theory of heat against Rumford, who had just propounded his opinion that heat is not a constituent part of bodies ; and he maintained that chemical affinity was a function of the mass of bodies as was astronomical attraction. The germ of truth in Berthollet's views, which were approved by Laplace, but cast into oblivion under the influence of Proust and Richter's theory of fixed proportions, has in recent times been shown by Lothar Meyer ('Modern Theories of Chemistry,' Introduction), and by Ostwald ('Allgemeine Chemie,' vol. ii. p. 557, 1st ed., also 'Die Energie und ihre Wandlungen,' Leipzig,

1888, p. 20). If the astronomical view of molecular phenomena prevented Berthollet from accepting Proust's doctrine of fixed proportions and definite combinations, Richter injured his own reputation by adhering to the nomenclature of the phlogiston theory after it had been discarded by French chemists, and in Germany after Klaproth's determinations in 1792. The oxygen theory of combustion of Lavoisier got such a firm hold on the minds of Continental chemists that the labours of those who, like Cavendish in England and Richter in Germany, put forward important discoveries in the language and on the principles of the older theory, were temporarily forgotten. See Kopp, 'Entwickelung der Chemie,' p. 271, &c.

[1] Stœchiometry comes from the Greek τὰ στοιχεῖα, the constituent parts, and μετρεῖν, to measure. All Richter's works are connected with the application of mathematics to chemistry ; his inaugural dissertation, which appeared in 1789, bearing the title 'de usu matheseos in chymia' (Kopp, 'Geschichte der Chemie,' vol. ii. p. 350). "Richter était préoccupé de l'idée d'appliquer les mathématiques à la chimie, et en

first table of chemical equivalents, taking sulphuric acid as the standard with the figure 1000.

The conviction that chemical substances combine according to fixed and simple proportions gained ground on the Continent, chiefly during the discussion in which Proust finally disproved and defeated Berthollet's theory of chemical affinity; but it is to Dalton that the doctrine of fixed and multiple proportions is indebted for a consistent exposition. Dalton based it upon a mental representation which ever since has been the soul of all chemical reasoning.

When Newton, from the measurable data of the movements of cosmic bodies, deduced the celebrated gravitation formula, he had to descend to molar—nay, even to molecular—dimensions, and to express it as a relation referring to the very elements of matter, before he could apply it in a useful manner: he had to express it as a formula which had reference to the smallest portions of matter. In the same way, the measurements made by

8.
Dalton.

particulier de découvrir des relations numériques entre les quantités des corps qui se combinent. Ses efforts, dans cette direction, n'ont pas été également heureux ; car, s'il a reconnu et énoncé le premier la loi de proportionnalité entre les quantités de bases qui s'unissent au même poids d'acide et entre les quantités d'acides qui s'unissent au même poids de base, fait important et exact, il a cherché à démontrer, d'un autre côté, que ces quantités formaient des séries numériques dont les termes augmentent suivant des relations simples, ce qui est erroné. . . . Ces erreurs n'ont pas échappé, sans doute, à l'attention des contemporains de Richter et ont contribué à discréditer ses travaux.

. . . Mais nous n'avons pas à insister sur ce dernier point. Relevons, dans l'œuvre de Richter, les idées justes et les découvertes fondamentales qui recommandent d'autant plus son nom à l'attention reconnaissante de la postérité qu'il est demeuré méconnu et presque ignoré de son temps " (Wurtz, 'La Théorie atomique," 7me ed., 1893, p. 9, &c.) "L'opposition même, qu'il professait pour les doctrines du réformateur [Lavoisier] semble avoir contribué à discréditer les travaux de Richter : son heure n'était pas venue ; l'intérêt était ailleurs, et en Allemagne, comme en France et en Angleterre, les esprits étaient entraînés par le courant des idées nouvelles " (ibid., p. 13).

many chemists previous to Dalton had to be interpreted as referring not only to such quantities as the balance could determine, but to the very smallest immeasurable particles of which chemical substances consist. For this purpose Dalton adopted what was known as the atomic view of matter. The conception of matter as made up of independent particles, which for our means and methods prove not only indestructible but likewise indivisible, was revived as the ancient theory of attraction had been. Combined with the Newtonian view that weight is a universal property of all matter, it made the two fundamental rules of chemical action intelligible: the two facts—*first*, that the total weight of substances remains always the same, be they combined in ever so many different ways; and *secondly*, that all substances, be they in large or in small quantities, combine with each other, or separate from each other, in definite and fixed proportions. This view could not be consistently maintained, except it was referred to the smallest particles into which matter is practically divisible: the figures expressing the combining numbers were viewed by Dalton as representing the relative weights of the actual atoms or elements of matter. That the ultimate particles of matter have definite weights is the reason why substances combine in fixed proportions, and why the combining weight of the compound is the sum of the combining weights of the constituents.

As the gravitation formula had given rise to a surprising activity in physical astronomy, to a long series of exact measurements, and to theoretical deductions of a purely mathematical kind, so the atomic theory of Dalton in the early years of the century fixed the task of chemists for a long time ahead.

To begin with, an enormous amount of work had to be done in determining the actual proportions in which elementary substances combine. A very large share of this work belongs to Berzelius, who by a great number of very accurate determinations confirmed inductively the correctness of Dalton's theory. And even more important than the conformation of the theory was the great harvest of actual knowledge of the things and processes of nature which was collaterally gathered, whilst chemists were trying to prove or to refute existing opinions.

Indeed, whilst the atomic theory of Dalton was the first step towards a systematic and comprehensive study of chemical phenomena—*i.e.*, of the qualitative varieties under which matter presents itself to us on the surface of this globe—the extension which was gained in the domain of actual facts was much greater than the simplification which the theory had attempted to give. The number of elements or simple bodies, which in Lavoisier's time hardly exceeded thirty, increased before the year 1830 to more than double : the number of new compounds, unknown before, has probably never been counted. Compared with this growth of actual knowledge of facts, the development of the theory was slow and uncertain. The view of nature from the atomic point of view marks indeed a great contrast to that from the astronomical point of view. We now live about as long after the reform of chemistry through Lavoisier and Dalton as Laplace lived after the reform of physical astronomy through Newton. But who could compare the state of chemistry at the present day with that of astronomy in the age of Laplace? There, every step had tended to show that the one Newtonian formula sufficed to comprehend all cosmic phenomena; here, the simplification introduced by Dalton has had to give way to a series of modifications which have rendered the atomic theory one of the most complicated machineries ever introduced into science. Let us review in brief the fate of Dalton's hypothesis during the century which followed. Quite in the early years of the atomic theory, Wollaston prophetically foretold that if once an accurate knowledge were gained of the relative weights of elementary atoms, philosophers would not rest satisfied with the determination of mere numbers, but would have to gain a geometrical conception of how the elementary particles were placed in space. Van't Hoff's ' La Chimie dans l'Espace '—published at Rotterdam in 1875—was the first practical realisation of this prophecy. Many stages had to be gone through before this latest phase of the atomic view was attained. Had it been the case that every elementary substance combines with any other substance only in one fixed numerical proportion, no necessity would have existed to look upon the atomic numbers as anything else than equivalents. But it was found that though the combining numbers were fixed they were not always the same; it was found that if a substance combined in two or more proportions with any other, the larger proportions were always exact multiples of the smallest proportion. And this—the rule or law of *multiple proportions*—was

11.
Wollaston's
prophecy.

12.
Rule of multiple proportions.

exactly what gave to Dalton's view its great plausibility,[1] for if the elementary atom of each substance had a definite weight, it might be that not one atom only combined with one other, but that one combined with two, or two with three, and so on. Indeed it was soon found that this was

[1] The different factors of thought which combined to give the atomic theory that definiteness and usefulness which it attained through and since Dalton lay ready-made before him; but no one had seen so clearly as he did how to combine them. Proust had taught how to distinguish between chemical compounds and mixtures. When he prepared carbonate of copper artificially, he found that it had the same composition as the mineral which he found in nature. Richter had shown that definite proportions describe the quantities in which acids and bases exist in neutral salts. Fischer had attached to his translation of Berthollet's work the first table of equivalent quantities of bases and acids which combine to neutralise each other. Richter, and after him Gay-Lussac, had also found that the quantities of different metals which dissolve in the same quantity of acid to form saturated solutions combine also with the same weights of oxygen to form oxides. Richter, and after him Proust, had found that certain metals, like iron and mercury, form more than one fixed compound with oxygen, but without perceiving that the different quantities of oxygen in these fixed compounds stand in simple proportions to each other. So far as the theoretical side is concerned, the idea that bodies are formed of distinct particles—the notion of the ultimate heterogeneousness or discontinuity of matter—was not only familiar to the ancients, but was adopted by many physicists before Dalton; though the

chemical specialists who prepared the way for Dalton do not seem to have made use of this idea. Boerhaave, and before him Boyle, had spoken of atoms and of the *massulæ* or particles. Theories were not wanting that these ultimate particles differed in size and form, nor the opposite view, that the particles which combined had the same weight. The latter was the view of Higgins, in the exposition of which (1790) he entangled himself in contradictions, losing his chance of being one of the founders of the atomic theory. As Wurtz and Kopp and others who have carefully investigated the rival claims have said: This honour of founding the atomic theory belongs undividedly to Dalton. It seems important to notice that his experiments with mixtures of gases, which must have begun about 1790, impressed upon him the idea that different gases could exist independently of each other in the same space, suggesting the conception that neither of them filled the whole space, but that they consisted of discontinuous particles. He himself refers to these first investigations as containing the germ of his later opinions. It must, however, be borne in mind that Dalton was only imperfectly acquainted with the writings of contemporary — especially Continental—writers, and that he had a wholesome distrust for statements of facts which he had not verified or observed himself. All this is very clearly stated in Kopp's 'Entwickelung der Chemie,' p. 285, &c.

actually the case.   The lowest number according to which any substance entered into combination with any other was called the atomic weight or equivalent.

There was, so far, no necessity to look upon atomic weights as anything else than numbers fixing a proportion.   The unit could be selected arbitrarily.   It was not long before that element, hydrogen, which entered into compounds in the relatively smallest weight was taken as an arbitrary unit, and all other elements and compounds were tabulated according to the relative amount of their weights required to form compounds with hydrogen or with any other element—*e.g.*, oxygen—the equivalent of which with hydrogen was known.[1]

13.
Equivalents.

[1] For many years after the enunciation of the atomic theory great uncertainty and much difference of opinion existed on this and other points.   The man who did most to elaborate the edifice of which Dalton had laid the foundations, who filled in the outlines and invented the language of chemistry, was Berzelius.   He proceeded inductively and gathered materials from all sides ; to him are also owing the greatest number of accurate analyses, especially of inorganic substances.   When he began his labours he was favourably disposed towards Dalton's hypothesis ; he clearly saw its capabilities, but also that it was based only upon a happy suggestion, that it was introduced more by deductive than by inductive reasoning, and that it needed to be exhaustively tested and verified.   After ten years, during which he published in Gilbert's 'Annalen' and in Thomson's 'Annals of Philosophy' many series of investigations, he was able in 1818 to publish, in his 'Essay on Chemical Proportions and on the Chemical Effects of Electricity' (French translation, 1819 ; German translation, 1820), the first systematic and complete exposition of the atomic theory.   The beginning of a really exact treatment of chemistry has been dated by H. Rose, the greatest analytical chemist of the century, from this year 1818—the year in which Dalton's hypothesis was proved and generally accepted.   Others have dated the beginning from 1808, when Dalton published his theory ; others again from 1776, when Lavoisier destroyed the older phlogiston theory and appealed to the balance ; others again from Black's discovery of latent heat in 1760.   In an international history of thought it is not of much interest to decide whose claims to be the founder of modern chemistry as a science are best established.   Every one of these dates marks an epoch in the advance of an important and independent branch of research.   Black took an important step in the foundation of physical chemistry through his introduction of the conception of the quantity

A great door was now opened, not only for actual observation and research, but also for speculation—*i.e.*, for abstract thought. Some substances, if they entered into combination with hydrogen, required more than one unit of hydrogen, and it might therefore be that the proportion of the combining weight of hydrogen with any substance did not correctly give the atomic weight of the latter, but merely a multiple or sub-multiple of it. Thus, assuming oxygen combined with hydrogen in the proportion of 8 parts of the former to 1 part of the latter, a possibility was that the proportion might more correctly be written 16 to 2 than 8 to 1. Then, again, were the equivalent or atomic weights necessarily whole numbers? Were combinations all binary, such as acids and alkalies forming salts? and were more complex compounds resolvable into binary compounds of simpler binary compounds? Further, assuming the proportions fixing the combining weights to be known, how did the volumes of bodies combine?—was there a rule of volumes as there was of weights? and lastly, what was the reason or cause which made substances change their combinations, forming new ones, what did chemical affinity consist in, what did it depend on, how could it be defined and measured?

Considering that we have to do with a large number of independent, apparently unchangeable, elements, entering into many thousands of differing compounds, the task of

of heat. Lavoisier led the way in the development of the purely arithmetical department of chemistry, in the exclusive study of which physical chemistry was greatly neglected. Dalton suggested a formula which lent itself admirably to the representation of these purely arithmetical relations, and Berzelius elaborated this and invented a practical nomenclature. Black and Dalton threw out novel ideas ; Lavoisier and Berzelius elaborated great systems and created great schools which numbered many converts and industrious workers.

the chemist was enormous, offering a large, almost limitless, field of research and speculation. Let us see under what leading ideas this knowledge has been arranged.

In the gradual development and clearer definition of these conceptions a general rule of thought seems to have unconsciously guided philosophers probably more than in any other department of knowledge. It is the rule of simplicity.[1] How the human mind should have arrived at the old formula of "simplex sigillum veri" is difficult to understand on any other ground than that of convenience and expediency. The prevailing impression, indeed, which the world of phenomena makes on the mind of an unbiassed observer must be the very reverse of simplicity or unity of law and purpose. That, nevertheless, the knowledge of some simple relations in time, number, and space would enable the human intellect to acquire a considerable insight into the course of events and the order of Nature's processes must have come to philosophers

14.
"Simplex
sigillum
veri."

---

[1] The progress of chemical theory is the history of the attempt to find simple relations of number and form, representing the countless combinations of elementary substances; and of the growing conviction that nearly every simplification must, in course of time, be abandoned. No formula remains unchallenged except the doctrine of fixed and fixed multiple proportions, and that only if we confine ourselves to solid compounds; but the proportions themselves are not accurately known, though no phenomenon exists which disproves the assumption that they are invariable. The original conception of the atom as a round hard body had to be abandoned for the more complicated notion of a molecule, an assemblage of atoms; the conception of elementary bodies had to be amplified by that of compound elements or radicles; the idea that the atomic weights were multiples of a lowest number had to be abandoned; the binary theory of the combination of bodies was replaced by the theory of radicles, of nuclei, of types; the simple nature of the elementary particles had to give way to a complicated atomicity, from which there had to be again distinguished the valency or capacity of saturation of the elementary constituents. It is a progress from simpler to more and more complex methods of representation.

as a kind of revelation, and it is not surprising that it came late in the course of civilisation.[1]

Nothing can have tended more in this direction than the success of the Newtonian gravitation formula, and of the simple laws of motion, which, at the time of the birth of modern chemistry, stood firmly established as the key to all problems of physical astronomy. No wonder that men were on the look-out for correspondingly simple—perhaps analogous—relations in the world of molecular phenomena. One of the earliest suggestions, which came forward soon after Dalton's atomic view had helped to establish the prevailing rule of fixed and of multiple proportions in the chemical combinations and reactions of matter, was the idea that, as to each element belonged a definite combining number, all these numbers must be the multiple of the lowest among them, the equivalent or

15.
Prout's
hypothesis.

atomic weight of hydrogen. This is Prout's celebrated hypothesis, which had some ardent admirers, and which has been repeatedly abandoned and revived in the course of this century.[2] It is hardly possible to maintain it any longer, since the accurate and elaborate measurements of

[1] Except indeed the Pythagorean notions are regarded as an anticipation of it.

[2] The hypothesis of Prout, published anonymously in 1815, and warmly defended by Thomson, has been again and again revived. From the beginning it was put forward together with the suggestion that the different elementary substances might after all turn out to be all derived from one and the same primary form of matter, and that the atoms of this might in the atoms of our present elements merely be aggregated in different numbers and figures, held together by forces, which by the means and processes at our command could not be broken up. This primary substance might then be either hydrogen, the lightest in weight of known substances, or some other substance of which hydrogen itself was an atomic multiple. Abroad, Prout's hypothesis was disproved by Berzelius's accurate determinations, in England by Turner's, and about 1830 it fell into oblivion. It was again revived in 1840 by Dumas, who, as well as his followers, Laurent and Gerhardt, favoured the idea that the explanation of the different properties of chemical compounds, notably organic compounds, was to be found in the arrangement

Stas, who began with a belief in the hypothesis, led to the result "that the simplicity supposed by Prout's hypothesis to exist in the ratios of weights which come into play in chemical processes has experimentally not been found; it does not exist in reality."[1]

of the elementary atoms, in the structure rather than in the material difference of the elements themselves. The development of this view in the modern chemistry of "types" and "structures" will always go hand in hand with an avowed or tacit belief in the existence of an ultimate uniformity of substance, out of which by a diversity of configuration of atoms the infinite variety of compounds is produced. The accurate measurements of Stas had again about the year 1860 disproved the hypothesis of Prout. It has, however, again turned up in recent scientific literature. The theories of evolution, physical and philosophical, the discoveries of the spectroscope regarding the small number of elements contained in the photosphere of the sun, the periodic laws of Lothar Meyer and Mendeléeff and the stereometric theory of the carbon-compounds, of which I shall speak later on, all point to the conclusion that our so-called elements are composite bodies, and favour a view, similar to that of Prout, that possibly a single kind of matter may form the only substance of which atoms, molecules, elements, and compounds are made up. Professor Crookes in his address to the chemical section of the British Association in 1886 revived interest in the subject. After quoting a variety of authorities, he sums up : "From these passages, which might easily be multiplied, it plainly appears that the notion—not necessarily of the decomposibility, but at any rate of the complexibility of our supposed elements—is, so to speak, in the air of

science, waiting to take a further and more definite development. It is important to keep before men's minds the idea of the genesis of the elements ; this gives some form to our conceptions, and accustoms the mind to look for some physical production of atoms." Further on he coins the word "protyle" (from πρώτη and ὕλη) to denote the original kind of matter, and thus reminds us that, though speculations of this nature are not infrequent in English philosophy since Roger Bacon, the English language has no word to denote what the Germans call "Urstoff," the Romans "prima materia," the Greeks τὸ στοιχεῖον or simply ὕλη. The line of thought which again and again leads philosophers to speculate on this "prima materia" and upon a hypothesis similar to that of Prout is interesting and noteworthy, though it must be acknowledged that, so far, no real scientific benefit has been derived from it, and that it rather tends to upset the only firm foundation of modern chemistry, the fixity of the equivalent proportions as we now use and know them. Mendeléeff himself, in his excellent Faraday lecture on the periodic law ('Journal of the Chemical Society,' 1889, p. 634, &c.) distinctly refuses to recognise any connection between the periodic law and the idea of an unique matter.

[1] Stas, quoted by Ostwald, 'Lehrbuch der Allgemeinen Chemie,' vol. i. 2nd ed., Leipzig, 1891, p. 129. The revival of the hypothesis of Prout about the middle of the century was owing to the discovery by Dumas and Stas of the fact that Berzelius's figure, 12·20, for the

Prout's simple but incorrect assumption belongs to the age which witnessed the decomposition of many compounds into their two constituents by Davy's successful use of the galvanic battery, at the poles of which the two elements of substances made their separate appearance.   Substances which had always been considered as elemental and permanent, such as many oxides and earths, came to be ranged among the list of binary compounds.   This lent plausibility to the idea that even the supposed elements themselves might ultimately prove to be aggregates—differing in number and figure—of the elementary particles of one and the same primary substance.   Though with Prout's hypothesis this view has been repeatedly held and refuted, another theory—recommended likewise by its simplicity—had its origin in the discoveries of Davy, and the further development of them by Berzelius.   This is the so-called electro-chemical or binary theory of chemical compounds.   The dual combination of one elementary substance with another, and again of two dual compounds with each other, and so on, even to the most complicated compounds, was to be the simple type of chemical combination.   This view, so

atomic weight of carbon, taking oxygen as 16, was incorrect. An account of the long series of determinations of this important constant will be found in the same work, p. 82, &c. I believe that in the first edition of this work will also be found the first consistent attempt to introduce into chemical data an estimate of the degree of accuracy or the amount of error which attaches to our knowledge of the constants of nature and the so-called laws of phenomena. This consideration, so familiar to astronomers, was, I believe, quite overlooked in many of the best handbooks during the earlier half of our century, and it is even yet hardly touched upon in the ordinary textbooks. The result is an entirely erroneous impression produced on the popular mind as to the degree of certainty which belongs to scientific statements.

simple and plausible, governed research for a long period, but has finally been abandoned as insufficient.[1]

Another blow was dealt at the simple theory by which

16.
Discovery of
isomerism.

[1] The electro-chemical theory of Davy and Berzelius was, after about fifteen years of development, during which period the use of the significant terms electro - positive and electro-negative was not consistent, finally enunciated by Berzelius in 1818 in his 'Essay on the theory of Chemical Proportions and on the Chemical Action of Electricity.' From that time it reigned almost supreme for twenty years, when both physical and chemical discoveries began to show its insufficiency. A very concise account of it is given in Kopp's 'Entwickelung der Chemie,' and in E. von Meyer's 'History of Chemistry,' translated by M'Gowan (Macmillan & Co., 1891). Berzelius clung to it to the last, and at the present moment there exists a widespread opinion that the future will see a revival and modified acceptance of the Davy - Berzelius theory. In relation to this Helmholtz's celebrated Faraday lecture of the year 1881 should be read (see the reprint in Helmholtz's 'Vorträge und Reden,' vol. ii.) The peculiarity of the electro-chemical theory was that it was an atomic theory as well as a theory of chemical affinity. When it was abandoned, the two distinct interests, that of developing the atomic view, so as to give a correct description of the constitution of chemical compounds and reactions, and that of giving an explanation of chemical affinity, fell for a time asunder. The former interest preponderated, owing mainly to two reasons, the one theoretical, the other practical. The theoretical reason was the need of a different method of systematically arranging the chaos of new organic compounds with which chemistry became crowded about the year 1840. Berzelius had created the nomenclature and notation of chemistry ; but this proved insufficient to describe and grasp the processes and products of the many carbon compounds. The practical reason which cast into the background the study of chemical affinity and its nature was the growing demands of manufacturing chemistry. This was during a long period occupied mainly with the analysis and synthesis of new products, or with new and simpler methods for producing well-known compounds. The study of reactions and of the products of bodies was practically of more interest than that of the forces which governed them. The question of the cost of producing chemical products was for a long time a secondary one. Towards the end of our century both theoretical and practical considerations forced upon chemists the necessity of making themselves acquainted with the different forms of energy which are at our command in chemical as well as in mechanical operations, and this has led to a renewal of the study of chemical and mechanical energy, and of the nature and laws of chemical affinity. Economy in practical chemistry can be divided into two branches : the economy of materials and the economy of energy. The great developments in the course of this century have consisted largely in utilising by-products and in avoiding waste of substance. We are now only approaching the second problem : how to put the energy which is at our command to the best use.

Berzelius united Dalton's and Davy's researches into a comprehensive system of chemistry. The identity or difference of chemical substances seemed in the early part of the century to be fixed by the constituent elements and their quantitative proportions determined by a qualitative and quantitative analysis. This simple view had to be abandoned when Wöhler in 1823, Liebig in 1824, and Faraday in 1825 found that entirely different qualities, indicating a different constitution, could belong to bodies having the same elements in the same numerical proportions.[1] The composition of a compound had to be distinguished from its constitution, the elementary from the constituent analysis and formula. It took forty years before the great variety of views which were brought forward with the purpose of explaining how composition and constitution of the same aggregate of elements might

[1] This phenomenon is termed "Isomerism," from the Greek word ἰσομερής, which signifies "having equal parts." The term was introduced by Berzelius in 1830, after he had satisfied himself that compounds existed, differing widely in their properties, which contain the same constituent elements in the same proportions, and which combine with other bodies in the same proportions to form neutral salts. This he found to be the case with "racemic" and "tartaric" acid. Up to that time he had hesitated in accepting the growing evidence that equal constituents in equal proportions did not constitute identity of compounds. Wöhler in 1823 and Liebig in 1824 had found the same numerical composition for "cyanate" and "fulminate" of silver. In 1825 Faraday found two hydrocarbons which contained the same proportions of carbon and hydrogen, but showed totally different properties, such as unequal density in the gaseous state. Two oxides of tin, having the same composition, were also known, and two modifications of "phosphoric acid." The explanation of these anomalies caused Berzelius much difficulty. He resorts to the notion of a difference of grouping of the constituent atoms. "The isomerism of compounds," he says, "in itself presupposes that the positions of the atoms in them must be different" (see E. von Meyer, 'History of Chemistry,' p. 238). A. Rau in his 'Theorien der modernen Chemie' (3 parts, Braunschweig, 1877-84) gives in the appendix to the third part a detailed history of isomerism. He denies that Berzelius refers to the different position of atoms in order to explain isomerism; he attributes this suggestion to Dumas in 1833.

differ, could be approximately brought into line and order. This period was filled by the development of the chemistry of organic compounds. The chemical substances which make up the framework and numerous tissues of all living beings, the juices and products of vegetable, the food and the excreta of animal organisms, consist mostly of a few elementary bodies, combined according to numbers which are highly complex and unintelligible. Most of these compounds, if removed from the organism which contained them, proved to be subject to rapid decomposition. An increasing number of stable compounds, however, were in course of time prepared from these residues, and these formed especially the subject of organic analysis. Already Lavoisier had indicated how some system might be brought into the apparent complexity of these organic bodies; and this view was adopted by Berzelius and incorporated in his dual or binary system.[1]

17.
Organic chemistry.

[1] Kopp's account of the development of Berzelius's views on organic compounds is most interesting and instructive. As late as 1814 he could not reconcile the composition of organic acids, such as oxalic acid, with the atomic theory; but renewed efforts and improved methods of analysis taught him in the following years how to apply the atomic formulæ to the description of such compounds. "He was the first to show the only right road to inform ourselves regarding the constitution of these bodies, the method, namely, of analysing their combinations with inorganic substances of known atomic weight. . . . He had also a great share in establishing the view that the ratios of combinations in organic compounds are analogous to those of inorganic substances, and that theories of the former must begin by comparing them with the latter" ('Geschichte der Chemie,' vol. i. p. 398; cf. also 'Die Entwickelung der Chemie,' p. 532, &c.) To Berzelius is thus due more than to any other man the breaking down of the barrier which had before his time divided the chemistry of organic from that of inorganic substances. For a considerable time Berzelius did not look upon organic compounds as binary—in fact, in 1814 he assumed that the difference between organic and inorganic compounds lay in this, that the latter were all binary, whereas the former were ternary or quaternary. The French chemists, under the influence of Lavoisier's oxygen theory, favoured the binary view, and this was much strengthened by Gay-Lussac's researches on cyanogen (in

It was supposed that the simple and well-known elements of these bodies might have the property of forming primarily combinations which were more firmly knit together than others, that these primary combinations might then as it were take the place of elements and act like them, forming with others of similar constitution, or with the simple elements themselves, more complex compounds. In these higher compounds they might behave like elementary bodies, entering into and being expelled from them in their own proper combinations without being broken up into the ultimate elementary constituents. One of the functions of the living organism was by the action of the vital forces to produce these primary compounds or complex atoms. It was thus thought that as inorganic bodies were made up of constituents which were elements, so organic bodies were made up of constituents which were themselves partly compounds. A new term had to be coined for those constituents which might comprise both elementary bodies and these primary compounds which behaved like elements in organic substances. This was the term "Radicle." A radicle might be an element or a compound.[1] For a long time it was thought that these

---

1815), a compound of carbon and nitrogen, which was shown to behave like an element. Ampère in the following year showed how the salts of ammonia could be brought into line with the salts of other alkalies by considering them to contain a compound element (consisting of nitrogen and hydrogen) in place of a simple element. In his celebrated essay of 1818 Berzelius defines organic acids as binary compounds of oxygen with com-

pound elements or radicles (Kopp, 'Geschichte der Chemie,' vol. iv. p. 269).

[1] The term "radicle," to designate the principal constituent of a compound, was used as far back as 1787 in the discussions through which the French chemists reformed the nomenclature of chemistry (Kopp, 'Geschichte,' &c., vol. iv. p. 266). It acquired a more definite meaning about the year 1835, when Liebig, in common with Ber-

complex radicles, as distinguished from the elements, were produced mainly—if not exclusively—in the organism of the plant or of the animal. Liebig himself, who favoured this view, and who first brought organic chemistry in its application to agriculture and physiology under the notice of a large circle of readers, introduced this branch of the subject with the designation of the chemistry of compound radicles, inorganic or mineral chemistry being termed the chemistry of simple radicles. The radicles were, according to Liebig, the true elements of organic chemistry. The binary system of Berzelius received another attack led by the celebrated French chemists Laurent and Gerhardt, with whom Dumas temporarily allied himself. It was about the year 1840 that the idea of "substitution" entered the list of formulæ by which chemical philosophers attempted to systematise and simplify the ever-growing number of definite compounds, supplied mainly by organic analysis.[1] It was

18.
Liebig's definition of organic chemistry.

19.
Substitution.

zelius and with Dumas, established what is now called the older radicle-theory of organic compounds. As Kopp has shown ('Entwickelung der Chemie, p. 576, &c.), it remained undecided at that time whether these organic radicles had actual existence, or whether they were merely a convenient symbolism,— whether they could be isolated, like cyanogen, or whether they existed only in combinations, — whether they were fixed and unchangeable, or whether they could themselves be converted one into another,— whether the same compound could be referred—for convenience sake —to more than one constituent radicle. "By most chemists the definition of organic chemistry given by Liebig ('Organic Chemistry,' 1843)

was adopted, that it was the chemistry of compound radicles; . . . that these radicles really existed in the compounds as definite constituents; and if it was then said that these radicles were mostly hypothetical, this was understood as meaning that some of them were known in the free state, others not" (p. 581).

[1] Even before that time the views of many eminent chemists had been greatly influenced by the discoveries and experiments of two great natural philosophers of this country who kept themselves free from the theoretical considerations which had led Berzelius in the elaboration of his electro-chemical and binary system. These were the researches of Davy regarding the so-called hydro-

found that one or more atoms in an organic compound,
notably of hydrogen, might be replaced by an equal
number of atoms of other elements, and that such products of substitution retained similar qualities, and could
be mutually converted into each other, the type of the
compound remaining the same. The process of substitution led to the conception of " Types," which remained
the same whilst the individual compounds varied according to the different elements which were introduced.

gen acids of chlorine, bromine, and
iodine, and the investigations of
Graham into the salts of phosphoric
acid and its different modifications.
Davy, though together with Berzelius the founder of the electro-
chemical theory, had found it necessary to modify the oxygen theory
of Lavoisier—*viz.*, that oxygen was
necessarily the acid - forming element : he, and after him Dulong
in France, had explained the so-
called oxygen acids like sulphuric
acid as hydrogen compounds of
certain compound radicles (SO_4)
exactly as hydrochloric acid is a
hydrogen acid of the simple radicle
chlorine. Graham's discovery of
three modifications of phosphoric
acid, and of the different power of
saturation of these three modifications, led to long discussions as to
what is really meant by a neutral
salt. Liebig in the year 1838, in
an important memoir gathering together the conclusions which these
facts, not easily reconciled with
Berzelius's system, had led him to,
emphasised there the twofold possibility of regarding metallic salts
either with Berzelius as binary
combinations of oxides with an-
hydrous acids, or else as products
of substitution of hydrogen compounds, hydrogen being replaced
by metals. The choice might then
depend on considerations of convenience : the one view might be
more suitable for inorganic—notably
metallic—compounds, the other for
organic compounds. The hydrogen
theory was thus introduced alongside of the oxygen theory ; substitution was introduced alongside of
simple combination. Though in
this stage the radicle theory was
already threatened, it was still possible to uphold the binary theory,
though it was not necessary. Chlorine could act in the same way as
oxygen, being an electro-negative
element. But when, in pursuing
the line of investigation opened out,
it was found that chlorine, the
electro-negative element, could take
the place of hydrogen in organic
compounds without changing their
chemical character, the binary
theory, based upon polar (electrical) contrasts, became insufficient
as a means of explanation or even
of classification. Dumas was the
first to indicate this (1834), though
he attempted to save the electro-
chemical or polar theory by stating
that the two electrically opposite
constituents of an organic compound might contain the same
elements in the opposite electrical
positions (Kopp, ' Entwickelung der
Chemie,' pp. 564, 595, &c.)

Whilst the " Radicle" theory of Berzelius and Liebig sought to simplify the study of chemical compounds by reducing them to a definite number of complex atoms, the " Type " theory of Laurent and Gerhardt sought to attain the same object by establishing a small number of simple formulæ, corresponding to well-known simple substances, under which the vast number of organic compounds could be grouped.[1] The conception of a "type" exhibiting

20.
Type theory.

[1] The type theory was slowly and hesitatingly developed. Dumas, whose researches about 1835 prepared the way, did not himself draw the immediate consequences ; this was done by Laurent, "who maintained that the structure and chemical character of organic compounds are not materially altered by the entrance of chlorine and the separation of hydrogen" (E. v. Meyer, 'History of Chemistry,' p. 261). Laurent then elaborated his theory of "Nuclei." They remind one of Berzelius's and Liebig's radicles. The nuclei were the groundwork of organic compounds ; they were not unalterable as the radicles had been considered to be. Dumas, who at first repudiated Laurent's ideas, was later on, through his own experimental discoveries, led to adopt similar views. The "radicle," as the permanent constituent in organic compounds—corresponding to the elements in inorganic chemistry —had given way to the changeable nucleus, which only preserved its form ; the unchangeable principle was found in the form, the structure or type, instead of in the substance of the simple or composite constituents. This led to an extensive study of the forms of chemical compounds—as expressed by their formulæ, and apart from the study of the properties of the original constituents. Types were invented, frequently in a somewhat arbitrary manner. "The ultimate result was that an empty scheme of formulation carried the day over what was really good in this doctrine" (ibid., p. 264). "The unitary conception was to step into the place of the dualistic. . . . Every chemical compound forms a complete whole, and cannot therefore consist of two parts. The chemical character is dependent primarily upon the arrangement and number of the atoms, and in a lesser degree upon their chemical nature" (p. 265). This is the beginning of the second great step which was taken in the elaboration of the atomic view of matter and nature. The atomic view first became a scientific instrument, when arithmetical relations of a definite and unalterable kind were suggested and proved to exist ; it became a yet more useful instrument, when to the arithmetical there were added geometrical conceptions. Position, arrangement, and structure are conceptions which involve ideas of distance and space. It is true that for a long time these terms were used merely symbolically ; the ultimate consequences of such conceptions can however not be avoided. The history of chemical theory in the second half of the nineteenth century is a proof of this.

certain stable qualities with a multitude of changing
varieties was a notion familiar to other branches of natural
history. The idea of substituting one element for another
gave the death-blow to the theory of Berzelius, which
assumed that elements paired with each other, according
to some polar contrast. It was found, for instance, that
the element chlorine, which stood on one side of the
scale—the electro-negative—could take the place of the
opposite electro-positive element hydrogen.

In the course of time the conception of types was much
changed, and became more and more complicated; it had
however the effect of finally destroying the binary view of
chemical composition, and restoring in its place the older
unitary conception.

All these attempts to simplify the study of chemical
compounds, by reducing them to simple or complex elements, or to pairs of simpler combinations, or by ranging
them according to types, were useful in many ways in
extending the knowledge of bodies, in indicating new
methods of inquiry, and in suggesting instructive experiments:[1] none of them were universally accepted in the

[1] About that time — so far as
chemistry proper, *i.e.*, the study of
compounds and of reactions was
concerned—there existed two main
currents of thought, the most illustrious and influential representatives of which were Kekulé (1829-
96, first professor at Ghent, then
since 1865 at Bonn), and Kolbe
(1818-1884, first professor at Marburg, then since 1865 at Leipsic).
As teachers and centres of academic influence, though in different, frequently opposite directions,
these two eminent men continued
the work started in Germany by
Liebig, Wöhler, and Bunsen. To
them as a third can be added the
name of A. W. von Hofmann (1818-
1892), who, through his twenty
years' residence in London, did much
to introduce a knowledge of German
chemistry and German teaching
methods in England, and who from
1865 established the modern Berlin
school of chemistry. It would be
impossible to enter here into details
as to how—mainly through the influence of these three men—the work
begun by Liebig and Wöhler was
extended, and how especially also
the great development of chemical

middle of the century.[1]   It thus happened that a variety of circumstances combined to bring into prominence, and subsequently into general acceptance, the modern view of

21.
Uncertainty
in chemical
theory about
the middle
of the cen-
tury.

industry in Germany was brought about ; a creation almost as characteristic of German intellect, and probably more lastingly beneficial, than the political changes which mark the same period in history. More important for a history of Thought is it to note how Kolbe attached himself to the school of Wöhler and Berzelius, and tried to preserve the continuity of thought in developing the fruitful ideas contained in the writings of the latter. "He united the conclusions from his own researches with the declining theory of Berzelius ; he endued the latter with new life by throwing aside whatever of it was dead, and replacing this by vigorous principles. From his own and other investigations he came to the conclusion that the unalterability of radicles, as taught by Berzelius, could no longer be maintained, since the facts of substitution had to be taken into account." He especially developed Berzelius's idea of paired compounds. (See E. v. Meyer's 'History of Chemistry,' p. 295.) Kolbe's joint work with Frankland was of the greatest importance to science. The influence of Kolbe was also largely of a polemical nature, inasmuch as he and some others, notably F. Mohr (whose name will have to be mentioned in a later chapter), protested energetically against the formal character of much of the writings and work produced by the French school which opposed the views of Berzelius. This school, of which Dumas, Laurent, and Gerhardt were the founders, and which exerted a very marked and beneficial influence through the teaching and the finished literary productions of

Wurtz (1817-84), was closely allied with the school of Kekulé in Germany, who indeed began by logically developing Gerhardt's ideas, being afterwards led to special views and methods of his own, through which he became the real founder of the so-called structural formulæ, and of the doctrine of the linking of atoms. I must here especially record my indebtedness to the admirable historical essays of Wurtz ('Théorie atomique,' 7me ed., 1893, and 'History of Chemical Theory,' transl. by Watts). For clearness and elegance of style, they are quite as marked as are Kopp's historical works for breadth, impartiality, and philosophical insight.

[1] The adherents of the theory of substitution and types, sometimes called the "modern," also the "French," school, urged against the followers of Berzelius, which adhered to the "electro-chemical" or "radicle" view, that since an electro-positive element could be replaced by a contrary one, there was no sense in upholding the polar difference. They pointed out that organic substances were not electrolytic ; and they criticised the artificial invention and multiplication of new radicles which had no real existence, as arbitrary. On the other side, the followers of Berzelius objected to the entire ignoring by the new school of the really existing electro-chemical differences, and reproved them for having destroyed the connection between organic and inorganic chemistry, and for having introduced a purely formal systematisation according to merely external differences. They rightly upheld

the "atomicity" or "valency" of chemical substances—
be they elements or compounds. This most recent development of chemical systematisation originated in England,[1] whereas the "radicle" theory belonged more to the

the view that an understanding of
chemical reactions must ultimately
depend upon a study of the nature
and degree of chemical affinity, and
maintained that so far the connection of chemical with electrolytic
phenomena afforded the only clue
to the comprehension of the nature
of chemical affinity. The atomic
theory had now absorbed all interest, to the detriment of a physical theory of chemical affinity such
as Berthollet had attempted. It
was held that by ignoring the
electro-chemical differences, the
"modern" school lost the only remaining chance of explaining, and
not merely classifying, chemical phenomena. A good exposition of the
latter argument will be found in
A. Rau, 'Die Theorien der modernen Chemie.'

[1] The number is small of the English names which about the middle
of this century figured prominently
in the discussions by which, in the
German and French annals of
science, correcter views on the constitution of chemical compounds
were gradually elaborated. Kane's
work was overlooked, but William-
son, Odling, and Frankland have
had a very marked influence; and,
as in so many other sciences, pioneer
work in modern chemistry was done
in this country, notably by Frankland. Liebig, after his visit to
England in 1837, wrote to Wöhler:
"I have traversed England, Ireland,
and Scotland in all directions, have
seen much that is astonishing, but
have learnt little: whence is scientific knowledge to come in England,
as the teachers are so inferior?
Among older men, Thomson is still
the best; among younger men,

Graham: modest and unassuming,
he makes the most beautiful discoveries. Nevertheless, a splendid
nation," &c. &c. ('Liebig's und
Wöhler's Briefwechsel,' vol. i. p.
113.) From what I stated above
(chapter iii. p. 296, &c.), we are,
however, quite prepared to find
that the idea which more than any
other has brought some order and
system into modern chemical theory,
and which has united the diverg-
ing currents of the foreign schools,
has come from England. Frankland more than any other must
be looked upon as the origina-
tor of the modern theory of the
atomicity or valency of chemical
elements and compounds. The
history of this conception can be
well studied in the collection of
scientific papers which he published
with valuable introductions in 1877
('Experimental Researches in Pure,
Applied, and Physical Chemistry,'
London, van Voorst). His researches commenced in those years
when great confusion existed in organic chemistry, "when the wildest
theories of the constitution of organic compounds created but little
surprise; the assertion, for instance,
that an atom of carbon was united
with four atoms of hydrogen and
two of chlorine would scarcely have
been considered intrinsically improbable, and certainly not impossible"
(loc. cit., p. 26). The idea existed
that bodies could enter into combination with other bodies, notably organic radicles, and could still retain
in such combination their original
affinities unimpaired; a new term,
that of "conjugate," "copulated,"
or "paired" compounds, had been
invented and adopted by Berzelius.

German, and the "type" theory to the French, school of chemists. But the idea of the "atomicity" and "valency" or saturating capacity of the element of any substance was not possible without the clear notion of the "molecule" as distinct from the "atom." This idea had lain dormant in the now celebrated but long forgotten law of Avogadro, which was established in the year 1811, almost immediately after the appearance of Dalton's atomic theory.

The atomic theory may be regarded in two distinct ways, and it is instructive from the point of view of the history of thought to see how these two different aspects of the theory have gradually presented themselves. The older and vague atomic theory professed to be a theory of the constitution of bodies, and to afford the basis for an explanation of physical phenomena; in order to do this, forces of attraction and repulsion between the particles of

22.
Two aspects of the atomic theory.

It appears that this theory was largely based upon a compound prepared by Bunsen, and called "cacodyl." This compound was one of the few organic radicles which contained a metal—arsenic. Frankland, partly alone, partly in union with Kolbe, entered upon a series of researches which had two distinct objects. Both these objects were foreign to that school which had given up the radicle theory, and which, by looking upon organic compounds as essentially different from inorganic compounds, had lost that important clue—the connection of the two branches of chemistry. These objects were the isolation of the so-called radicles or compound elements and the preparation of other "organo-metallic" bodies. The latter research led to new insight into the nature of chemical combinations. "I had not proceeded far," says Frankland, "in the investigation of the organo-metallic compounds before the facts brought to light began to impress upon me the existence of a fixity in the maximum combining value or capacity of saturation in the metallic elements which had not before been suspected. . . . It was evident that the atoms of zinc, tin, arsenic, antimony, &c., had only room, so to speak, for the attachment of a fixed and definite number of the atoms of other elements, or, as I should now express it, of the bonds of other elements. This hypothesis, which was communicated to the Royal Society on May 10, 1852, constitutes the basis of what has since been called the doctrine of atomicity or equivalence of elements; and it was, so far as I am aware, the first announcement of that doctrine" (ibid., p. 145).

matter had to be assumed, and elaborate calculations as to the integral or resultant effect of these elementary forces had to be instituted, or at least formulated.   An interesting and typical case of these attempts was the theory of Boscovich, referred to in the last chapter.[1]   In looking back on the history of science, it can now be safely stated that, ingenious as those theories were, they led to no results in the direction of the calculation of the molar and molecular properties of bodies, or if they did, they yielded none which could not be gained by the opposite view which regarded matter as continuous.   The atomic theory, however, did good service from another point of view, when through Richter, Dalton, Proust, and Berzelius the fact that bodies combine only in definite proportions of weight, or their simple multiples, became firmly established.   The authors of this discovery were driven to the atomic view

[1] See also Berthollet, 'Statique chimique,' 1803, vol. i. : "Les puissances qui produisent les phénomènes chimiques sont toutes dérivées de l'attraction mutuelle des molécules des corps, à laquelle on a donné le nom d'affinité, pour la distinguer de l'attraction astronomique. Il est probable que l'une et l'autre ne sont qu'une même propriété" (p. 1). "Il y a des sciences qui peuvent parvenir à un certain degré de perfection sans le secours d'aucune théorie, et seulement par le moyen d'un ordre arbitraire qu'on établit entre les observations des faits naturels, dont elles s'occupent principalement ; mais il n'en est pas le même en chimie, où les observations doivent naître presque toujours de l'expérience même et où les faits résultent de la réunion factice des circonstances qui doivent les produire. Pour tenter les expériences, il faut avoir un but, être guidé par une hypothèse. . . . ainsi les suppositions plus ou moins illusoires et même des chimères qui sont aujourd'hui ridicules, mais qui ont engagé aux tentatives les plus laborieuses, ont été nécessaires, au berceau de la chimie. Par leur moyen les faits se sont multipliés, un grand nombre de propriétés a été constaté, et plusieurs arts se sont perfectionnés" (p. 4). "Si les propriétés chimiques des différentes substances sont dues à leur affinité et à leurs dispositions particulières, celles des combinaisons qu'elles forment dépendent de la saturation respective, des changements de constitution qui sont dus à l'action réciproque, du degré de la force qui maintient la combinaison ; ainsi les propriétés des substances simples sont non seulement la cause des combinaisons, mais encore celle de leurs propres affections " (vol. ii. p. 552).

of matter as the most convenient method of expressing the
formulæ of chemical compounds. Ever since that time
the atomic view has served as a kind of symbolism by
which different chemical elements could be characterised,
their compounds described, and the actual weights practically calculated. And here we must note the reserve
with which some of the greatest representatives of
chemical science expressed themselves up to the middle
of the century regarding the actual physical existence of
those elementary particles with which they operated so
freely in their formulæ, and which they even represented
by balls and coloured discs in their demonstrations.

23.
A conveni-
ent sym-
bolism.

Wollaston, one of the first who accepted Dalton's[1] views

[1] Dalton does not seem to have
been troubled by any philosophical
doubts or by the anticipation of
the mathematical difficulties which
would stand in the way of a consistent development of the atomic
view. He was led to formulate and
employ his atomic theory by ponder-
ing over the most convenient manner in which certain chemical facts
—the facts of definite and multiple
proportions—and certain physical
discoveries—the separate existence
of aqueous vapour from the other
constituents of the air—could be
represented, and he adopted the
view suggested by Newton in his
'Queries,' "that matter was formed
in solid, massy, hard, impenetrable,
movable particles" (see Sir H.
Roscoe, 'John Dalton,' Century
Series, p. 128, &c.) Wollaston and
Davy were much more cautious :
the former foresaw the complicated
and far-reaching mathematical problems which were involved in the
atomic view, the latter thought
the generalisation premature. His
labours had been largely in the
direction of showing that bodies
which had been looked upon as
elementary were compound, and
he "doubts whether we have yet
obtained elements" (ibid., p. 155).
Even as late as 1826, in his award
to Dalton of the Royal Medal, he
speaks of his "Development of the
Chemical Theory of Definite Proportions, *usually called the Atomic
Theory*," he emphasises its practical
usefulness, "making the statics of
chemistry depend upon simple
questions in subtraction or multiplication, and enabling the student
to deduce an immense number of
facts from a few well authenticated,
accurate, experimental results." He
refers to Wollaston's table of equivalents, which "separates the practical part of the doctrine from the
atomical or hypothetical part." It
has, in fact, been maintained that
the hesitancy which Wollaston displayed on this subject deprived him
of his well-deserved share of the
glory which the introduction of the
atomic view of matter has shed
upon Dalton and Berzelius. (See
Peacock, 'Life of Dr Young,' p.
469.)

as to fixed and multiple proportions, expressed himself with great reserve as to the value of the atomic hypothesis, and when drawing up a table of atomic weights, he preferred to call them equivalents—a term used already by Cavendish—as implying no other meaning than that they fix the proportions in which bodies combine into, or separate out of, compounds. Davy was hesitating and reluctant to admit any hypothesis as to the ultimate constitution of matter. Liebig[1] and Faraday,[2] at a somewhat

[1] "In endeavouring to develop the theory which at present prevails respecting the cause of the unchangeableness of chemical proportions, let it not be forgotten that its truth or falsehood has nothing whatever to do with the natural law itself. The latter is the expression of universal experience; it remains true, invariably and immutably, however our notions respecting its cause may from time to time vary and change." Thus wrote Liebig ('Familiar Letters on Chemistry,' 1844) at a time when great confusion existed as to the real atomic or smallest combining weights which should be assigned to the chemical elements; when in consequence many chemists preferred to discard the word "atomic weight" altogether, and to revert to the term equivalent (see Kopp, 'Entwickelung der Chemie,' p. 718, &c.) Dumas in 1840 declared that the term atomic weight did not deserve the confidence with which chemists made use of it: if he could he would banish the word atom from chemistry, convinced as he was that science should not transgress the limit of that which could be known by experience. Liebig, in 1839, about the time when his important memoirs on the constitution of organic bases and acids appeared in his 'Annals,' em-

phasised likewise the fact that equivalents never change; but he doubted whether chemists would ever agree as to the relative atomic weights, and he hoped the time was not far distant when they would all return again to equivalents (ibid., p. 438). In France an influential school, headed by the eminent M. Berthelot, up to the present day limits itself to the use of equivalents. See Berthelot, 'La Synthèse chimique,' 7me éd., p. 164 n.

[2] The objections which Faraday urged against the notion of atom and atomic weight seem to come from a different quarter. In 1834, when explaining his researches on electro-chemical action, he says ('Exper. Res.,' No. 869): "If we adopt the atomic theory or phraseology, then the atoms of bodies which are equivalents to each other in their ordinary chemical action have equal quantities of electricity naturally associated with them. But I must confess I am jealous of the term *atom;* for though it is very easy to talk of atoms, it is very difficult to form a clear idea of their nature, especially when compound bodies are under consideration." Ten years later, in his 'Speculation touching Conduction and the Nature of Matter' (see 'Exper. Res.,' vol. ii. p. 285),

later date, appeared similarly averse to admit the physical existence of atoms in the older sense, and warned chemists against the introduction of unnecessary and unproven hypotheses. Even Gerhardt, as late as 1856, opposed the idea that chemical formulæ could express the actual constitution of substances : they were merely a convenient symbolism, a kind of alphabet, by which reactions between different elements or compounds could be conveniently described, and the proportional weights of the constituents or the products could be ascertained.[1] Accordingly, it was also maintained that formulæ could be written in very different ways, expressive of the different processes and reactions which had in special cases to be considered.[2]

Although, therefore, chemical research was governed all through the century by the atomic view of matter, it does

---

he says : "The word atom, which can never be used without involving much that is purely hypothetical, is often *intended* to be used to express a simple fact. . . . There can be no doubt that the words definite proportions, equivalents, primes, &c., which did and do express fully all the *facts* of what is usually called the atomic theory in chemistry, were dismissed because they were not expressive enough, and did not say all that was in the mind of him who used the word atom in their stead ; they did not express the hypothesis as well as the fact." He then enlarges on the necessity of the atomic view, and expresses his preference for the form which Boscovich had given to it over "the more usual notion," as according to the latter "matter consists of atoms and intervening space," whilst with the former "matter is everywhere present, and there is no intervening space unoccupied by it."

(ibid., pp. 290, 291). It is evidently the objection to action at a distance, uncommunicated action, which is implied in the ordinary atomic view of matter, that makes Faraday jealous of the term atom. This objection was quite foreign to the chemists abroad who in the middle of the century elaborated the atomic view of matter and nature ; it belongs to a different direction of thought, which will occupy us in a later chapter.

[1] In his 'Traité de Chimie organique,' which he brought out as a continuation of the French edition of Berzelius's 'Treatise of Inorganic Chemistry' in the years 1853 to 1856. See Kopp, 'Entwickelung der Chemie,' pp. 747, 796, 800, 809, 819, 834.

[2] Even the combining weight or equivalent of an element, that datum upon which—since Richter and Dalton—the whole system of chemistry has been built up, was

not appear that philosophers considered the existence and usefulness of chemical formulæ as a proof of the physical existence of atoms, or of smallest indivisible particles of matter, in the older sense of the theory. Hand in hand with this purely formal and experimental treatment of chemical phenomena went the almost absolute neglect with which questions referring to chemical affinity were treated. The word was little more than a name for an unknown something.

24.
Neglect of
the study
of affinity.

How it came to pass that substances had more or less affinity for each other, what was meant by a chemical compound, symbolically expressed by writing two or more letters, near or above each other, in a square or in a circle, united by parentheses or brackets, did not seem to trouble chemical philosophers at all. To compare the problem of chemistry with that of astronomy, the former for a great part of our century resembled that phase of astronomical knowledge in which stellar maps and catalogues, plans of orbits and orreries, were considered sufficient, giving a picture of a certain constellation of the heavenly bodies, but no idea of how these configurations were maintained and altered. In fact, chemistry was for a long time a science purely of numbers, to which was attached a natural history of the substances to which these numbers belonged. The geometrical arrangement of the formulæ was usually looked upon as only symbolical: of the dynamical changes which take place in time, and imply the knowledge of

considered to be represented by more than one number in instances where the same metal had several basic or acid oxides, as in the case of nitrogen and phosphorus (ibid., p. 805). Laurent in 'Comptes

Rendus,'1844, vol. xix. p. 1099, says: " Le même corps simple se présente tantôt avec certaines propriétés, tantôt avec d'autres, il entre dans les corps composés, tantôt avec un certain poids, tantôt avec un autre."

forces or movements, few took any notice whatever.   In
spite of the enormous accumulation of well-arranged
knowledge, and the marvellous practical achievements of
chemistry, the foremost historian of that science could,
as late as 1873, write as follows: "No theory has as yet   25.
been formed in chemistry which, starting from a definite   Kopp on
chemical
principle, attempts to deduce the results of experience as   theory in
1873.
necessary consequences.   The doctrines which have been
termed in chemistry theoretical are still only such as permit us to bring connection into the results which practical
chemistry has gained in special directions; or to form a
picture how we might think of them as mutually related."[1]

[1] Kopp, 'Entwickelung der Chemie,' 1873, p. 844. A generation
earlier Dumas had written ('Comptes Rendus,' vol. x., 1840, pp.
171, 176, 178): "Dans les vues de
l'électrochimie la *nature* de leurs
particules élémentaires doit déterminer les propriétés fondamentales
des corps, tandis que dans la théorie
des substitutions, c'est de la *situation* de ces particules, que les propriétés dérivent surtout. . . . La
théorie des types . . . explique ce
que la loi des substitutions se con-
tente de préciser. Elle envisage
les corps organiques comme étant
formés des particules, qui peuvent
être déplacées et remplacées, sans
que le corps soit détruit, pour ainsi
dire. . . . Voilà donc en présence
deux systèmes: l'un qui attribue
le rôle principal à la nature des éléments, l'autre qui la réserve pour
le nombre et l'arrangement des
équivalents. Poussé à l'extrême
chacun d'eux . . . se trouverait
conduire à l'absurde." In 1861
Kekulé, in his 'Lehrbuch der organischen Chemie' (vol. i. p. 95),
declares that, "besides the laws of
fixed and multiple proportions of
weight (and in gaseous bodies also

of volume), chemistry had as yet
discovered no exact laws, . . . and
all so-called theoretical conceptions
were merely points of view which
possessed probability or convenience." And Wurtz ('La Théorie
atomique,' 1863) speaks of the
atomic hypothesis in terms which
might lead one to think we were on
the eve of an entirely different conception of the phenomena of nature:
"Nous retiendrons l'hypothèse aussi
longtemps qu'elle permettra d'inter-
préter fidèlement les faits; de les
grouper, de les relier entre eux et
d'en prévoir de nouveaux, aussi
longtemps, en un mot, qu'elle se
montrera féconde" (p. 2).   "Les
considérations sur la valeur de combinaison des éléments survivraient
à l'hypothèse des atomes si celle-ci
venait à être remplacée un jour
par une hypothèse plus générale.
Mais ce jour n'est pas arrivé; c'est
vainement qu'on chercherait à discréditer la première aussi longtemps
qu'elle se montrera féconde. Et sa
fécondité, sa puissance éclatent dans
les progrès incessants de la science.
C'est elle qui vivifie les découvertes
les plus récentes, comme elle a été
depuis Dalton son immortel auteur,

This statement implies that even as late as the end of the third quarter of the century, foremost thinkers hesitated to attach a more than provisional importance to chemical symbolism and the various elaborations of the atomic theory, as chemical text-books then exhibited them. Similar merely provisional theories have existed in other branches of science. The theory of the two fluids in electricity did good service for a long time in enabling philosophers to define their ideas, to describe, calculate, and predict phenomena. In optics, the so-called corpuscular theory of light is still used with advantage as a convenient means of summarising the laws of reflexion and refraction; similarly, in treatises on the conduction of heat, the old caloric theory still holds a place alongside of the more modern dynamical views. It may be questioned whether the celebrated periodic law of Newlands, Lothar Meyer, and Mendeléeff, which has brought some order into the atomic and other numbers referring to the different elements, and has even made it possible to predict the existence of unknown elements with definite properties, stands really in a firmer position than the once well-known but now forgotten law of Bode,[1] according to

26.
The periodic
law.

l'instrument le plus parfait pour les conceptions élevées de la théorie et le guide le plus sûr pour les recherches expérimentales" (p. 241). And quite mournfully does Kopp report at the close of his historical survey of the development of chemistry ('Entwickelung,'&c., p. 829) how that science about 1860 again "turned into the course which it had tried so often, and had so often abandoned as hopeless, endeavouring to gain a knowledge how the elementary atoms are arranged in the smallest particles of their compounds."

[1] According to the relation, first observed by Christian Wolff and Daniel Titius, that the distances of the planets from the sun obey approximately the formula $0\cdot4 + 0\cdot3 \times 2^n$, where n for Venus, Earth, Mars, &c., assumes the values 0, 1, 2, &c., the planet corresponding to $n=3$ was missing. When, on the discovery of Uranus in 1781, it was found that this planet's distance also agrees approximately with the formula, Bode and von Zach drew attention to this fact, and suggested a systematic search for the missing

which the gap in the series which gives the distances
of the planets from the sun indicated the existence of a

planet, "à chercher une aiguille dans une botte de foin." About the same time that this search was contemplated Piazzi found the first of the small planets, which—like the other subsequently discovered asteroids—corresponds very nearly with the expected position in the system. The periodic system of the elements, according to which the physical and chemical properties of all the elements show a periodic dependence upon the atomic weights, was first systematically stated by Newlands (in 1864) and by Lothar Meyer and Mendeléeff on the Continent. The latest edition of Meyer's treatise on "Modern Theories of Chemistry," of which only the first part, with the title 'Die Atome und ihre Eigenschaften' has been published (posthumously by the author's brother, Breslau, 1896), gives a good idea of how from small beginnings these statistics of the atomic theory of matter have grown into a great accumulation of interesting facts, upon which a system of inorganic chemistry can now be based which compares with the system of organic chemistry founded upon the types of Gerhardt in their original or in some modified form, and upon the "homologous" series of hydrocarbon compounds. As the typical arrangement of organic compounds, or rather of carbon compounds (for many real organic compounds are not easily classed by these methods), led to the suggestion of the existence of many compounds which were not known at the time, and have since been prepared, so the periodic arrangement enabled Mendeléeff to predict the properties of missing numbers of the periodic series. And although this mapping out of the

elements according to their atomic weights does not indicate how and where the missing numbers are to be found, as is the case with the law of Titius and Bode, and still more so with the homologous series of carbon compounds, still it is interesting to be able to state that in several instances — notably on the discovery of the new elements, gallium (by Lecoq de Boisbaudran in 1878), scandium (by Nilson in 1880), and germanium (by Winkler in 1886)—the properties of these substances confirmed to a very great extent the predictions of Mendeléeff. And when in 1894 Lord Rayleigh and Professor Ramsay announced their discovery of a new element in atmospheric air, which, from its inertness, was called argon, interesting suggestions as to its properties were drawn from speculations regarding its probable position in the periodic curve (see Lothar Meyer, *loc. cit.*, p. 165). It is true that these numerical regularities, which for some minds possess a great fascination, are, so far, purely statistical. It is possible to arrive by interpolation or extrapolation at valuable suggestions in statistics, in meteorology, and in mining operations; but so long as the actual cause or intrinsic connection is not known, which explains the necessity of these regularities, they are apt to be misleading, and have to be used with great caution. Still, the fact alone that they bring some order into a bewildering mass of figures and data makes them almost indispensable. For similar reasons many chemists adopted Gerhardt's types and homologous series as affording a ready method of classification, though not a rational explanation of phenomena.

planet between Mars and Jupiter, anticipating the discovery of the Asteroids, which have accordingly been
regarded as the fragments of the missing planet.

27.
Difference
between
chemical
and physical
reasoning.

It thus appears that purely "chemical reasoning," as it
has been called, has proved insufficient to establish the
atomic view of nature on the same firm basis as has
supported the mechanical or astronomical view ever since
the age of Galileo and Newton.[1] In the second half of
the century, the atomic view of matter has however
been put forward from a different side, and independent
researches have, in combination with the older chemical
theories, introduced so much definiteness into this line
of thought that " the Newtonian theory of gravitation is

[1] "Many diagrams and models
of compound molecules have been
constructed. These are the records of the efforts of chemists to
imagine configurations of material
systems by the geometrical relations of which chemical phenomena
may be illustrated or explained.
No chemist, however, professes to
see in these diagrams anything
more than symbolic representations
of the various degrees of closeness
with which the different com-
ponents of the molecule are bound
together. In astronomy, on the
other hand, the configurations and
motions of the heavenly bodies are
on such a scale that we can ascertain them by direct observation ;
. . . the doctrine of universal gravitation not only explains the observed motions of our system, but
enables us to calculate the motions
of the system in which the astronomical elements may have any
values whatever" (Clerk Maxwell,
"On the Dynamical Evidence
of the Molecular Constitution of
Bodies," June 1875, 'Scientific
Papers,' vol. ii. p. 418). "The

chemists ascertain by experiment
the ratios of the masses of the
different substances in a compound.
From these they deduce the chemical equivalents of the different substances, that of a particular substance being taken as unity. The
only evidence made use of is that
furnished by chemical combination.
It is also assumed, in order to account for the facts of combination,
that the reason why substances
combine in definite ratios is, that
the molecules of the substances
are in the ratio of their chemical
equivalents, and that what we call
combination is an action which
takes place by a union of a molecule of one substance to a molecule
of the other. This kind of reasoning, when presented in a proper
form, and sustained by proper evidence, has a high degree of cogency.
But it is purely chemical reasoning ;
it is not dynamical reasoning. It
is founded on chemical experience,
not on the laws of motion" (Id.
article "Atom," 'Ency. Brit.,' 1875 ;
ibid., vol. ii. p. 456).

not surer to us now than is the atomic or molecular theory in chemistry and physics—so far, at all events, as its assertion of heterogeneousness in the minute structure of matter, apparently homogeneous to our senses, and to our most delicate direct instrumental tests." [1]

This side of the atomic view of matter has been developed by the study of the properties of bodies in the gaseous state, and, in its modern form, goes back to the experiments of Gay-Lussac, which were almost simultaneous with those of Dalton.[2] It is interesting to note how little the latter recognised the importance of these researches, when he rejected the so-called law of volumes, according to which gases, under the same pressure, and at equal temperatures, enter into, or separate out of, chemical combination in definite and very simple proportions of their volume. As, according to the law of definite proportions, bodies (including gases) combine only

28.
The kinetic theory of gases.

[1] Lord Kelvin on "Capillary Attraction," 1886. See 'Popular Lectures and Addresses,' vol. i. p. 4.

[2] The first results referring to the combining volumes of oxygen and hydrogen gas in forming water were given by Gay - Lussac and Humboldt in a joint memoir. Their experiments were carried on in 1805. Gay-Lussac continued the experiments alone, extended them to gaseous compounds, and published his results in 1809 in the second volume of the 'Mémoires d'Arcueil.' This was one year after the publication of Dalton's 'New System of Chemical Philosophy,' and two years after Thomas Thomson had published a sketch of the atomic theory in his text-book on Chemistry. The law of equal expansion of all gases with temperature was published by Dalton in 1801 ; the law of pressures—that the volume of a gas, at the same temperature, is inversely as the pressure—was published by Boyle in 1662. It goes on the Continent under the name of Mariotte, who first made it generally known about twelve years later (see on this the fourth appendix to the 2nd edition of Tait's 'Properties of Matter,' 1890). The law of temperatures was published in 1802 by Gay-Lussac in the 'Annales de Chimie et de Physique' (vol. xliii. p. 137), where he remarks that Charles, Professor of Physics at the "Conservatoire," had fifteen years earlier noted the property indicated by this law. Both these so-called laws of gases are only accurate within certain [not very wide limits of temperature and pressure.

according to definite proportions of their weight, it follows that in the gaseous state these combining weights of bodies have either equal volumes or such as stand in very simple proportions. Now the amount of matter (measured by weight) in the same volume is called the density of a gas. It therefore follows, by putting Dalton's and Gay-Lussac's discoveries together, that the combining weights of gases are either directly proportional to their densities or to a simple multiple thereof. Some years after this discovery in 1809, Gay-Lussac extended his statement so as not only to embrace elementary gases, such as hydrogen, oxygen, and nitrogen, but also compounds, such as ammonia, carbonic acid, hydrochloric acid, and showed how, if they enter into chemical combination, they likewise do so in the simple proportions of one volume of one, to one or two volumes of the other.

Whilst chemists such as Gay-Lussac, Berzelius, and others [1] recognised in the facts discovered by the first a

[1] Dalton was the only person who doubted the correctness of Gay-Lussac's figures, although both Thomson and Berzelius pointed out to him the great support they afforded to the atomic theory. Berzelius also saw the usefulness of the law of volumes in fixing the smallest combining or atomic numbers in cases where the reference to weight alone left the matter undecided. Thus he correctly inferred that the formula of water should be H_2O, as we write it to-day, because two volumes of hydrogen combined with one of oxygen. But it was unfortunate that, through his want of appreciation of Avogadro's further expositions, he was unable to reconcile more completely the appeal to volume with that to weight, and that in consequence great uncertainty reigned for a long time in these matters. This induced L. Gmelin to disregard the volumetric relations in his system of equivalents, to the great detriment of those who in the middle of the century were brought up with very vague and unsatisfactory explanations on this subject—different numbers being used in books on organic and inorganic chemistry. A great confusion existed at that time, Gerhardt showing good reasons, based upon his observations of the substitution of hydrogen in organic compounds and the system of classification which he introduced, why several of Gmelin's figures should be doubled ; but the matter was not cleared up till Cannizzaro

method for determining the combining weights of elements
or their simple multiples, they did not draw the natural
consequences as to the physical constitution of bodies in
the gaseous state which followed from these and other
facts which had been known before.   It had been known
since the time of Boyle and Mariotte that equal volumes of
different gases under equal pressure change their volumes
equally if the pressure is varied equally, and it was also
known through Gay-Lussac himself that equal volumes of
different gases under equal pressure change their volumes
equally with equal rise of temperature.   The like be- 29.
Avogadro's
haviour of equal volumes of different gases towards pres- hypothesis.
sure, temperature, and chemical combination suggested
to Avogadro, and almost simultaneously to Ampère, the
very simple assumption that this is owing to the fact that
equal volumes of different gases contain an equal number of smallest independent particles of matter.   This is
Avogadro's celebrated hypothesis.   It was the first step in
the direct physical verification of the atomic view of matter, and if maintained by further experience, it was destined to be one of the most important proofs of this view.
But this assumption or hypothesis had to be reconciled
with facts.   It was, for instance, observed that a given
quantity of hydrochloric acid gas occupied the same

showed the real meaning and importance of Avogadro's hypothesis.
A good exposition of the difference
of opinions which were held at that
time will be found in A. Wurtz,
'La Théorie atomique,' p. 55, &c.
See also Prof. Bedson's 'Memorial
Lecture' on Lothar Meyer (1896),
in the 'Journal of the Chemical
Society,' p. 519, &c., and especially the graphic description by L.
Meyer himself of the meeting held
in September 1860 at Carlsruhe
for the purpose of ventilating these
important theoretical questions (L.
Meyer's translation of Cannizzaro's
'Sunto di un corso di filosofia
chimica,' in Ostwald's 'Classiker
der exacten Wissenschaften,' No.
30, Appendix, p. 58).

volume as did each of the equivalent quantities, hydrogen and chlorine, out of which it was compounded, and it appeared that accordingly double the number of atoms were condensed into the same volume. To explain this, and yet maintain his original hypothesis, Avogadro was forced into the conception of compound atoms or particles —*i.e.*, into the assumption that the smallest independent particles need not be the elementary atoms of hydrogen and chlorine themselves, but might be made up of two or more of such atoms, chemically connected in such a way that the expansion of the gas under increasing temperature or decreasing pressure did not affect this complex of elementary particles.[1] Such a compound

[1] Avogadro published his memoir in the 'Journal de Physique' in 1811, and Ampère expounded similar views three years later in the form of a letter to Berthollet in the 'Annales de Chimie.' Neither the celebrity of Ampère nor the exhaustive explanations of Avogadro, who was then an unknown author, prevented this hypothesis, which is now looked upon as a cornerstone of the atomic view, from falling into oblivion. Whewell does not mention it. Even Kopp, whose labours for many years covered a field little cultivated by most other chemists, that of physical chemistry, makes no mention of Avogadro's and Ampère's hypothesis in his great work on the History of Chemistry, published between the years 1843 and 1847. In his later work ('Die Entwickelung der Chemie,' 1873) he enters elaborately into the causes which made chemical philosophers overlook so valuable a suggestion (p. 353, &c.) Like Whewell's History, Poggendorf's Dictionary (1863) was silent about Avogadro. The distinc-

tion between molecules and atoms seemed to complicate matters; besides, the new hypothesis was not launched in conjunction with any new experimental discoveries, as had been the case with Dalton's, Davy's, and Gay-Lussac's theories. The first who again drew attention to the subject was Dumas, who in 1826 began his investigations regarding the specific weight of vapours—*i.e.*, of bodies in a gaseous state. He there drew attention to the necessity of distinguishing between chemical and physical particles, but he does not yet consistently use the terms atom and molecule to denote the former and the latter. In the meantime, however, a very important step had been taken in the development of the atomic view. In 1819 Dulong and Petit published their experimental researches concerning the specific heat of a large number of elementary bodies—*i.e.*, the measured quantities of heat (compared with a standard substance) which were required to raise a number of metals by one degree in tempera-

atom or complex was termed a molecule, and it was assumed that molecules, or smallest individual particles of chemical substances, might be made up of one or more atoms of the same or of different substances. Avogadro was able in this way to explain how a certain number of molecules of hydrogen—each made up of two atoms— combine with an equal number of molecules of chlorine ; these being likewise composed of two atoms of chlorine, in order to form an equal number of molecules of hydrochloric acid, each of these consisting of two atoms—*viz.*, one of chlorine and one of hydrogen. This view, which Ampère likewise adopted, did not recommend itself to chemists for many years ; not indeed till, about the year 1840, several eminent chemists—notably Laurent—were independently led to consider chemical compounds as formed by what is termed substitution instead of simple combination.[1] For, according to Avogadro's view, the for-

30.
Neglect of
same.

ture. They then found that these quantities stood very nearly in inverse proportions to the atomic or combining numbers. They at the same time pointed out the uncertainty which — in consequence of the law of fixed multiple proportions — existed regarding the smallest figure which was to determine the combining weights ; they chose those numbers which brought out clearly the physical regularity and coincidence which they had discovered ; and they expressed their result in the rule that the atoms of all elementary bodies have the same capacity for heat. Whereas Berzelius ignored the theoretical discussions of Avogadro and Ampère, he hailed the experimental data of Dulong and Petit as most useful in helping to fix correctly the real equivalent numbers, a task to which,

as the fundamental requisite of all chemistry, he devoted so much time and labour. It must, however, be noted that the law of Dulong and Petit, now universally accepted as a fundamental fact in the atomic theory, is, as little as the laws of Boyle, Charles, and Gay - Lussac, rigidly correct : it obtains within certain limits. The experiments of Dulong and Petit were extended to compounds by F. Neumann in 1831. The connection of the specific heat or thermal capacity of compounds and that of their constituents was fully investigated by Regnault. A statement of the difficulties and anomalies which still exist will be found in L. Meyer's ' Die Atome und ihre Eigenschaften' (p. 73, &c.)

[1] A very important influence in contributing to the gradual recog-

mation of the molecule of hydrochloric acid depended upon an exchange of places of the atomic constituents in the molecules of the elementary substances, an atom of chlorine being substituted for an atom of hydrogen in the hydrogen molecule, and *vice versá* in the chlorine molecule.

About the middle of this century the conviction was thus firmly established in the minds of chemical philosophers that the simple symbolism by which Dalton and Berzelius expressed chemical combinations and processes was insufficient for the purpose of systematically arranging the

nition of the difference between atom and molecule belongs also to Gerhardt, who emphasised a fact known already to Berzelius—*viz.*, that hydrogen according to his notation appeared to combine with other bodies always in paired atoms. This fact remained unnoticed if the atomic number of hydrogen was put at 1, oxygen at 8, as was done by English chemists and reintroduced by Gmelin. Berzelius did not attach a fundamental importance to this fact. Blomstrand ('Die Chemie der Jetztzeit,' 1869, p. 30) has shown that this originated in his clinging to Lavoisier's oxygen theory. Oxygen was made the centre and measure of everything in chemistry, also of the equivalence of substances : Berzelius thus started from a unit which was too large, and with which the smaller value of hydrogen could not be measured. Gerhardt fully recognised the importance of this fact ; showed in many examples that the combining or atomic weight of hydrogen had been fixed too high ; and proposed to halve most of the organic formulæ. In this way he proposed to bring harmony into the theory of combining volumes and the atomic theory. He partially succeeded in doing so, although in the

case of inorganic elements he went too far. This important step, which has been extolled by some, and depreciated by other historians of chemistry, is lucidly expounded by Rau in his 'Theorien der modernen Chemie' (vol. ii. p. 107, &c.) Wurtz ('Théorie atomique,' p. 64) considers Gerhardt's influence as a reform, and alludes to it as bringing again into view the hypothesis of Avogadro : "Voilà le thème d'Avogadro et d'Ampère, qui revient à l'horizon, comme une étoile dirigeante, après une longue éclipse. Et pourtant on ne peut pas dire qu'elle ait été pour Gerhardt, à cette époque du moins, un guide exclusif. Les considérations maîtresses qu'il a invoquées sont plutôt d'ordre purement chimique. Elles étaient justes, et il s'est trouvé qu'elles concordaient avec une idée également juste, et qui était tombée dans l'oubli. La distinction entre deux espèces de petites particules, molécules et atomes, qu'Avogadro et Ampère avaient introduite inutilement dans la science, que M. Dumas avait essayé de faire revivre dans sa Philosophie chimique, cette distinction était peut-être faite dans l'esprit de Gerhardt, mais elle n'apparaissait pas encore dans son langage."

growing volume of chemical knowledge ; that the conception of the atom must be extended and more closely defined ; that the proportions of weight were inadequate for
the purpose of distinguishing and identifying the many
organic compounds; and especially that the relations of
volume and the arrangements of particles of matter in space
must be taken notice of, if the atomic view of matter was
to be made further serviceable for scientific purposes. That
purely geometrical relations, such as can be grasped only
by our space conceptions, are of importance in the chemical composition of substances, was very evident, for
instance, in some of the optical properties of crystallised
organic substances.   The discoveries of Pasteur, published
in 1850, mark in this respect an epoch in science.[1]   He
showed that there exist chemical substances which are
different, but only as a right-hand glove differs from a
left-hand one, a right-handed screw from a left-handed,

31.
Develop-
ment of the
atomic view.

32.
Pasteur's
discovery of
"chirality."

---

[1] A special line of " physical " or
"mechanical" reasoning which bears
upon the atomic view of matter began with Biot's discovery in 1815
that certain fluids—notably organic
—have the property of rotating the
plane of polarisation of light which
passes through them.   Later on he
extended this observation to the
vapours formed by such fluids.
Faraday found in 1846 that substances which are optically "inactive" become active in the
manner described under the influence of powerful electro-magnets.
An explanation of the phenomenon
by Fresnel, which was based upon
crystalline structure, would — for
liquids and vapours—have to be
applied to the structure of the molecule itself.   Pasteur found in 1850
that there exist two modifications

of tartaric acid, which differ in this
only, that one of them turns the
plane of polarisation to the right,
the other to the left, and that a
mixture of both in the proper proportions is inactive.   As far back
as 1860, in his ' Leçons de Chimie,'
he put the question, "whether
the atoms in tartaric acid are arranged like the turns of a right-
handed screw, or situated in the
corners of an irregular tetrahedron,
or have they any other asymmetrical
grouping? . . . There can be no doubt
that the atoms have an unsym-
metrical arrangement after the fashion of mirrored images which cannot
be made to fall into each other "
(quoted by Van't Hoff, 'Die Lagerung der Atome im Raume,' German translation, 2nd ed., p. 9).

the image in a mirror from the original. Was it possible any longer to suppress the conviction that the smallest particles of matter, in forming chemical compounds, do so not only in definite proportions of weight, but also in definite geometrical distances and positions ?

About the middle of the century the atomic view of matter had thus received considerable modifications. Originally suggested only to explain, describe, or symbolise the fact that different substances combine in fixed, and especially in fixed multiple proportions, it had to be modified by a recognition of the fact that in gases at least a distinction exists between particles which are closely knit together—as it were, geometrically inseparable—and such as can move away from each other. The latter explain the increase of volume under increasing temperature or decreasing pressure. Geometrical distance came in as the means of distinguishing the molecule from the atom. And lastly, about 1850, the phenomena of right- and left-handedness,[1] discovered by Pasteur, suggested the idea of geometrical position as well as of distance. The atom had become a molecule, with a definite geometrical arrangement.

33.
Atom and
molecule.

It took, however, a full generation before, in the second half of the century, these different suggestions for a modification of the atomic view became clear, before philosophers took seriously the opinion that molecules and atoms existed in reality, and were not merely a convenient symbolism, as many great chemists during the first half of the century were inclined to think. This change in the habit of chemical thought has no doubt been greatly

[1] Called by Lord Kelvin "chirality."

brought about by the development of the so-called kinetic theory of gases in the second half of the century. This is a physical, not a chemical, theory.

The kinetic theory of gases, invented for the purpose of explaining the pressure which all bodies in the gaseous state exert on the walls of the containing vessels, will always be identified with the two names of Clausius in Germany and Clerk Maxwell in England.[1] But if we

[1] Before the atomic view of matter had, in the course of the last fifty years, closely and definitely allied itself with the kinetic view, it had been allied with the astronomical view of matter. In the last century and the earlier decades of the present century we frequently find the behaviour of a complex of molecules or atoms compared with that of a planetary system ; but in addition to the forces of attraction, those of repulsion had to be resorted to in order to explain the expansiveness of gases. Heat was then considered to be a material substance, the particles of which repelled each other. Dalton favoured this view in the introduction to his 'New System of Chemical Philosophy' ; so did Berthollet and most of the French physicists who were brought up in the school of Newton and Laplace. Lasswitz, in his 'Geschichte der Atomistik' (2 vols., Hamburg, 1890), has traced the 'Decline of Kinetic Atomism' in the seventeenth century under the influence of the 'Corpuscular Philosophy.' The kinetic view of matter was allied with the Cartesian physical philosophy, which was dispelled by Newtonianism in France and by Kant's philosophy in Germany. In consequence, when in Germany A. Krönig published his 'Grundzüge einer Theorie der Gase' in 1856, philosophers who had been speculating in the direction of a Newtonian atomism (see Fechner's 'Atomenlehre,'1855 ; Redtenbacher's 'Dynamiden System,' 1857 ; and other publications quoted by Rosenberger, 'Geschichte der Physik,' vol. iii. p. 536, &c.) were much taken by surprise. It had the immediate result of inducing R. Clausius, who had been occupied with similar researches since 1850, to publish his celebrated memoir, 'Ueber die Art der Bewegung welche wir Wärme nennen' (Poggendorf's 'Annalen,' vol. c., 1857). These two publications first called general attention to the subject.   Joule's paper, which appeared in the 'Memoirs of the Lit. and Phil. Soc. of Manchester,' had remained unnoticed, but was reprinted by him, at the request of Clausius, in the 'Philosophical Magazine' (4th ser. vol. xiv.) in 1857.   Subsequently, the researches of Paul du Bois-Reymond and others unearthed a whole list of authors who, in more or less definite ways, had resorted to the hypothesis of a rectilinear translatory motion of the molecules in order to explain the phenomena of pressure and other properties of gases. Among these, Daniel Bernoulli (in his 'Hydrodynamica,' 1738) seems to have expressed the clearest views, and he is now usually named as the father of the hypothesis. The fullest statement of the historical data will be found in the posthumous second edition of

agree to date the real birth, not the incubation, of any
scientific idea from the moment when it was set forth
in definite figures, and with mathematical precision per-
mitting of a precise verification by actual test, the modern
theory of gases was born in Manchester in the school
of Dalton, when Joule in 1857 actually calculated the
velocity with which a particle of hydrogen at ordinary
atmospheric pressure and temperature must be moving,
assuming that this atmospheric pressure is equilibrated by
the rectilinear motion and impact of the supposed particles
of the gas on each other and the walls of the containing
vessel. This meant taking the atomic view of matter in
real earnest, not merely symbolically, as chemists had done.
Joule gave up the older and vague ideas of a rotatory or a
vibratory motion of the particles of a gas which had been
floating about since the time of Hooke[1] in various theories,
and adopted the suggestion of Daniel Bernoulli, known to
him through Herapath, that all particles of gaseous matter
are in a natural state of rectilinear motion, which is
changed only by the encounter with other particles or by
the walls of the containing vessel on which they impinge,
and from which they rebound.[2]

34.
Joule's cal-
culations.

Clausius, 'Die mechanische Wärme-
theorie' (Braunschweig, 1889 - 91,
p. 2, &c.) See also O. E. Mayer,
'Die kinetische Theorie der Gase'
(2nd ed., Breslau, 1895, part i. p. 11).
   [1] See Tait, 'Properties of Matter,'
2nd ed., p. 289, also J. P. Joule's
Memoir on 'Heat and the Constitution of Elastic Fluids,' 1848, reprinted in 'Scientific Papers,' vol.
i. p. 290, &c.
   [2] The real proof that the kinetic,
in contradistinction to what we may
call the Newtonian, view of the
motion of the molecules of a gas is
the correct one, and that Newtonian
(attracting and repelling) forces
play only a subordinate, if any, part
in the observable phenomena of
gaseous bodies, is based upon Joule
and Thomson's experiments made
in 1853. It belongs to quite a
different line of reasoning, neither
chemical nor mechanical, but going
upon the principle introduced into
scientific thought about the middle
of the century, that heat and work
are convertible terms and equivalent
quantities. Now, it was generally
assumed, before Joule and Thomson

This idea of the rectilinear motion of the particles of matter in a free, *i.e.*, a gaseous, state (the first attempt to explain the physical properties of matter by giving a numerical value to a molecular, not molar, quantity) was not regarded by chemists, for it was indeed of little use in explaining chemical combinations and reactions. It, however, very soon received an important addition under the treatment of Clausius.[1]

35.
Clausius's
firstmemoir.

The kinetic theory of gases had not been propounded for the purpose of explaining chemical phenomena; it had grown out of repeated attempts to explain the nature of heat, and the fact, established about ten years earlier by Mayer and Joule, that heat can be transformed into the mechanical energy of molar motion. The idea suggested itself that if heat can disappear and be replaced by the measurable motion of molar (measurably large) masses, and *vice versâ*, heat itself may be merely the energy of the directly immeasurable movements of molecular (immeasurably small) masses; and as every body

made their careful experiments, that if gaseous bodies were allowed to expand, without doing work, no change of temperature took place—*i.e.*, that heat neither appeared nor disappeared. This would mean that no work of either repelling or attracting forces was done. Joule and Thomson showed that there was indeed a very slight cooling, indicating that a small amount of heat or energy was used up in doing work against attracting forces —the forces of cohesion. Had repelling forces existed, their work would have shown itself in a rise of temperature. This line of reasoning will occupy us in a subsequent chapter (see O. E. Meyer, 'Theorie der Gase,' vol. i. p. 7, &c., also

Joule's 'Scientific Papers,' vol. ii. p. 216, &c.)

[1] How little chemical and physical reasoning went hand in hand before the middle of the century is seen from the fact that only after Clausius had published his first paper (see note, p. 433), in which he came to the conclusion that the molecules or smallest physical particles of simple (elementary) substances consist of several atoms, was his attention drawn to the fact that some French chemists, notably Dumas, Laurent, and Gerhardt, had already, by different arguments, arrived at the conclusion that the molecules of simple (elementary) gases consist of several atoms (see Clausius, *loc. cit.*, p. 22, &c.)

in the gaseous state shows the mechanical energy which
we call pressure or expansiveness, the attempt was made
to explain the phenomena of expansion, pressure, and
temperature of gases by a purely mechanical hypothesis.
This answered remarkably well. On the assumption that
the particles of a perfect gas possess a rectilinear motion,
the experimental formulæ of Boyle and Mariotte, of Dalton, and of Gay-Lussac, could be theoretically deduced.
It also became evident that under this conception the
forgotten statement of Avogadro must be correct, according to which equal volumes of different gases, under equal
pressures and at equal temperatures, contain an equal
number of freely moving particles.

36.
Internal
energy of
molecules.

And when Clausius showed further that in perfect
gases only a portion of the quantities of energy which
are measured as motion or as heat can be explained
by the assumed rectilinear motion of the particles of
gases, and that an internal motion of the particles themselves must be assumed, the new ideas became still more
exactly defined; they included the conception familiar to
chemists of compound atoms or molecules. The smallest
individual particles of matter in the free state were themselves not simple bodies, but systems of still smaller
particles; they were molecules composed of atoms; the
symbols of chemists became descriptive of real physical
conditions; the vague notions of radicles, types, or compound atoms began to acquire geometrical and mechanical
definiteness.

Thus the atomic theory, known to the ancients, revived
by Dalton in the early years of the century, and employed by chemical philosophers for half a century as a

convenient symbolism, had, about the year 1860, been accepted by physicists, and used not merely as a convenient symbolism, but as a physical reality.

37.
The atomic
theory ac-
cepted as a
physical
theory about
1860.

Joule had actually calculated the velocity of a particle of hydrogen gas. The atomic view of nature was now taken in real earnest. To establish it still further, there were required definite numerical data [1] as to the size of the smallest particles (henceforth sometimes called atoms, sometimes more correctly molecules) and their number, and also clearer views as to the composition of the molecules out of their elements, the chemical atoms.

The interest which attaches to this latest development of the atomic theory is very great: it has brought about a union of the researches of chemists and physicists, and has made chemistry a province of natural philosophy.[2] No one has done more than the late Professor Clerk Max-

---

[1] Numerical data regarding the size and number of smallest physical particles contained in a given volume of matter have been supplied by various methods or various "lines of reasoning." The best summary will be found in Lord Kelvin's lecture, "On the Size of Atoms" (1883: reprinted in 'Popular Lectures and Addresses,' vol. i. p. 147 *sqq.*) The four lines of reasoning are founded on the undulatory theory of light, on the phenomena of contact electricity, on capillary attraction, and on the kinetic theory of gases. They "agree in showing that the molecules of ordinary matter must be something like the one ten-millionth, or from the one ten-millionth to the one hundred-millionth of a centimetre in diameter."

[2] "We can distinguish two kinds of motion, atomic motion and molecular motion. . . . To this dis-

tinction corresponds the division of natural philosophy into physics and chemistry, not rigidly, yet in so far as chemistry is mainly occupied with the equilibrium of the atoms, physics with the mechanics of the molecules. Chemical equilibrium, unchanged condition of the molecules, exists if the affinity which holds together the atoms equilibrates the forces which tend to loosen the composition of the molecule: these forces consist in the motion of the atoms. . . . As accordingly in a chemically stable compound the atomic motions remain in lasting dynamical equilibrium with the chemical forces, . . . there remains for the examination of the purely physical phenomena in the first instance only the molecular movements" (O. E. Meyer, 'Die kinetische Theorie der Gase,' vol. i. p. 6).

well to develop the novel conceptions which here force themselves upon us.   Especially are we indebted to him for the idea—marking an epoch in the history of scientific thought—of the difference between historical knowledge of natural phenomena and a merely statistical summary of average results.[1]   If the atomic view of nature has to be adopted seriously, as the development of the kinetic

38.
Clerk Maxwell. The statistical view of nature.

[1] See Clerk Maxwell's memoir, 'Illustrations of the Dynamical Theory of Gases' (1859 : reprinted in 'Scientific Papers,' vol. i. p. 377). Clausius had in his second paper, "On the average mean path of a particle" (Poggendorf's 'Annalen,' 1858), given an expression for this quantity as depending on the average distance of two particles and on the average diameter of the sphere of action of a particle. As these quantities are all only mean or average quantities, he had been obliged to resort to a method which was then novel in physical science, the method of averages and the calculus of probability, which is its mathematical expression. He had calculated the probability of a certain motion of a particle. Maxwell, who had in 1856 been engaged in writing his Adams prize essay "On the stability of the motion of Saturn's rings," had there considered the possibility of these rings being composed of a cloud of scattered particles moving with all possible velocities towards each other and round some attracting centre : he was thus familiar with physical problems in which the given data could be only average quantities. He now undertook to develop systematically the methods necessary for treating such problems, of which we have only statistical knowledge, and he there developed his famous law which gives the distribution of different velocities in a crowd of particles moving at random and in their collisions obeying the condition of the conservation of energy. This investigation marks an epoch in mathematical physics and in the history of the atomic view of nature. Like all theorems connected with the theory of probability, it has provoked a large literature, the foundations of the proof and the different steps in the logic of the deductions having been examined and criticised in the most searching manner. The expression given by Maxwell has stood all these criticisms,—"he has demonstrated the possibility of calculating in a strict manner the averages which before him had only been estimated, but which were required for a further development of the theory of gases." See O. E. Meyer, 'Die kinetische Theorie der Gase,' 2nd ed., vol. i. p. 45, &c., where also a complete account is given of the various steps by which the doubts which attached to Maxwell's theories and his proofs were at length removed, and the "variety of traps and pit-falls" avoided "which are met with even in the elements of the subject" (see Tait, "On the Foundations of the Kinetic Theory of Gases," 'Trans. of the Royal Soc. of Edinburgh,' 1886, vol. xxxiii. part 1, p. 66). In a later chapter of this history I intend to trace the development of the statistical view of nature, and shall then have occasion to revert to this subject.

theory of gases suggests, we begin to realise the enormous numbers of individual elements of matter with which we have to do in any physical or chemical operation or experiment. The step which enabled mathematicians to calculate molar and cosmical phenomena by looking upon them as made up of an immeasurably, nay infinitely, large number of elementary parts, be these of space or time, was taken by Newton and Leibniz : its result was the invention, development, and application of the infinitesimal calculus. Our fundamental notions applied only to integrals, to a summation of these differential properties. It was the problem of the new calculus to deduce from the simple differential properties, expressed in what is called the differential equation, the results of finite observable quantities. This was done by a process of summation or integration. In this process the elements were, however, all considered to be equal. This was an assumption which, for the purposes of simplicity, might be safely made in a first approximation. When, however, the kinetic theory of gases took seriously into account the motion, velocity, number, and size of the constituent particles of matter contained in any finite measurable volume, or portion of matter, two distinct views presented themselves : the one which looks only at the total or average result and aspect of the phenomena, the other which looks at the actual behaviour and properties of the component parts, be these ever so numerous or ever so small. These latter could no longer be regarded as differentials which lose their independent existence in the process of summation : they had individual properties, which were not lost in the aggregate. It is evident that chemists had been studying those properties of matter that are preserved distinct in ever so large a number of individuals which are characteristically and specifically alike : while physicists had been mainly studying the properties of distance, motion, velocity, and size, which, if added together, merge themselves into a common sum, integral or average. It does not follow that, even so far as these latter properties are concerned, the numberless individual particles of matter behave alike; their sizes, velocities, and movements may be very different : indeed it is evident that, in a large crowd of moving particles, they must be widely different.

39.
Doctrine of
averages.

In assigning numbers to these data, it was therefore clear that only average or mean values could be meant, and that our actual physical knowledge of the individual elements resembles that statistical information which we possess, for instance, regarding the mortality, average age, and general properties and ways of the members of a great population. It is statistical knowledge, it is not individual, historical, or biographical knowledge, that we possess.

The individual behaviour of the single molecules, their sizes, their velocities, the length of their paths, their vibrations, rotations, and internal motions, remain unknown. What can be known is only the average magnitudes of these quantities, and possibly the extreme limits within which these individual magnitudes vary. The great differences exhibited by larger portions of different kinds of matter—i.e., the chemical differences or qualities—were reduced to the actual composition and qualities of the molecules and atoms themselves. Chemists and physicists were now alike compelled to venture on some more definite hypothesis, descriptive of the great variety of constitution which the molecules of chemically distinct substances exhibit. These molecules show in their combining numbers, and in their physical properties, great fixity, excluding apparently all gradual transitions. The manner in which they enter into, and again separate out of, combinations and compounds, always regaining and showing their original characteristics, forced more and more upon natural philosophers the conviction that compounds were merely geometrical arrangements of individually independent atoms, and that these atoms must possess geometrically different forms and figures, enabling them, without loss of their individuality, to enter into varying configurations.

40.
Geometrical arrangement of atoms.

The conception of the molecule as a system of atoms, geometrically arranged, had gradually grown from vague suggestions in the minds of physicists as well as chemists —i.e., of students of the quantitative as well as of those of the qualitative properties of substances. To the former it was especially the forms of crystals, to the latter the different degrees of saturation of chemical substances, that suggested a geometrical arrangement of atoms as the constitution of the smallest particles or molecules of different substances.

Ever since the study of the regular forms of minerals or of artificially prepared crystals was reduced to an exact science by the labours of Haüy, at the end of the last century,[1] the forms of these regular shapes have been valued by investigators, for two distinct rea-

41.
Crystallography.

[1] See above, chapter i. p. 116.

sons. They seemed to afford a practical means of recognising and obtaining in the laboratory substances in their qualitative or chemical purity, if they were elements, or in identical chemical combinations, if they were compounds. And secondly, these regular, recurring forms, which, in many cases, exhibited characteristic and geometrically fixed arrangements of plane surfaces, appeared the only means by which we could gain an insight into the grouping and the shape of the ultimate particles, out of which, according to the atomic view, molar substances were constituted. If the particles of any substance, when set free to follow their most natural movements by solution, by fusion, or by volatilisation, meet again during the process of solidification in definite, always recurring forms, the conclusion seems obvious that the individual and ultimate particles possess marked peculiarities in the different directions of space. And it is almost inconceivable that these peculiarities should consist in anything else than in distinct primitive forms, arranged in varying, but geometrically definable, meshes of a network. Accordingly, different systems have been elaborated ever since the age of Haüy, which have the object of easily classifying, recognising, and measuring crystalline structures, or, more ambitiously, of discovering the number of simple forms and arrangements of networks of which our spatial conceptions admit. It is satisfactory to be able to state that investigations of the latter kind, carried on from seemingly different beginnings, have resulted in the recognition of a certain limited number of forms of symmetry. This symmetry is referred to points, called centres, or to lines, called axes, or to planes of symmetry.[1] French and German investigators have deduced in different ways the different possible forms of symmetry, and have shown that in all thirty-two different forms of symmetry or groups are geometrically possible. These thirty-two fundamental groups of crystals can be gathered up into six classes or types, according to the different systems of crystallographic axes or the number of planes of symmetry belonging to them.[2]

[1] The question may be raised, to what extent crystallography is obliged to assume a molecular structure of matter, or what support does the atomic view receive from it? On this point see Ostwald's 'Allgemeine Chemie,' vol. i. p. 855, &c. The geometrical forms of crystals can either be derived from elementary polyhedra, as Haüy attempted to do by his "molécules intégrantes" and his theory of decrescences, space being in this system considered as continuously filled ; or the elementary particles may be considered to consist of meshes of points geometrically arranged in the corners of a primitive figure in three dimensions ; or elementary spheres or ellipsoids may be supposed to be piled on each other like cannon-balls. The two latter systems assume vacant spaces ; the first view refers to the crystalline shape to some primitive crystal, and, therefore, does not explain it. It has accordingly been said that "the structure of crystals is one of the principal supports of the molecular theory. In assuming continuous matter without at least points which are geometrically or kinematically distinct, the anisotropic structure of crystals is quite unthinkable." (Lehmann, 'Molecular-physik,' vol. ii. p. 376). This view does not agree with what Ostwald says ('Allgemeine Chemie,' vol. i. p. 868) ; he considers that the structure of crystals affords no proof for the molecular constitution of matter, as the data of elasticity by no means necessarily require a molecular arrangement, but formally can be ascribed as easily to continuous matter. "Nevertheless the molecular view has the advantage of greater evidence, and leads to the same results with much greater simplicity, and hence more convincingly." It seems, however, that if chemical facts and physical theory force upon us the atomic view, crystallographic phenomena force us to complete it by some conception of geometrical arrangements.

[2] This purely geometrical treatment was introduced by Bravais in his 'Études crystallographiques' (1851), the much earlier work of Hessel ('Krystallometrie,' 1831) having been forgotten. It was further developed by L. Sohnke ('Entwickelung der Theorie der Krystallstructur,' 1879), and completed by Curie (1884) and Minnigerode (1886). A concise summary will be found in Liebisch, 'Physikalische Krystallographie,' Leipzig, 1891, pp. 3 to 50 ; also Groth, 'Physikalische Krystallographie,' Leipzig, 1895, p. 324, &c.

42.
Analogy
between
crystallo-
graphic and
atomic laws.   An analogy has been pointed out [1] between the atomic
theory in chemistry, by which Dalton explained the fixed
simple and multiple proportions of the combining weights
of various substances, and the molecular theory of crystalline structures, by which the fundamental forms of crystals
are defined and the accessory forms derived from them.
It has been found that if once a crystal has been defined
by a fundamental plane referred to three axes at fixed
angles, all other planes or faces can be defined by simple
multiples of the numbers which belong to the fundamental
plane, and which are called the parameters of the crystal.
This fundamental rule or law of crystallisation, termed by
Haüy the law of derivation, stands thus in the same relation to the corpuscular theory of the structure of bodies
as the law of fixed multiple proportions stands to the
original atomic view of matter, and it is thought that it
may in the future lead to important results.[2]

43.
Isomor-
phism.   Another very remarkable discovery had been made by
Mitscherlich in 1823.[3] This is the property which various
compounds possess of crystallising in the same forms,
although they contain different elements—such elements
being, however, joined together by similar formulæ. The
elements are, as it were, interchangeable. This phe-

---

[1] See Ostwald, "Allgemeine Chemie,' vol. i. p. 870.

[2] A question arises in this connection as to the accuracy of the crystallographic law of the fixity of the
angles. In respect of this Ostwald
says : "On examining the validity
of the fundamental laws of crystallography, it becomes evident that
they are only approximate, or perhaps more correctly, that there exist
numerous circumstances which permit them to show themselves only in
a somewhat disturbed manner" (loc.
cit., vol. i. p. 890). This I understand to mean that, if disturbing
circumstances could be removed,
the law of the fixity of angles and
the simple multiples of the indices
would obtain with the same accuracy as do the combining numbers
and their multiples in chemical
combinations.

[3] See supra, chap. ii. p. 191 and
note.

nomenon has been called isomorphism. The discovery has been of great practical value, as well as theoretical interest. If the definite and invariable form of existence which the crystal exhibits is considered as a proof of the purity of a chemical substance, and if in the same crystal one elementary substance can be replaced by one or several other substances, then this substitution must take place in definite proportions of weight, in the equivalent proportions. Thus the production of such isomorphous crystals affords a method of determining the relative atomic weights or equivalents. As such it was hailed by Berzelius; the more so, as in no case did the equivalents thus obtained contradict the numbers he had found by other methods.[1] Theoretically, the property of isomorphism acquired a still greater interest when Mitscher-

[1] In the early days of the atomic theory as developed by Berzelius, great uncertainty existed as to the numbers which were to be chosen for the atomic weights of the elements. This was owing to the property of fixed multiple ratios—it remaining undecided which was the smallest submultiple of a given combining ratio in which any special element could enter into combination. Other methods were then used to assist in deciding this point. The law of volumes, and later the properties of isomorphism, were therefore hailed by Berzelius as welcome aids in fixing the atomic numbers. Both these methods are still used, though the latter is not always decisive. The most important method according to the present state of our knowledge is the determination of the vapour density, where such can be got, and that of the specific heat in the solid state. It is mainly owing to Cannizzaro (1858) that the apparent contradictions, which were supposed to exist in the numbers arrived at by various methods, were explained by reverting to Avogadro's forgotten hypothesis. The periodic law or arrangement of the elements into classes showing similar physical properties is likewise of use. A complete, lucid, and exhaustive statement of the most recent position of our knowledge of the true atomic weights of the elements will be found in Lothar Meyer's posthumous tract, 'Die Atome und ihre Eigenschaften,' Breslau, 1896. In this valuable book, as also in Ostwald's 'Allgemeine Chemie,' vol. i., will also be found an account of the degree of accuracy which attaches to our present knowledge of the atomic and combining numbers, which form the solid foundation of all quantitative chemistry and all practical applications.

lich discovered another crystalline property of certain chemically pure substances. He found that some substances can crystallise in more than one distinct and definite form. The alums and vitriols are typical of isomorphism. As typical of the second property, which was termed by him dimorphism or polymorphism, we have the well-known mineral calc-spar, which is dimorphous with aragonite, both having the same chemical constitution and properties. A typical example of dimorphism is the mineral rutile, which is chemically the same substance as the mineral anatase, both being chemically pure titanic oxide. Among the elements, pure sulphur crystallises in two different forms. The property of dimorphism seemed at first to contradict the inference which Mitscherlich had drawn from his first discovery—*viz.*, that the crystalline shape is expressive of the number and chemical connection of the smallest particles or atoms; but the further discovery, that if of two isomorphous bodies one is dimorphous, the other is likewise so, gave again a great support to the geometrical conception of atomic complexes—*i.e.*, to the idea that chemical individuality is ultimately to be explained not only by the number, but also by the mutual fixed position and shape, of the atoms. And yet it seemed a long way, and is a long way still, from the external, visible, and well-marked shape of a crystal, with its peculiar and well-defined geometrical, elastic, optical, and thermal properties, to the primitive molecule, made up of still more simple atoms, in the form, number, and arrangement of which we are again and again tempted to see the nature of chemical or qualitative individuality. To obtain a clear view in this way would be to work our way from

44.
Polymor-
phism.

outside inward—a method which has rarely led to definite results in scientific research.

A department of chemical science called structural chemistry—which has quite recently developed into stereo-chemistry—has during the last fifty years of the century been working by the opposite method. Even those organic chemists who ridiculed the notion that a chemical formula, which on the surface of the paper on which it is written cannot help making use of geometrical position and proximities, is in any way a picture of the arrangements of atoms in real space, were nevertheless forced to avail themselves of this symbolism. About the middle of the century, especially through the researches of Frankland, followed by those of Couper and Kekulé, the phenomenon of multiple proportions was explained by introducing the notion of saturation. An element which can combine with one or more atoms of the same or of different elements or definite chemical compounds was looked upon as having a chemical affinity which might be wholly or only partially satisfied. The different compounds arising out of such combinations would then represent different degrees of saturation of the first element; and it was evident that elements as well as compounds could be arranged according to the degrees of saturation of which they were capable. A compound containing elements which possessed a greater capacity for saturation than the combination afforded was called unsaturated. The term valency was introduced to denote the degrees of saturation of elements and compounds, which were therefore mono-, di-, or poly-valent, according to the compounds existing in fixed simple or

45.
Structural and stereo-chemistry.

46.
Valency.

fixed multiple proportions. In a table of the valencies or saturating capacities of elements and compounds, the element hydrogen forms the unit and point of reference, as it does in the scale of the atomic or combining weights, and very remarkable relations and analogies have been established between the periodic law of Mendeléeff and the valency of the different elements. Nevertheless it must be remarked that the valency of an element or compound does not, according to our present knowledge, show such absolute fixity as the equivalents or combining weights do, or as the angles of crystallisation of chemically pure substances do.[1]

The introduction of the conception of valency has had an enormous influence on the development of the science of chemistry, and this in a twofold direction. Its practical use was demonstrated by Kekulé, when he placed the idea of the tetravalency, or fourfold saturating capacity, of carbon in the front of his treatise of organic chemistry,[2] and by so doing gave a great impetus to organic research. One of the first symbols used to denote

[1] Not only are many of the elements, such as oxygen and phosphorus, classed differently by different chemists according as their valency or saturating capacity is put at a higher or lower multiple, but compounds which are universally considered to be saturated compounds, such as neutral salts and water, form chemical combinations according to their combining numbers, which are quite definite and stable : such are the hydrated crystallised salts and the double salts. These compounds are called "molecular compounds." Various explanations have been attempted, but the fact remains that "no characteristic distinction has been found, either in physical or chemical behaviour, between the ordinary compounds and the molecular compounds ; and therefore, strictly speaking, from the phenomena exhibited, at present no other conclusion can be drawn except that chemical compounds do undoubtedly exist which cannot be included in the structure scheme which is based on the doctrine of a constant valency" (see Nernst, 'Theoretical Chemistry,' transl. by Palmer, London, 1895, p. 246).

[2] A. Kekulé (1829-1896), 'Lehrbuch der organischen Chemie,' 1st ed., Erlangen, 1859, and later.

the valency of an element was to attach to it as many lines as it possessed capacities of saturation. The capacities of saturation or valencies thus appeared very early as points of saturation, and the saturation itself as a linkage. These geometrical artifices or expressions were, for a long time, used merely as symbols, and to the present day many eminent chemists refuse to attach to them any real meaning: formulæ of this kind were called formulæ of structure, not of constitution. One of the most remarkable instances of the exact use of linkages to explain the difference of a series of organic compounds, all closely connected with each other, is the theory of the so-called aromatic compounds, derived from benzene, which we owe to Kekulé. It has stood the criticism of more than a quarter of a century, and has led to the most wonderful practical knowledge of a large number of old and new compounds.

47. Atomic linkage.

It is not astonishing if, in the face of these remarkable strides which geometrical symbols have led to, an attempt has been made to form an actual conception of the geometrical figure and grouping of the atoms of which chemical molecules and compounds are made up.

Space relations are the only ones in which the difference of symmetry and asymmetry can be at all conceived by us; and when chemical compounds were discovered which show no other difference than that one of them turns the plane of polarisation of a ray of light passing through it to the right, the other to the left side, the time seemed ripe to seek an explanation of this in a purely stereometrical difference of form or grouping.

In 1874 two chemists, Le Bel and Van't Hoff, suggested independently a picture of the tetravalent carbon atom, which would explain how it could enter with its four points or capacities of saturation into two compounds having the same saturating substances, but arranged in ways which were not geometrically superposable, but only symmetrical, like a right- and left-hand glove, or the images in a mirror. The suggestion amounts to this, that the carbon atom has the shape of a tetrahedron, the four corners representing the four valencies or capacities of saturation.[1]

48.
The carbon
tetrahedron.

The carbon tetrahedron is the last step which has been taken in the development of the atomic view of matter and of nature. No book on organic chemistry can now well avoid introducing this and other similar ways of representing chemical relations. On the further specialisation of this conception will probably depend to a large extent the future of our chemical theory—*i.e.*, of our attempts to grasp the qualitative nature of different substances. It is clear that we are far on the way to realising Wollaston's prophecy of the year 1808—*viz.*, " that the

---

[1] This speculation was at first looked upon with very great doubt. Only few chemists of note took it up ; others, such as Kolbe, who led a consistent opposition to the ideas and developments of structural chemistry, treated it with ridicule. Van't Hoff, ten years after the publication of the first edition of his pamphlet, 'La Chimie dans l'Espace' (Rotterdam, 1875) reviewed the position in his 'Dix Années dans l'Histoire d'une Théorie' (translated by Marsh, Oxford, 1891), and, after reproducing the two opposite reviews, with which the original theory was met by Wislicenus and Kolbe, was able to state " that the theory in question now forms part of elementary chemical teaching, and is to be found enunciated in the most widely used text-books" (translation, p. 19). Further applications of the theory, especially to the compounds of nitrogen, will be found in the 2nd edition of the German translation ' Die Lagerung der Atome im Raume' (Braunschweig, 1894).

atomic theory could not rest contented with a knowledge of the relative weights of elementary atoms, but would have to be completed by a geometrical conception of the arrangement of the elementary particles in all the three dimensions of solid extension." [1]

But though a further development of the atomic view, not only " pondere " but also " mensura," may be expected in the near future, the progress of chemistry, which has benefited so much by this view of nature, will not depend exclusively upon this line of thought, nor perhaps to so large an extent as it has done during the greater part of the century. We have seen how the atomic theory of Dalton rose to the position of being more than a convenient symbolism, and how it became a physical theory of matter and of nature mainly by the support which it received from a different line of reasoning.

49.
Defects and insufficiency of the atomic view.

The development of this line of reasoning led to the employment of the statistical method, a view quite foreign to other branches of physical science.

The kinetic theory of gases itself had been elaborated in connection with still another line of reasoning, with the endeavour to get a clearer and more comprehensive view of the nature of the different forces which the astronomical as well as the atomic views had merely accepted as given quantities without further examination. We are thus necessarily led on to trace the history of

---

[1] See Wollaston's memoir, "On Super-acid and Sub-acid Salts," read before the Royal Society, Jan. 8, 1808 (' Phil. Trans.,' 1808, p. 96, &c.), where he even suggests the examination of the stability of aggregates of particles in different configurations, mentioning the tetrahedron, since become celebrated through Pasteur and Van't Hoff.

these other views of nature, which up to the middle of the century had grown up independently.

The next chapter will accordingly deal with the kinetic view of nature.

At the time when the atomic theory was firmly established and defined, the great founders of chemical science were well aware that the investigation and measurement of chemical forces, of what was termed affinity, was just as important a problem as the fixing of the combining weights and the formulæ of chemical compounds.

Accordingly we find men like Bergmann, Berthollet, Davy, Berzelius, and Faraday all propounding or suggesting theories of chemical affinity, some of which, like the electro-chemical theory, remained long in use. The difficulty, however, which was experienced in defining, and still more in measuring, chemical affinity, and the absence of a general system for the computation and calculation of all physical quantities, retarded the progress of this line of research compared with the study of the weights or proportions of mass which existed in chemical processes, and which were more easily ascertained by means of the balance, and made intelligible by the atomic theory.

50.
Theories of
chemical
affinity.

The tendency of chemical reasoning during the first half of the century lay therefore in the direction of a one-sided development of the knowledge of matter, its definite constituents and infinite compounds, rather than in a study of that equally important but more subtle quantity, now called energy, which appears or disappears, but is never created or destroyed in physical or chemical processes.

A clear recognition of this fundamental doctrine—nay,

even a name for the thing implied—did not exist before the middle of the century. How both were gradually introduced will be shown in another of the following chapters.

The atomic view or theory which gave such good help in classifying and in studying the characteristic feature of all chemical processes—the fact that they take place according to definite proportions of weight—had also the effect of promoting a somewhat one-sided habit of thought in the domain of chemical science itself.

The search for the elements, the fixing of their combining weights and properties, absorbed a great deal of time, labour, and ability.

The practical demands of the arts stimulated the preparation of metals, of acids, and of alkalies, all of which possessed useful properties in their isolated, as distinguished from their natural, condition. This gave a stimulus in practice to the invention of processes of disintegration, and in reasoning to processes of analysis. The synthesis or putting together was expected to take place easily, if once the elements or constituent parts were got. In mineral chemistry and metallurgy this is indeed very frequently the case. It was soon found that it is not so in organic chemistry, and that when in organic chemistry a synthesis is effected, the product is frequently unlike that original natural substance from the analysis or disintegration of which the constituents or elements were procured.

51.
Practical
influences.

It soon became evident that synthesis does not mean merely addition. A certain order had to be observed in the way of putting together, and this led to the introduction of structural, further of geometrical, formulæ. Even then, however, it was found that if a synthesis succeeded, it did not always produce a natural, but frequently a purely artificial, compound. The practical effect of this discovery has been remarkable, not to say astonishing. New industries have been founded, and a branch of science has been created called "organic chemistry," but more correctly the "chemistry of carbon compounds," which was undreamt of in the beginning of the century. At that time "organic chemistry" meant that branch of the science which dealt with the compounds which were found in the structures of the vegetable and animal kingdoms, and which were peculiar to them.[1] This meaning of the term "organic chemistry" has disappeared; but the branch of science which deals specially with the substances contained in living matter has not disappeared. Only the development of chemistry on the lines pre-eminently prescribed by the atomic view of nature has diverted the attention of many investigators and philosophers from the original problems of organic chemistry—the study, the analysis, and the reproduction or synthesis of such compounds as are immediately connected with living matter.

To the extent that these problems which have not lain

52.
Change in
definition of
organic
chemistry.

[1] The merit of having upheld the twofold aspect of organic chemistry and of having urged the necessity of two distinct ways of analysing organic substances, belongs in this century pre-eminently to Chevreul. Not only are his 'Recherches sur les Corps gras d'Origine animale,' carried on from 1813 to 1823, a model work of great theoretical and practical value; but he has in various writings, notably in his historical memoirs ('Journal des Savants,' 1852-60), insisted on the necessity of studying what he terms, after Fourcroy, "les principes immédiats, qui constituent les végétaux et les animaux." This study is based upon quite a different method from that usually called "analyse élémentaire." Chevreul's great work has been continued and developed by M. Berthelot in his celebrated book, 'Chimie organique fondée sur la Synthèse,' 1860, two vols.

specially on the lines marked out by the atomic view of
nature have, in the course of time, reasserted themselves,
the atomic view itself has been regarded with less favour
by students who have made these problems their especial
study. In fact, one meets not infrequently with an inclination to disparage the atomic theory, to point out
that it is merely a hypothesis, and that as such it
should only assist, but not govern, scientific research.[1]

In the domain of specially chemical reasoning we meet
with severe criticisms of the one-sided and formal development to which the atomic view has led, of the playing with
symbols and of their empty formalism; notably structural
chemistry and stereo-chemistry have not escaped severe
ridicule.[2] Whilst it is not very evident how the school
from which these criticisms proceed can in the long-run
escape those logical consequences which are embodied
in stereo-chemistry, other criticisms claim our attention

53.
Criticisms of
the atomic
view.

[1] See Berthelot, 'La Synthèse
chimique,' 7me éd., 1891, p. 167.
'Le principal reproche, que l'on
puisse adresser à la théorie atomique, comme à toutes les conceptions analogues, c'est qu'elles con-
duisent à opérer sur ces rapports
numériques des éléments et non
sur les corps eux-mêmes, en rap-
portant toutes les réactions à une
unité type, nécessairement imag-
inaire. Bref elles enlèvent aux
phénomènes tout caractère réel,
et substituent à leur exposition
véritable une suite de considérations
symboliques, auxquelles l'esprit se
complaît, parce qu'il s'y exerce
avec plus de facilité que sur les
réalités proprement dites . . . les
symboles de la chimie présentant
à cet égard d'étranges séductions
par la facilité algébrique de leurs
combinaisons et par les tendances
de l'esprit humain, naturellement
porté à substituer à la conception
directe des choses . . . la vue plus
simple . . . de leurs signes repré-
sentatifs."

[2] The late eminent Professor
Hermann Kolbe of Leipsic, whose
labours both alone and jointly with
Frankland have done so much to
break down the formalism of the
older type theory, was especially
conspicuous by his virulent attacks
on the representatives of 'Modern
Chemistry.' The controversy is
elaborately and lucidly treated by
A. Rau in 'Die Theorien der
modernen Chemie' (Braunschweig,
1877-84, 3 parts), which contains
very valuable historical references.
I am afraid it is greatly owing to
this party spirit that Kolbe's own
greatness is hardly sufficiently
known in this country.

because they follow from distinctly defined and independent lines of reasoning. The three criticisms can be
summed up in three distinct arguments, all three demanding our special and exhaustive study. These three
arguments may be summarised as follows:—

First. The atomic view is a hypothesis resting upon the
fact that substances combine in fixed and fixed multiple
proportions, and upon the further observation that bodies
both in the solid and liquid state show different properties
in different directions of space. But as to the nature
of the differences of the elements the atomic view gives no
information; it simply asserts these differences, assumes
them as physical constants, and tries to describe them by
number and measurement.

The atomic view is therefore at best only a provisional
basis, a convenient resting-place,[1] similar to that which
Newton found in physical astronomy, and on which has
been established the astronomical view of nature.

Second. The atomic view in its present development
gives us no insight into the nature of those forces on which
depend the formation or destruction of chemical compounds. It neglects the study of chemical affinity. This
must be conducted on different lines of observation and
reasoning.[2]

[1] As these and other points referred to here will be taken up and
fully treated in future chapters of
this work, I abstain from giving
exhaustive references, limiting myself to such writings as will
give the reader a general idea of
the various attempts which have
been made to go beyond or behind
the Atomic View of Nature or to
supplement it by other views.

Very suggestive in the first instance
is Lord Kelvin's address to the
mathematical and physical section
of the British Association in 1884,
reprinted in the first volume of his
'Popular Lectures and Addresses,'
p. 218, &c., "Steps towards a Kinetic Theory of Matter."

[2] In respect of this the Introduction to the first edition of Lothar
Meyer's 'Modern Theories in Chem-

Third. The atomic view, as developed in chemical formulæ, has unduly favoured and promoted the analytical tendency of research and thought, limiting synthesis to such compounds as can be artificially prepared, but neglecting that kind of synthesis by which compounds are formed in nature, and especially in living organisms.[1]

As representative of these three lines of argument, leading beyond or outside of the atomic view of nature, I mention the three names of Lord Kelvin in England, coupled with the kinetic—specially the vortex—theory of matter; of Professor Ostwald in Germany, coupled with the modern doctrines of chemical affinity; and of M. Berthelot in France, as especially identified with the development of modern synthetical methods in chemistry. In the next chapter I shall take up the line of thought embodied in the first of these developments—the kinetic view of nature.   In order to understand the history of this view, we shall have to go back to opinions held

istry,' written in 1862 and reprinted in the subsequent editions and also in the English translation by Bedson and Williams (London, 1888), gives a very lucid summary of the historical developments. The publication of Meyer's book, by the controversies it produced, did a great deal to give "theoretical" or "physical" chemistry a distinct and independent position.   Separate chairs and laboratories for physical chemistry have since been inaugurated, first at Leipsic and subsequently at other German universities.   See Ostwald's article on "Physikalische Chemie," in Lexis, 'Die deutschen Universitäten,' vol.

ii. p. 50, &c.   Professor Ostwald is also the editor, since 1857, of the first periodical devoted to physical chemistry.   To his great work, entitled 'Allgemeine Chemie,' which, since its first appearance in 1884, has done so much for "general" as distinguished from "systematic" chemistry, and to his numerous suggestive addresses, I shall frequently have occasion to refer.

[1] See the works of M. Berthelot, quoted above, pp. 454, 455; also an address by Prof. Meldola before the chemical section of the British Association in 1895.

already in antiquity; just as I showed that the astronomical and atomic views of nature grew out of vaguer theories of older times, and that they owe their revival and scientific usefulness to the fact that they have received in recent days the precise treatment of exact measurement and mathematical reasoning.

END OF THE FIRST VOLUME.

A CATALOGUE OF SELECTED DOVER BOOKS
IN ALL FIELDS OF INTEREST

WHAT IS SCIENCE?, *N. Campbell*
The role of experiment and measurement, the function of mathematics, the nature of scientific laws, the difference between laws and theories, the limitations of science, and many similarly provocative topics are treated clearly and without technicalities by an eminent scientist. "Still an excellent introduction to scientific philosophy," H. Margenau in *Physics Today.* "A first-rate primer . . . deserves a wide audience," *Scientific American.* 192pp. 5⅜ x 8.
                                                                    S43   Paperbound $1.25

THE NATURE OF LIGHT AND COLOUR IN THE OPEN AIR, *M. Minnaert*
Why are shadows sometimes blue, sometimes green, or other colors depending on the light and surroundings? What causes mirages? Why do multiple suns and moons appear in the sky? Professor Minnaert explains these unusual phenomena and hundreds of others in simple, easy-to-understand terms based on optical laws and the properties of light and color. No mathematics is required but artists, scientists, students, and everyone fascinated by these "tricks" of nature will find thousands of useful and amazing pieces of information. Hundreds of observational experiments are suggested which require no special equipment. 200 illustrations; 42 photos. xvi + 362pp. 5⅜ x 8.
                                                                    T196   Paperbound $2.00

THE STRANGE STORY OF THE QUANTUM, AN ACCOUNT FOR THE GENERAL READER OF THE GROWTH OF IDEAS UNDERLYING OUR PRESENT ATOMIC KNOWLEDGE, *B. Hoffmann*
Presents lucidly and expertly, with barest amount of mathematics, the problems and theories which led to modern quantum physics. Dr. Hoffmann begins with the closing years of the 19th century, when certain trifling discrepancies were noticed, and with illuminating analogies and examples takes you through the brilliant concepts of Planck, Einstein, Pauli, Broglie, Bohr, Schroedinger, Heisenberg, Dirac, Sommerfeld, Feynman, etc. This edition includes a new, long postscript carrying the story through 1958. "Of the books attempting an account of the history and contents of our modern atomic physics which have come to my attention, this is the best," H. Margenau, Yale University, in *American Journal of Physics.* 32 tables and line illustrations. Index. 275pp. 5⅜ x 8.   T518   Paperbound $2.00

GREAT IDEAS OF MODERN MATHEMATICS: THEIR NATURE AND USE, *Jagjit Singh*
Reader with only high school math will understand main mathematical ideas of modern physics, astronomy, genetics, psychology, evolution, etc. better than many who use them as tools, but comprehend little of their basic structure. Author uses his wide knowledge of non-mathematical fields in brilliant exposition of differential equations, matrices, group theory, logic, statistics, problems of mathematical foundations, imaginary numbers, vectors, etc. Original publication. 2 appendixes. 2 indexes. 65 ills. 322pp. 5⅜ x 8.
                                                                    T587   Paperbound $2.00

THE BAD CHILD'S BOOK OF BEASTS, MORE BEASTS FOR WORSE CHILDREN, and A MORAL ALPHABET, *H. Belloc*
Hardly and anthology of humorous verse has appeared in the last 50 years without at least a couple of these famous nonsense verses. But one must see the entire volumes — with all the delightful original illustrations by Sir Basil Blackwood — to appreciate fully Belloc's charming and witty verses that play so subacidly on the platitudes of life and morals that beset his day — and ours. A great humor classic. Three books in one. Total of 157pp. 5⅜ x 8.
Paperbound $1.00

THE DEVIL'S DICTIONARY, *Ambrose Bierce*
Sardonic and irreverent barbs puncturing the pomposities and absurdities of American politics, business, religion, literature, and arts, by the country's greatest satirist in the classic tradition. Epigrammatic as Shaw, piercing as Swift, American as Mark Twain, Will Rogers, and Fred Allen, Bierce will always remain the favorite of a small coterie of enthusiasts, and of writers and speakers whom he supplies with "some of the most gorgeous witticisms of the English language" (H. L. Mencken). Over 1000 entries in alphabetical order. 144pp. 5⅜ x 8.
Paperbound $1.00

THE COMPLETE NONSENSE OF EDWARD LEAR.
This is the only complete edition of this master of gentle madness available at a popular price. *A Book of Nonsense, Nonsense Songs, More Nonsense Songs and Stories* in their entirety with all the old favorites that have delighted children and adults for years. The Dong With A Luminous Nose, The Jumblies, The Owl and the Pussycat, and hundreds of other bits of wonderful nonsense. 214 limericks, 3 sets of Nonsense Botany, 5 Nonsense Alphabets, 546 drawings by Lear himself, and much more. 320pp. 5⅜ x 8.
Paperbound $1.00

THE WIT AND HUMOR OF OSCAR WILDE, *ed. by Alvin Redman*
Wilde at his most brilliant, in 1000 epigrams exposing weaknesses and hypocrisies of "civilized" society. Divided into 49 categories—sin, wealth, women, America, etc.—to aid writers, speakers. Includes excerpts from his trials, books, plays, criticism. Formerly "The Epigrams of Oscar Wilde." Introduction by Vyvyan Holland, Wilde's only living son. Introductory essay by editor. 260pp. 5⅜ x 8.
Paperbound $1.00

A CHILD'S PRIMER OF NATURAL HISTORY, *Oliver Herford*
Scarcely an anthology of whimsy and humor has appeared in the last 50 years without a contribution from Oliver Herford. Yet the works from which these examples are drawn have been almost impossible to obtain! Here at last are Herford's improbable definitions of a menagerie of familiar and weird animals, each verse illustrated by the author's own drawings. 24 drawings in 2 colors; 24 additional drawings. vii + 95pp. 6½ x 6.
Paperbound $1.00

THE BROWNIES: THEIR BOOK, *Palmer Cox*
The book that made the Brownies a household word. Generations of readers have enjoyed the antics, predicaments and adventures of these jovial sprites, who emerge from the forest at night to play or to come to the aid of a deserving human. Delightful illustrations by the author decorate nearly every page. 24 short verse tales with 266 illustrations. 155pp. 6⅝ x 9¼.
Paperbound $1.50

THREE SCIENCE FICTION NOVELS,
John Taine
Acknowledged by many as the best SF writer of the 1920's, Taine (under the name Eric Temple Bell) was also a Professor of Mathematics of considerable renown. Reprinted here are *The Time Stream*, generally considered Taine's best, *The Greatest Game*, a biological-fiction novel, and *The Purple Sapphire*, involving a supercivilization of the past. Taine's stories tie fantastic narratives to frameworks of original and logical scientific concepts. Speculation is often profound on such questions as the nature of time, concept of entropy, cyclical universes, etc. 4 contemporary illustrations. v + 532pp. 5⅜ x 8⅜.

T1180   Paperbound $2.00

SEVEN SCIENCE FICTION NOVELS,
H. G. Wells
Full unabridged texts of 7 science-fiction novels of the master. Ranging from biology, physics, chemistry, astronomy, to sociology and other studies, Mr. Wells extrapolates whole worlds of strange and intriguing character. "One will have to go far to match this for entertainment, excitement, and sheer pleasure . . ."*New York Times*. Contents: The Time Machine, The Island of Dr. Moreau, The First Men in the Moon, The Invisible Man, The War of the Worlds, The Food of the Gods, In The Days of the Comet. 1015pp. 5⅜ x 8.

T264   Clothbound $5.00

28 SCIENCE FICTION STORIES OF H. G. WELLS.
Two full, unabridged novels, *Men Like Gods* and *Star Begotten,* plus 26 short stories by the master science-fiction writer of all time! Stories of space, time, invention, exploration, futuristic adventure. Partial contents: *The Country of the Blind, In the Abyss, The Crystal Egg, The Man Who Could Work Miracles, A Story of Days to Come, The Empire of the Ants, The Magic Shop, The Valley of the Spiders, A Story of the Stone Age, Under the Knife, Sea Raiders,* etc. An indispensable collection for the library of anyone interested in science fiction adventure. 928pp. 5⅜ x 8.

T265   Clothbound $5.00

THREE MARTIAN NOVELS,
Edgar Rice Burroughs
Complete, unabridged reprinting, in one volume, of Thuvia, Maid of Mars; Chessmen of Mars; The Master Mind of Mars. Hours of science-fiction adventure by a modern master storyteller. Reset in large clear type for easy reading. 16 illustrations by J. Allen St. John. vi + 490pp. 5⅜ x 8½.

T39   Paperbound $2.50

AN INTELLECTUAL AND CULTURAL HISTORY OF THE WESTERN WORLD,
Harry Elmer Barnes
Monumental 3-volume survey of intellectual development of Europe from primitive cultures to the present day. Every significant product of human intellect traced through history: art, literature, mathematics, physical sciences, medicine, music, technology, social sciences, religions, jurisprudence, education, etc. Presentation is lucid and specific, analyzing in detail specific discoveries, theories, literary works, and so on. Revised (1965) by recognized scholars in specialized fields under the direction of Prof. Barnes. Revised bibliography. Indexes. 24 illustrations. Total of xxix + 1318pp.

T1275, T1276, T1277   Three volume set, paperbound $7.50